Algebra Connections
Version 3.1

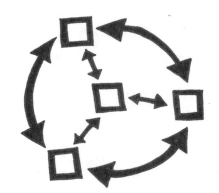

Managing Editors

Leslie Dietiker
Phillip and Sala Burton Academic High School
San Francisco, CA

Evra Baldinger
Phillip and Sala Burton Academic High School
San Francisco, CA

Contributing Editors

Carlos Cabana
San Lorenzo High School
San Lorenzo, CA

John Cooper
Del Oro High School
Loomis, CA

Mark Coté
Beaver Lake Middle School
Issaquah, WA

Joanne da Luz
The Life Learning Academy
San Francisco, CA

David Gulick
Phillips Exeter Academy
Exeter, NH

Patricia King
Holmes Junior High School
Davis, CA

Lara Lomac
Phillip and Sala Burton Academic
High School, San Francisco, CA

Bob Petersen
Rosemont High School
Sacramento, CA

Ward Quincey
Gideon Hausner Jewish Day School, Palo
Alto, CA

Barbara Shreve
San Lorenzo High School
San Lorenzo, CA

Michael Titelbaum
University of California
Berkeley, CA

Illustrator

Kevin Coffey
San Francisco, CA

Technical Manager

Bethany Armstrong
Davis, CA

Technical Assistants

Erica Andrews
Elizabeth Burke
Elizabeth Fong
Keith Lee

Eric Baxter
Carrie Cai
Rebecca Harlow
Michael Leong

Program Directors

Leslie Dietiker
Phillip and Sala Burton Academic High School
San Francisco, CA

Brian Hoey
Christian Brothers High School
Sacramento, CA

Judy Kysh, Ph.D.
Departments of Mathematics and Education
San Francisco State University

Tom Sallee, Ph.D.
Department of Mathematics
University of California, Davis

Consultants from San Lorenzo High School

Ashanti Branch	Laura Evans	Eric Price	Estelle Woodbury
Suzanne Cristofani	Lisa Jilk	Ana Ruiz	Dorothy Woods
Kristina Dance	Karen O'Connell	Hannah Witzemann	Lisa Wright

Assessment Contributors:

Evra Baldinger, Managing Editor
Phillip and Sala Burton Academic High School
San Francisco, CA

Carlos Cabana
San Lorenzo High School
San Lorenzo, CA

Mark Coté
Beaver Lake Middle School
Issaquah, WA

Leslie Dietiker
Phillip and Sala Burton Academic High School
San Francisco, CA

Laura Evans
San Lorenzo High School
San Lorenzo, CA

Judy Kysh, PhD
Departments of Mathematics and Education
San Francisco State University

Contributing Editors of the Parent Guide:

Bev Brockhoff
Glen Edwards Middle School
Lincoln, CA

Elizabeth Coyner
Christian Brothers High School
Sacramento, CA

Brian Hoey
Christian Brothers High School
Sacramento, CA

Patricia King
Holmes Junior High School
Davis, CA

Bob Petersen, Managing Editor
Rosemont High School
Sacramento, CA

Editor of Extra Practice:

Bob Petersen
Rosemont High School
Sacramento, CA

Technical Manager of Parent Guide:

Rebecca Harlow
Stanford University
Stanford, CA

5 6 7 8 9   10 09 08 07   ISBN-10: 1-931287-46-5

Printed in the United States of America   Version 3.1   ISBN-13: 978-1-931287-46-3

A Note to Students:

Welcome to a new year of math! In this course, you will be exposed to a powerful set of mathematical tools called algebra. As a set of tools, algebra is the foundation of higher mathematics. In fact, future courses will build from what you learn here. While you learn algebra, we also hope you become used to a new way of thinking: a way of investigating new situations, discovering relationships, and figuring out what strategies can be used to solve problems. Learning to think this way is useful in mathematical contexts, other academic disciplines, and situations outside the classroom.

In meeting the challenges of algebra, you will not be working alone. During this course you will collaborate with other students as a member of a study team. Working in a team means speaking up and interacting with others. You will explain your ideas, listen to what others have to say, and ask questions if there is something you do not understand. In algebra, a single problem can often be solved several ways. You will see problems in different ways than your teammates do. Each of you has something to contribute while you work on the lessons in this course.

Together, your team will complete problems and activities that will help you discover mathematical ideas and methods. Your teacher will support you as you work, but will not take away your opportunity to think and investigate for yourself. Each topic will be revisited many times and connected to other topics. If something is not clear to you the first time you work with it, you will have more chances to build your understanding as the course continues.

Learning math this way has a significant advantage: as long as you actively participate, make sure everyone in your study team is involved, and ask good questions, you will find yourself understanding mathematics at a deeper level than ever before. By the end of this course, you will have a powerful set of mathematical tools at your disposal. You will see how these tools connect with each other so that you can use them to solve new problems. With your teammates you will meet mathematical challenges you would not have known how to approach before.

In addition to the support provided by your teacher and your study team, CPM has also created online resources to help you, including help with homework, a parent guide, and extra practice. You will find these resources and more at www.cpm.org.

We wish you well and are confident that you will enjoy learning algebra!

Sincerely,
The CPM Team

Algebra
Connections
Table of Contents

Student Edition

Chapter 5 Multiplication and Proportions   189

Chapter 6 Systems of Equations   229

CHAPTER 7

Linear Equations

Chapter 7 will complete the focus on linear equations that began in Chapter 1 and continued through Chapters 3, 4, and 6. In this chapter, you will analyze the geometric meaning of slope and will explore the idea of slope as a rate of change. You will also use trend lines to make predictions from existing data about future events.

In this chapter, you will learn:

➤ How to find the slope (steepness) of a line given its equation, its graph, or any two points on the line.

➤ How the slopes of parallel and perpendicular lines are related.

➤ How slopes can represent rates of change in real-life applications.

➤ How to find the equation of a trend line to fit linear data.

➤ How to find the slope of a line without graphing it.

Guiding Questions

Think about these questions throughout this chapter:

What is slope?

What is a rate?

What information is necessary to find the equation of a line?

How are the slopes of two lines related?

Chapter Outline

Section 7.1 In this section, you will find equations of lines that fit data and will learn how to measure the steepness of a line on a graph. You will also study the difference between lines that point upward, lines that point downward, and lines that are horizontal.

Section 7.2 In this section, you will investigate situations where slope represents a rate in a real-life context, culminating in an activity called "The Big Race."

Section 7.3 In Section 7.3, you will develop a method for finding the equation of a line when given only two points on the line. This section ends with several activities for which you will pull together your understanding of slope and $y = mx + b$ to solve problems.

7.1.1 What's the equation of the line?

$y = mx + b$

Previously, you developed ways to find the growth of a line using its rule, table, and graph. You also learned how the y-intercept is present in each of the multiple representations. In this chapter, you will complete your study of lines and will develop ways to find the equation of a line using different pieces of information about the line, such as two points that are on it. Today's lesson will help you review **connections** you made in previous chapters by challenging you to find equations for lines from multiple representations.

7-1. GETTING TO KNOW YOU, Part Three

Your teacher will give you a card with a representation of a line (a table, graph, rule, or situation). Consider what you know about the line represented on your card. Then find the other students in your class that have a representation of the same line. These students will be your teammates. Be prepared to **justify** how you know your representation matches those of your teammates.

7-2. THE LINE FACTORY, Part One

Congratulations! You have recently been hired to work at the city's premiere Line Factory. People from all over the country order lines from your factory because of their superior quality and excellent price.

However, lately the Line Factory is having a serious problem: Too many customers have placed orders and then received a line different from the one they wanted! The factory has hired your team to eliminate this problem.

Your Task: Review the recent orders (the bulleted items that follow) and decide if there is anything wrong with each customer's order. If the order is correct, then pass it on to your production department with a rule, a table, and a graph (on graph paper). However, if the order is incorrect, explain to the customer how you know the order is incorrect and suggest corrections.

Problem continues on next page →

7-2.   *Problem continued from previous page.*

- **Customer A** wants a line that has *y*-intercept at (0, –3) and grows by 4. She ordered the line $y = -3x + 4$.

- **Customer B** wants the line graphed at right. He ordered the line $y = 3x + 2$.

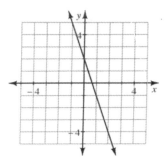

- **Customer C** wants a line that passes through the points (2, –4) and (5, 2). She ordered the line $y = 2x - 8$.

- **Customer D** wants the line that is represented by the table below.

IN (x)	–3	–2	–1	0	1	2	3
OUT (y)	–4	–1	2	4	7	10	13

- **Customer E** ordered the line $2x - y = 4$ and wants the line to grow by 2 and pass through the point (5, 6).

- **Customer F** wants a line that starts at (0, 1), grows first by 3, and then grows by 5.

7-3.   For the customer order that your team is assigned, prepare a team transparency or poster with your analysis from problem 7-2. Every team transparency or poster should include:

- The original customer order, complete with any given table, rule, graph, or statements.

- An explanation of any errors your team found in the order. If your team did not find any errors, the transparency or poster should **justify** this fact as well.

- Suggestions for how the customer can fix his or her order. You may want to suggest an equation that you suspect the customer wanted. If no mistake was made, then write a note to the company's production department with a rule, a table, and a graph for the order.

7-4.   Examine the tile pattern shown at right.

a.   On graph paper, draw Figure 0 and Figure 4.

Figure 1   Figure 2   Figure 3

b.   How many tiles will Figure 10 have? **Justify** your answer.

276   *Algebra Connections*

7-5.   Match the system of equations in the left column with its solution in the right column.

a. $6x - y = 4$ 1. $(0, -4)$
      $3x + y = 5$

b. $x = y + 4$ 2. $(3, 7)$
      $2x + 3y = -12$

c. $5x - 2y = 1$ 3. $(1, 2)$
      $y = 2x + 1$

7-6.   Use proportional reasoning to solve each of the problems below.

a.   At the zoo, three adult lions eat 250 pounds of food a day. If two more adult lions joined the group, how much food would the zoo need to provide each day?

b.   Byron can read 45 pages in an hour. How long will it take him to read the new 700-page Terry Cotter book?

7-7.   Graph $y = -\frac{1}{2}x + 6$. Find its x- and y-intercepts.

7-8.   Solve each equation below for the indicated variable.

a. $4x - 2 + y = 6 - 2x$ for y b. $4x - 2 + y = 6 - 2x$ for x

c. $3(6 - x) + 2x = 15$ for x

7-9.   Little Evan has 356 stuffed animals, all of which are either teddy bears or dogs. He has 17 more than twice as many dogs as teddy bears. How many teddy bears does he own? Write and solve an equation (or a system of equations) to solve this problem. Be sure to define your variable(s).

7.1.2 How can I use an equation?

Using Equations to Make Predictions

Previously, you have learned to find and **extend** patterns in data and to make predictions using rules, equations, and graphs. Today you will **apply** these math tools to a real situation in which your data does not make a perfect pattern.

7-10. Today you will use your new knowledge of $y = mx + b$ to solve "Newton's Revenge," problem 1-15, which is summarized below.

Newton's Revenge, the new roller coaster, has a tunnel that thrills riders with its very low ceiling. The closest the ceiling of the tunnel ever comes to the seat of the roller-coaster car is 200 cm. Although no accidents have yet been reported, rumors have been spreading that very tall riders have been injured as they went through the tunnel with their arms raised over their heads. The management needs your help in convincing the public that the roller coaster is safe.

Your Task: To help determine whether the tunnel is safe for any rider, no matter how tall, plot the data collected in problem 1-15 into a grapher, such as a graphing calculator. The height and reach should both be measured in centimeters. If you do not have the data from Chapter 1, your teacher may instruct you to use the data provided at right. As you enter the data into the grapher, answer the questions below.

Height (cm)	Reach (cm)
166.4	127
169	133
172.8	133
179	139
170	139
183	137
162.5	121
165	126
157.5	128
165	123
169	132
156	119

a. What window should you use to be able to see all of your data in a scatter plot? Set up the appropriate window and make a scatter plot with your grapher.

b. Is this plot useful for making predictions? Why or why not? If not, how could you change the plot to make it more useful?

7-11. Use your grapher to help you find the **trend line** (the equation of the line that best approximates your data). Once you have an equation that can best represent the data, you will be able to use the equation to verify that the roller coaster is safe.

If you have not done so already, set the window on your grapher to show the *x*-axis from 0 to your highest *x*-value and the *y*-axis from 0 to your highest *y*-value.

a. Guess an equation that you think might come close to your data. Enter the equation into your grapher and graph it in the same window as your data. Did you come close?

b. Change the numbers in your equation to numbers you think might fit the data more closely. Graph the equation again and see what happens. Keep trying new numbers until you find an equation that you think comes close to fitting the data. What is your equation?

c. Now reset the window to zoom in on your data. Does your equation still seem to fit the data well? If not, adjust your equation until you are satisfied with how it fits the data.

d. Zoom back out and find the *y*-intercept. What does this point represent? Does this make sense? If necessary, change your equation so that your equation makes sense at $x = 0$.

7-12. The amusement park wants Newton's Revenge to be safe for tall riders. For example, the famous basketball player Yao Ming is 7 feet 6 inches (about 228.6 cm) tall. Is the roller coaster safe for him? Use your grapher to confirm your decision.

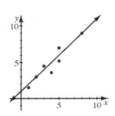

(M)ETHODS AND MEANINGS

MATH NOTES

Trend Lines

A **trend line** is a line that represents a set of data. It does not need to intersect each data point. Rather, it needs to approximate the data. A trend line looks and "behaves" like the data, as shown in the example at right.

7-13.   Evaluate each expression below for a when $a = \frac{2}{3}$, if possible.

a. $24a$ b. $3a$ c. $\frac{a}{0}$ d. $\frac{0}{a}$

7-14.   Find the distance between each pair of points.

    a. $(3, 7)$ and $(8, 7)$ b. $(-13, 7)$ and $(8, 7)$

    c. $(x, 7)$ and $(c, 7)$ d. $(5, 2)$ and $(5, 38)$

    e. $(5, -4)$ and $(5, 34)$ f. $(5, y)$ and $(5, f)$

7-15.   Solve each equation below for x. Check your solution.

    a. $3x - 7(4 + 2x) = -x + 2$ b. $-5x + 2 - x + 1 = 0$

7-16.   Find the solution for each system of equations below, if a solution exists. If there is not a single solution, explain why not. Be sure to check your solution, if possible.

    a. $x + 4y = 2$ b. $2x + 4y = -10$
          $3x - 4y = 10$ $x = -2y - 5$

7-17.   The figures below are **similar** (meaning they have the same shape). Use the information given about the lengths of the sides to solve for x and y.

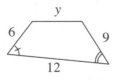 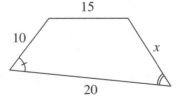

7-18.   Assume that a baby's length can be determined by the equation $l = 23 + 1.5t$, where l represents the length of the baby in inches and t represents the age of the baby in months.

    a.   How fast is the baby growing each month? How can you tell?

    b.   How long was the baby when it was born? How can you tell?

    c.   How long will the baby be when it is 3 months old?

    d.   If the baby was born in January, during what month will it be 39.5 inches long?

7.1.3 How can I measure steepness?

Measuring Steepness: An Introduction to Slope

You have been investigating what factors determine the steepness and position of a line and have seen that m in a $y = mx + b$ equation determines the direction of a line on a graph. In this lesson you will use all of your knowledge about m to determine the accurate value of m for an equation when you see the graph of a line.

During this lesson, ask your teammates the following focus questions:

What does m tell you about a line?

What makes lines steeper? What makes lines less steep?

How is growth related to steepness?

7-19.   In Chapter 4 you worked with tile patterns and **made connections** between tile patterns and graphs. Think back on your work from that chapter to answer these questions about the tile patterns A and B represented in the graph below.

a.   By looking at the graph, what statements can you make about the two tile patterns? What do the patterns have in common? What is different? Be specific.

b.   On the Lesson 7.1.3 Resource Page you receive from your teacher, draw growth triangles for each line. If available, use different colors for the triangles on each line. Label each triangle with its dimensions.

c.   What does the steepness of a line tell you about the growth of the tile pattern?

d.   Write an equation (rule) for each tile pattern.

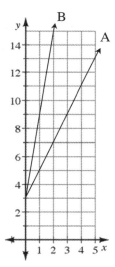

7-20.   The graph at right shows a line for a tile pattern you may recognize from Chapter 4. What is the growth factor for this line? That is, how many tiles are added each time the figure number is increased by 1? Explain how you found the growth factor.

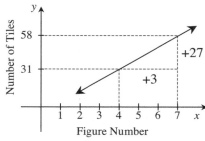

7-21.   The growth triangles in problem 7-20 are also
         called **slope triangles**. **Slope** is a measure of the
         steepness of a line. It is the ratio of the vertical
         distance to the horizontal distance of a slope
         triangle. The vertical part of the triangle is called
         Δy (read "change in y"), while the horizontal part
         of the triangle is called **Δx** (read "change in x").
         Note that " Δ " is the Greek letter "delta" that is
         often used to represent a difference or a change.

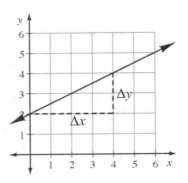

   a.   What is the vertical distance (Δy) for this
         slope triangle?

   b.   What is the horizontal distance (Δx) for this slope triangle?

   c.   Find this graph on the resource page. Draw miniature slope triangles for this
         line that have a horizontal distance (Δx) of 1. Use one of these mini-triangles
         to find the slope (growth factor) for this line.

   d.   How could you use Δy and Δx to find the slope of this line?

   e.   What is the equation of this line?

7-22.   Find the line graphed at right with slope triangles
         A, B, and C on the resource page.

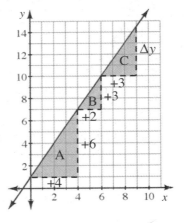

   a.   Find the slope using slope triangles A and B.
         What do you notice?

   b.   What is the vertical distance (Δy) of slope
         triangle C? Explain your reasoning.

   c.   Draw a slope triangle on the line with a
         horizontal distance (Δx) of 1 unit. Find the
         vertical distance (Δy) of this new triangle.
         What do you notice?

7-23.   What is special about the line that has $\Delta y = 0$? How can you describe a line for
         which $\Delta x = 0$? Draw a diagram for each case to demonstrate your answer.

Algebra Connections

7-24. Michaela was trying to find the slope of the line shown at right, so she selected two **lattice points** (locations where the grid lines intersect) and then drew a slope triangle.

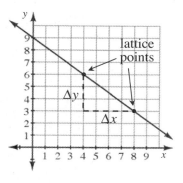

Her teammate, Cynthia, believes that $\Delta y = 3$ because the triangle is three units tall, while her other teammate, Essie, thinks that $\Delta y = -3$ because the triangle is three units tall and the line is pointing downward.

a. With whom do you agree and why?

b. When writing the slope of the line, Michaela noticed that Cynthia wrote $\frac{-3}{4}$ on her paper, while Essie wrote $-\frac{3}{4}$. She asked, "Are these ratios equal?" Discuss this with your team and answer her question.

c. Find the equation of Michaela's line.

METHODS AND **M**EANINGS

Introduction to Slope

MATH NOTES

Slope is a measure of the steepness of a line. It is the ratio of the vertical distance to the horizontal distance of a slope triangle. The vertical part of the triangle is called Δy (read "change in y"), while the horizontal part of the triangle is called Δx (read "change in x").

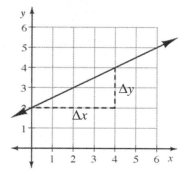

In the example at right, $\Delta y = 2$ and $\Delta x = 4$, so the slope is $\frac{2}{4} = \frac{1}{2}$.

Note that "Δ" is the Greek letter "delta" that is often used to represent a difference or a change.

7-25.   What shape will the graph of $y = x^2 + 2$ be? How can you tell? **Justify** your prediction by making a table and graphing $y = x^2 + 2$ on graph paper.

7-26.   Carol has two rose bushes: one with red flowers and another with yellow flowers. Her red rose bush has three times as many flowers as her yellow rose bush. Combined, they have 124 flowers. How many of each color flower does she have? Write an equation (or a system of equations) and solve.

7-27.   Artemis thinks that all lines eventually cross the x-axis. Do you agree? If not, provide a counterexample (that is, find a rule and a graph of a line that does not have an x-intercept).

7-28.   For each equation below, solve for x and check your answer.

   a. $10(2x - 1) = 100$ b. $\frac{1}{3}x - 6 = 8$

   c. $(x - 2)(x + 1) = x^2 + 4x$ d. $9x - 21 + 9 = 2(5 - x)$

7-29.   Write and solve an equation (or a system of equations) for the situation below. Define your variables and write your solution as a sentence.

          Jennifer has a total of four and a half hours to spend on the beach swimming and playing volleyball. The time she spends playing volleyball will be twice the amount of time she spends swimming. How long will she do each activity?

7-30.   Use a generic rectangle to multiply the expressions below. Write each answer as a product and as a sum.

   a. $(5x + 3)(x - 7)$ b. $-6x(4x - 3)$

Algebra Connections

7.1.4 How steep is it?

Comparing Δy and Δx

In Lesson 7.1.3, you discovered how to use the dimensions of a slope triangle to measure the steepness of a line. Today you will use the idea of stairs to understand slope even better. You will examine the difference between positive and negative slopes and will learn how to draw a line when given information about Δx and Δy.

During the lesson, ask your teammates the following target questions:

How can you tell if m is positive or negative?

What makes lines steeper? What makes lines less steep?

What does a line with a slope of zero look like?

7-31.   One way to think about slope or growth triangles is as stair steps on a line.

a.   Picture yourself climbing (or descending) the stairs from left to right on each of the lines on the graph (shown below, at right). Of lines A, B, and C, which is the steepest? Which is the least steep?

b.   Examine line D. What direction is it traveling from left to right? What number should be used for Δy to represent this direction?

c.   Find this graph on the Lesson 7.1.4 Resource Page and label the legs of one of the slope triangles on each line. Then find the slope of each line.

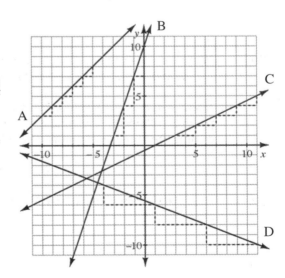

d.   How does the slope relate to the steepness of the graph?

e.   Cora answered part (d) with the statement, "The steeper the line, the greater the slope number." Do you agree? If so, use lines A through D to support her statement. If not, change her statement to make it correct.

7-32. Find the graph shown below on the Lesson 7.1.4 Resource Page.

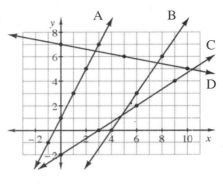

a. Which is the steepest line? Which is steeper, line B or line C?

b. Draw slope triangles for lines A, B, C, and D using the highlighted points on each line. Label Δx and Δy for each.

c. Match each line with its slope using the list below. Note: You will have slopes left over.

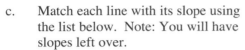

$m = 6 \qquad m = 2 \qquad m = -\frac{1}{5} \qquad m = \frac{3}{2}$

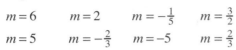

$m = 5 \qquad m = -\frac{2}{3} \qquad m = -5 \qquad m = \frac{2}{3}$

d. Viewed left to right, in what direction would a line with slope $-\frac{3}{5}$ point? How do you know?

e. Viewed left to right, in what direction would a line with slope $-\frac{5}{3}$ point? How do you know? How would it be different from the line in part (d)?

7-33. Examine lines A, B, C, and D on the graph at right. For each line, decide if the slope is positive, negative, or zero. Then draw and label slope triangles on your resource page and calculate the slope of each line.

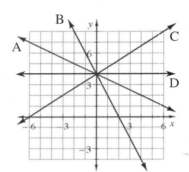

7-34. On graph paper, graph a line to match each description below. List the slope of each line.

a. A line with $\Delta y = 6$ and $\Delta x = 1$.

b. A line that goes up 3 each time it goes over 5.

c. A line with $\Delta x = 4$ and $\Delta y = -6$.

d. A line that has $\Delta y = 0$ and $\Delta x = 3$.

7-35. What happens to the slope when the slope triangles are different sizes? For example, the line at right has three different slope triangles drawn as shown.

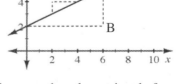

a. Find the slope using each of the slope triangles. What do you notice?

b. The triangle labeled A is drawn above the line. Does the fact that it is above the line instead of below it affect the slope of the line?

c. On the resource page provided by your teacher, draw another slope triangle for this line so that $\Delta x = 1$. What is the height (Δy) of this new slope triangle?

7-36.   Revisit the target questions for this lesson (reprinted
         below). Use the ideas you have developed in class to
         answer these questions in your Learning Log. Label
         this entry "Positive, Negative, and Zero Slope" and
         label it with today's date.

How can you tell if m is positive or negative?

What makes lines steeper? What makes lines less steep?

What does a line with slope zero look like?

MᴇᴛHODS AND Mᴇᴀɴɪɴɢꜱ

More Solving Systems by Elimination

MATH NOTES

In Chapter 6, you learned how to
solve systems of equations by
eliminating a variable. Suppose you
want to solve the system of equations
shown at right.

$$\begin{cases} 3x + 2y = 11 \\ 4x + 3y = 14 \end{cases}$$

multiply
by 3

multiply
by -2

$$9x + 6y = 33$$
$$-8x - 6y = -28$$

The goal is to *eliminate* either x or y when
you add the equations together. In this
case, you need to do something to *both*
equations before you add them. To
eliminate y, you can multiply the first
equation by 3 and multiply the second
equation by -2.

$$9x + 6y = 33$$
$$\underline{-8x - 6y = -28}$$
$$x = 5$$

Then eliminate the y-terms by adding the two new equations, as shown above.

Since you know that $x = 5$, you can substitute to find that $y = -2$. Therefore,
the solution to the system of equations is $(5, -2)$.

You could also solve the system by multiplying the first equation by 4 and the
second equation by -3. This would cause x to be eliminated when the
equations are added together.

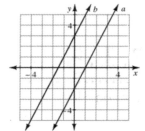

7-37. When Yoshi graphed the lines $y = 2x + 3$ and
$y = 2x - 2$, she got the graph shown at right.

    a.   One of the lines at right matches the equation
$y = 2x + 3$, and the other matches $y = 2x - 2$.
Which line matches which equation?

    b.   Yoshi wants to add the line $y = 2x + 1$ to her graph.
Predict where it would lie and sketch a graph to
show its position. **Justify** your prediction.

    c.   Where would the line $y = -2x + 1$ lie? Again, **justify** your prediction and add
the graph of this line to your graph from part (b).

7-38. Find the point of intersection for each system of linear equations below. Be sure to
check your solutions. Which method did you use for each system and why?

    a. $5x - y = 2$ b. $6x + 2y = 7$ c. $5x + 2y = 7$
          $3x + y = -10$ $4x + y = 4$ $2y + 5x = 7$

7-39. Solve each of the following equations.

    a. $2x + 8 = 3x - 4$ b. $1.5(w + 2) = 3 + 2w$

    c. $8(x + 6) + 23 = 7$ d. $3(2x - 7) = 5x + 17 + x$

7-40. Copy and complete these generic rectangles on your paper. Then write the area of
each rectangle as a product of the length and width and as a sum of the parts.

    a.   6 | $13x$ | -21

    b. x, -5 ; x, $+3$

    c. $16x^2$ | $-24x$ | 4

    d. $3x$, -2 ; x, $+4$

7-41. When Malcolm hops 15 times down the
hallway, he travels 18 feet. How many
times would he need to hop to travel to class
(66 feet away)?

288

Algebra Connections

7-42.   On graph paper, graph a line with *y*-intercept (0, –4) and *x*-intercept (3, 0). Find the equation of the line.

7.1.5   What information determines a line?

More on Slope

Today you will complete your focus on finding slope as well as using slope and the *y*-intercept to find the equation of a line. During this lesson, keep the following questions in mind:

Is there enough information to graph the line?

How are parallel lines related?

How can you find the slope of a line without graphing it?

7-43.   WHAT'S MY LINE?

How much information is necessary to know where a line is on a graph? For example, if you only know two points on the line, is that enough information to know where the line is graphed? What if you only know one point? Consider each of the lines described in parts (a) through (e) below.

If possible, graph each line and find its equation. If you do not have enough information to draw one specific line, draw at least two lines that fit the given criteria. Then, for part (f), write a statement describing what information is necessary to determine a line.

a.   Line A goes through the point (2, 5).

b.   Line B has a slope of –3 and goes through the origin (the point (0, 0)).

c.   Line C goes through points (2, 8) and (3, 10).

d.   Line D has a slope of 4.

e.   Line E goes through the point (8, –1) and has a slope of $-\frac{3}{4}$.

f.   To graph a line and find its equation, what information do you need?

7-44. **SLOPES OF PARALLEL LINES**

How are the slopes of parallel lines related? How can this information be useful? Consider these questions as you answer the questions below.

a. On graph paper, graph the line $y = \frac{1}{2}x - 3$. Then, on the same set of axes, draw another line that is parallel to $y = \frac{1}{2}x - 3$. What is the slope of this line? Explain how you know.

b. What do you notice about the slope of parallel lines?

c. Use this idea to draw a line parallel to $y = -2x + 5$ that goes through the point (0, –5).

d. Now draw a line parallel to $y = \frac{1}{2}x - 3$ that goes through the point (2, –5). Find its rule.

7-45. **FINDING THE SLOPE OF A LINE WITHOUT GRAPHING**

While finding the slope of a line that goes through the points (6, 5) and (3, 7), Gloria figured that $\Delta y = -2$ and $\Delta x = 3$ without graphing.

a. Explain how Gloria could find the horizontal and vertical distance of the slope triangle without graphing. Draw a sketch of the line and validate her method.

b. What is the slope of the line?

c. Use Gloria's method (without graphing) to find the slope of the line that goes through the points (4, 15) and (2, 11).

d. Use Gloria's method to find the slope of the line that goes through the points (28, 86) and (34, 83).

e. Another student found the slope from part (d) to be 2. What error or errors did that student make?

7-46. **SLOPE CHALLENGE**

What is the steepest line possible? What is its slope? Be ready to **justify** your statements.

METHODS AND MEANINGS

MATH NOTES

The Slope of a Line

The **slope** of a line is the ratio of the change in y (Δy) to the change in x (Δx) between any two points on the line. It indicates both how steep the line is and its direction, upward or downward, left to right.

$$\text{slope} = \frac{\text{vertical change}}{\text{horizontal change}} = \frac{\Delta y}{\Delta x}$$

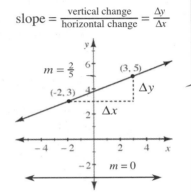

Note that lines pointing upward from left to right have positive slope, while lines pointing downward from left to right have negative slope. A horizontal line has zero slope, while a vertical line has undefined slope. The slope of a line is denoted by the letter m when using the $y = mx + b$ equation of a line.

To calculate the slope of a line, pick two points on the line, draw a slope triangle (as shown in the example above), determine Δy and Δx, and then write the slope ratio. You can verify that your slope correctly resulted in a negative or positive value based on its direction.

7-47.   Sam and Jimmica have both taken a speed-reading class and have been assigned to read a 300-page novel. Jimmica started reading at noon and read 10 pages per minute. Sam was on page 62 at noon and read 8 pages per minute. Will Jimmica ever catch up to Sam? Explain how you found your answer.

7-48.   Consider this system of equations:

$$y = 2x - 8$$
$$y = -\tfrac{2}{3}x$$

    a.   Use your knowledge of $y = mx + b$ to graph the lines without tables.

    b.   Use the graph to find the point of intersection.

    c.   Confirm this point of intersection by solving the system algebraically.

7-49.   Without graphing, find the slope of each line described below.

    a.   A line that goes through the points (4, 1) and (2, 5).

    b.   A line that goes through the origin and the point (10, 5).

    c.   A vertical line (one that travels "up and down") that goes through the point (6, –5).

    d.   A line that goes through the points (1, 6) and (10, 6).

7-50.   Solve the equations below for x. Check each solution by substituting the answer back into the equation.

    a. $4(2 - x) + 3x = x$ b. $x^2 - 5x + 2 = (x - 3)(x - 2)$

    c. $\tfrac{3}{x} = 6$ d. $-(-2x + 3) = -(-5)$

7-51.   Solve the equations below for the indicated variable.

    a. $6x - 3y = 12$ for y b. $y = -2x + 4$ for x

    c. $4 - 2(3x + 2) = 4x - 10$ for x d. $\tfrac{3-x}{4} = \tfrac{5}{2}$ for x

7-52.   Graph the curve $y = 3x^2 - 6x - 24$ using x-values between –3 and 5 on graph paper. What are the x- and y-intercepts?

7.2.1 What's the equation of the line?

Equation of a Line in Context

Today you will start to look at slope as a measurement of rate. Today's activity ties together the equation of a line and motion. Look for ways to **connect** what you know about *m* and *b* as you have fun.

7-53.   SLOPE WALK

Congratulations! The president of the Line Factory has presented your class with a special challenge: She now wants a way to find the equation of a line generated when a customer walks in front of a motion detector. That way, a customer can simply walk a line to order it from the factory.

Your Task: Once a motion detector has been set up with the correct software, have a volunteer walk **away** from the motion detector at a *constant* rate. In other words, he or she should walk the same speed the entire time. Then, once a graph is generated, find the equation of the line. Also find the equation of a line formed when a different volunteer walks **toward** the motion detector at a constant rate.

Discussion Points

What do you expect the first graph to look like? Why?

What will be different about the two graphs?

What would happen if the volunteer did not walk at a constant rate?

How does the volunteer's speed affect the graph?

7-54.   WALK THE WALK

To impress the president, you have decided to **reverse** the process: Write
instructions for a client on how to walk in front of the motion detector in order to
create a graph for a given rule.

Each team in the class will be assigned one or two rules from the list below. Then,
as a team, decide how to walk so that you will get the graph for your rule. After the
entire team understands how to walk, one member will try to graph the line by
walking in front of the motion detector. Pay close attention to detail! Your team
only has two tries!

a. $y = 3x + 2$ b. $y = -x + 10$

c. $y = 6$ d. $y = 2x + 4$

e. $y = -2x + 13$ f. $y = x + 5$

g. $y = -0.5x + 15$ h. $y = 1.5x + 3$

7-55.   Write a memo to the president of the Line Factory explaining why you cannot use a
motion detector to collect the data plotted below. The x-axis represents time in
seconds, and the y-axis represents the distance from the motion detector in feet.

a.   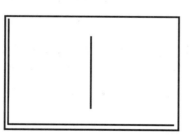   b.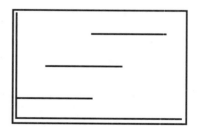

7-56.   On July 4th, Dizzyland had 67,000 visitors and collected approximately $2,814,000. How much money should Dizzyland expect to receive on New Year's Day, when park attendance reaches 71,000 people?

7-57.   The graph below represents the number of tiles in a tile pattern.

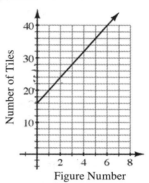

a.   Based on the information in the graph, how many tiles are being added each time (that is, what is the growth factor of the pattern)? Pay close attention to the scale of the axes.

b.   How many tiles are in Figure 0?

c.   How would the line change if the pattern grew by 12 tiles each time instead?

7-58.   Solve this system of equations:
$$y = \tfrac{2}{3}x - 4$$
$$2x - 3y = 10$$

a.   What does your solution tell you about the relationship between the lines?

b.   Solve the second equation for y.

c.   Does the slope of each line confirm your statement in part (a)? Explain how.

7-59.   Find the equation of each of the lines graphed at right. Then confirm algebraically that $(1, 1)$ is the point of intersection.

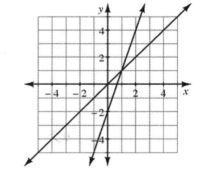

7-60.   Dominic simplified an expression using the Distributive Property and got this result: $15x^2 - 5x$. Can you find a possible expression that he started with?

7-61.   On graph paper, graph the line that goes through the points $(-6, 3)$ and $(-3, -1)$.

a.   What is the slope of the line?

b.   What is the y-intercept?

c.   Find the equation of the line.

7.2.2 What can slope represent?

Slope as a Measurement of Rate

Today you will focus on the meaning of slope in various contexts. What does a slope represent? How can you use it?

7-62.   THE BIG RACE – HEAT 1

Before a big race, participants often compete in **heats**, which are preliminary races that determine who competes in the final race. Later, your class will compete in a tricycle race against the winners of these preliminary heats.

In the first heat, Leslie, Kristin, and Evie rode tricycles toward the finish line. Leslie began at the starting line and rode at a constant rate of 2 meters every second. Kristin got an 8-meter head start and rode 2 meters every 5 seconds. Evie rode 5 meters every 4 seconds and got a 6-meter head start.

a.   On neatly scaled axes, graph and write an equation in terms of x and y for the distance Leslie travels. Let x represent time in seconds and y represent distance in meters. Then do the same for Kristin and Evie using the same set of axes.

b.   After how many seconds did Leslie catch up to Evie? How far were they from the starting line when Leslie caught up to Evie? Confirm your answer algebraically.

c.   If the race is 20 meters long, who won? Use both the graph and the rules to **justify** your answer.

d.   What is the slope of Kristin's line? How does the slope of her line explain her rate of travel (also known as her speed)?

e.   Kaye also rode in this heat. When her distance line is graphed, the rule is $y = \frac{2}{3}x + 1$. What was her speed? Did she get a head start?

Algebra Connections

7-63. **TAKE A WALK**

The president of the Line Factory is so
impressed with your work that you have been
given a special assignment: to analyze the
graphs below, which were created when a
customer walked in front of a motion detector.
The motion detector recorded the distance
between it and the customer.

Working with your team, explain what motion each graph describes. In other words,
how did the customer need to walk in order to create each graph? **Note:** Time is
measured in 1-second increments along the *x*-axis, while distance from the detector
is measured in 1-foot increments along the *y*-axis.

Make sure you describe:

- If the customer was walking **toward** or **away** from the motion detector.
- Where the customer began walking when the motion detector started
  collecting data.
- When the customer walked slowly and when he or she walked quickly.
- Any time the customer changed direction or stopped.

a. 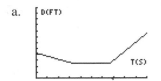   b. 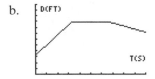   c.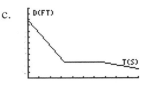

7-64. **OTHER RATES OF CHANGE**

Problems 7-62 and 7-63 concentrated on situations where the slope of a line
represented speed. However, many other situations can be graphed that do not
involve motion. Examine the graphs below and explain what real-world quantities
the slope and *y*-intercepts represent. Find the slope and *y*-intercept. Write the
measurement units with each of your answers. (For example, the slopes in problem
7-63 would be expressed in feet per second.)

a. 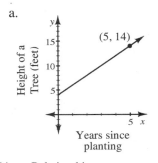   b. 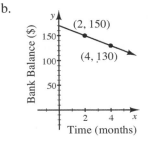   c.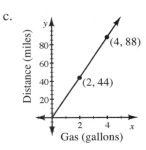

METHODS AND MEANINGS

MATH NOTES

Writing the Equation of a Line from a Graph

One of the ways to write the equation of a line directly from a graph is to find the slope of the line (m) and the y-intercept (b). These values can then be substituted into the general slope-intercept form of a line: $y = mx + b$.

For example, the slope of the line at right is $m = \frac{1}{3}$, while the y-intercept is $(0, 2)$. By substituting $m = \frac{1}{3}$ and $b = 2$ into $y = mx + b$, the equation of the line is:

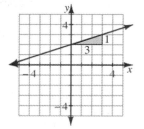

$$y = mx + b \quad \rightarrow \quad y = \tfrac{1}{3}x + 2$$

slope y-intercept

═══════════════ Review & Preview ═══════════════

7-65.   THE BIG RACE – HEAT 2

Barbara, Elizabeth, and Carlos participated in the second heat of "The Big Race." Barbara thought she could win with a 3-meter head start even though she only pedaled 3 meters every 2 seconds. Elizabeth began at the starting line and finished the 20-meter race in 5 seconds. Meanwhile, Carlos rode his tricycle so that his distance (y) from the starting line in meters could be represented by the rule $y = \frac{5}{2}x + 1$, where x represents time in seconds.

a.   Using the given information, graph lines for Barbara, Elizabeth, and Carlos on the same set of axes. Who won the 20-meter race and will advance to the final race?

b.   Find rules that describe Barbara's and Elizabeth's motion.

c.   How fast did Carlos pedal?

d.   When did Carlos pass Barbara? Confirm your answer algebraically.

Algebra Connections

7-66.   Salami and More Deli sells a 6-foot sandwich for
         parties. It weighs 8 pounds. Assume the weight
         per foot is constant.

    a.   How much does a sandwich 0 feet long
          weigh?

    b.   Draw a graph showing the weight of the
          sandwich (vertical axis) compared to the
          length of the sandwich (horizontal axis).
          Label the axes with appropriate units.

    c.   Use your graph to estimate the weight of a 1-foot sandwich.

    d.   Write a proportion to find the length of a 12-pound sandwich.

7-67.   Create a table and a graph for the line $y = 5x - 10$. Find the x-intercept and
         y-intercept in the table and in the graph.

7-68.   Match each expression in the left column with the equivalent expression on the right.
         Show and explain how you decided which ones matched.

    a. $(x+5)(2x-1)$ 1. $2x^2 + 9x - 5$

    b. $(2x-5)(x+1)$ 2. $2x^2 - 9x - 5$

    c. $(2x+1)(x-5)$ 3. $2x^2 - 3x - 5$

7-69.   Complete the missing entries in the table below. Then write the rule.

IN (x)	2	10	6	7	-3		-10	100	x
OUT (y)	4	28	16			10			

7-70.   Write and solve an equation (or a system of equations) for the situation below.
         Define your variable(s) and write your solution as a sentence.

         The Physical Education Department sells t-shirts for $12 and shorts for $8. One
         month, they sold 77 total items for $780 in total. How many t-shirts did they sell?

7.2.3 How can I use $y = mx + b$?

Rates of Change

Over the last four chapters you have found linear equations using many different strategies and starting from many different types of information. Today you are going to **apply** what you know about finding linear equations to solve a complicated puzzle: Who among you will win "The Big Race"?

7-71.   THE BIG RACE

Today is the final event of "The Big Race"! Your teacher will give you each a card that describes how you travel in the race. You and your study team will compete against Leslie and Elizabeth at today's rally in the gym. (Note: The information cards are also available at www.cpm.org.)

Your Task: As a team, do the following:

- Draw a graph (on graph paper) showing all of the racers' progress over time.

- Write an equation for each participant.

- Figure out who will win the race!

Rules:

- Your study team must work cooperatively to solve the problems. No team member has enough information to solve the puzzle alone!

- Each member of the team will select rider A, B, C, or D. You may not show your card to your team. You may only communicate the information contained on the card.

- Assume that each racer travels at a constant rate throughout the race.

- Elizabeth's and Leslie's cards will be shared by the entire team.

7-72.   Use your results from "The Big Race" to answer the following questions. You may answer the questions in any order, but be sure to **justify** each response.

a.   Who won "The Big Race"? Who came in last place?

b.   How fast was Rider D traveling? How fast was Elizabeth traveling?

c.   At one point in the race, four different participants were the same distance from the starting line. Who were they and when did this happen?

x- and *y*-Intercepts

Recall that the **x-intercept** of a line is the point where the graph crosses the *x*-axis (where $y = 0$). To find the *x*-intercept, substitute 0 for *y* and solve for *x*. The coordinates of the *x*-intercept are $(x, 0)$.

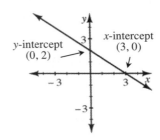

Similarly, the **y-intercept** of a line is the point where the graph crosses the *y*-axis, which happens when $x = 0$. To find the *y*-intercept, substitute 0 for *x* and solve for *y*. The coordinates of the *y*-intercept are $(0, y)$.

Review & Preview

7-73.   Find the point of intersection of the lines $3 = 6x - y$ and $3x - 2y = 24$.

7-74.   Sometimes the quickest and easiest two points to use to graph a line that is not in slope-intercept form are the *x*- and *y*-intercepts. Find the *x*- and *y*-intercepts for the two lines below and use them to graph each line. Write the coordinates of the *x*- and *y*-intercepts on your graph.

   a. $x - 2y = 4$

   b. $3x + 6y = 24$

7-75.   Find the slope of the line passing through each pair of points below.

   a.   (1, 2) and (4, −1)

   b.   (7, 3) and (5, 4)

   c.   (−6, 8) and (−8, 5)

   d.   (55, 67) and (50, 68)

   e.   Azizah got 1 for the slope of the line through points (1, 2) and (4, −1). Explain to her the mistake she made and how to find the slope correctly.

7-76.   MATCH-A-GRAPH

Match the following graphs with their equations. Pay special attention to the scaling of each set of axes. Explain how you found each match.

a. $y = \frac{1}{4}x + 4$

b. $y = \frac{1}{2}x + 4$

c. $y = 2x + 4$

d. $y = -\frac{2}{3}x + 4$

1.

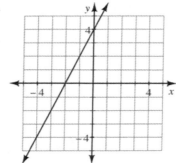

2.

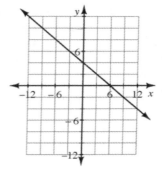

3.

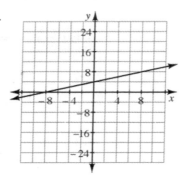

4.

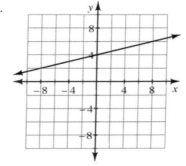

7-77.   Simplify the following expressions.

a. $15x^2 - 3x(4 + 5x)$

b. $\frac{1}{3}(24x - 9) + 10$

c. $(x - 3)(x + 1) + 2x$

d. $6x - 2 + 9 - 3y - x$

7-78.   **Multiple Choice:** The cost of a sweater is $3 less than the cost of a pair of jeans, while a hat is twice the cost of a sweater. If the pair of jeans costs j dollars, then which expression below represents the cost of the hat?

a. $2j$ b. $j - 3$ c. $2(j - 3)$ d. $2j - 3$

7.3.1 How can the solutions help find an equation?

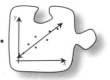

. . . .

Finding an Equation Given a Slope and a Point

To do well in "The Big Race," you had to find the equation of a line with a given rate (slope) that passed through a given point. Your method probably involved estimating the y-intercept of the line visually or working backward on a graph. What if the given point is far away from the y-axis? What if an estimate is not good enough in a particular situation?

During this lesson, you will develop an algebraic method for finding the equation of a line when given its slope and a point on the line.

7-79.   **DOWN ON THE FARM**

Colleen recently purchased a farm that raises chickens. Since she has never raised chickens before, Colleen wants to learn as much about her baby chicks as possible. In particular, she wants to know how much a baby chick weighs when it is hatched.

To find out, Colleen decided to track the weight of one of the chickens that was born just before she purchased the farm. She found that her chick grew steadily by about 5.2 grams each day, and she assumes that it has been doing so since it hatched. Nine days after it hatched, the chick weighed 98.4 grams.

Your Task: Determine how much the chick weighed the day it was hatched using two different representations of the chick's growth: a graph and an $x \rightarrow y$ table. Then, assuming the chicken will continue to grow at the same rate, determine when the chick will weigh 140 grams.

Discussion Points

What are you looking for?

What information are you given?

What do you expect the graph to look like? Why?

Which representation (graph or table) will give more accurate results? Why?

7-80.   USING A GRAPH

Use the information in problem 7-79 to answer these questions.

a.   What is the baby chick's rate of growth? That is, how fast does the baby chick grow? How does this rate relate to the equation of the line?

b.   Before graphing, describe the line that represents the growth of the chicken. Do you know any points on the line? Does the line point upward or downward? How steep is it?

c.   Draw a graph for this situation. Let the horizontal axis represent the number of days since the chick hatched, and let the vertical axis represent the chick's weight. Label and scale your axes appropriately and title your graph "Growth of a Baby Chick."

d.   What is the y-intercept of your graph? According to your graph, how much did Colleen's chick weigh the day it hatched?

e.   When will the chick weigh 140 grams?

7-81.   USING A TABLE

Use the information in problem 7-79 to answer these questions.

a.   Now approach this problem using a table. Make a table with two columns, the first labeled "Days Since Birth" and the second labeled "Weight in Grams." In the first column, write the numbers 0 through 10.

b.   Use Colleen's measurements to fill one entry in the table.

c.   Use the chick's growth rate to complete the table.

d.   According to your table, how much did the chick weigh the day it was hatched? When will the chick weigh 140 grams? Do these answers match your answers from the graph? Which method do you think is more accurate? Why?

————   *Further Guidance section ends here.*   ————

7-82.   FINDING AN EQUATION WITHOUT A TABLE OR GRAPH

Now you will explore another way Colleen could find the weight of her chick when it hatched without using a table or a graph.

a.   Since Colleen is assuming that the chick grows linearly, the equation will be in the form $y = mx + b$. Without graphing, what do m and b represent? Do you know either of these values?

b.   You already know the chicken's rate of growth. Place the slope into the equation of the line. What information is still unknown?

c.   In Lesson 7.1.5, you discovered that knowing the slope and a point is enough information to determine a line. Therefore, using the point (9, 98.4) should help you find the y-intercept. How can you use this point in your equation? Discuss this with your team and be ready to share your ideas with the rest of the class.

d.   Work together as a class to solve for b (the weight of the chick when it was hatched). Write the equation of the line that represents the weight of the chick.

e.   Does the y-intercept you found algebraically match the one you found using the graph? Does it match the one you found using the table? How accurate do you think your algebraic answer is?

f.   Use your equation to determine when Colleen's chicken will weigh 140 grams.

7-83.   Use this new algebraic method to find equations for lines with the following properties:

a.   A slope of –3, passing through the point (15, –50).

b.   A slope of 0.5 with an x-intercept of 28.

7-84.   MIGHTY MT. EVEREST

The Earth's surface is composed of gigantic plates that are constantly moving. Currently, India lies on a plate that is slowly drifting northward. India's plate is grinding into the rest of Asia. As it does so, it pushes up the Himalayan Mountains, which contain the world's highest peak, Mt. Everest. In 1999, mountain climbers measured Mt. Everest  with satellite gear and found it to be 8850 meters high. Geologists estimate that Mt. Everest may be growing by as much as 5 cm per year.

Your Task: Assuming a constant growth of 5 cm per year, determine how tall Mt. Everest was in the year 0. (The year 0 is the year that came 2000 years before the year 2000.) Write an equation for the height of Mt. Everest over time, with x representing the year and y representing the height of the mountain.

7-85.   The point (21, 32) is on a line with slope 1.5.

   a.   Find the equation of the line.

   b.   Find the coordinates of a third point on the line.

7-86.   Copy and complete each of the Diamond Problems below. The pattern used in the Diamond Problems is shown at right.

   a.   b.   c.   d.

7-87.   Solve the following systems of equations. Remember to check your solution in both equations to make sure it is the point of intersection.

   a. $y = 2x - 3$ b. $y - x = -2$
         $x - y = -4$ $-3y + 2x = 14$

7-88.   Solve each of the following equations for x.

   a. $\frac{x}{6} = \frac{7}{3}$ b. $3x + 2 = 7x - 8$

   c. $\frac{6}{x} = \frac{4}{x+1}$ d. $6(x - 4) = 42$

7-89.   The graph of the equation $2x - 3y = 7$ is a line.

   a.   Find the x- and y-intercepts and graph the line using these two points.

   b.   If a point on this line has an x-coordinate of 10, what is its y-coordinate?

7-90.   Without graphing, identify the slope and y-intercept of each equation below.

   a. $y = 3x + 5$ b. $y = \frac{5}{-4}x$ c. $y = 3$

   d. $y = 7 + 4x$ e. $3x + 4y = -4$ f. $x + 5y = 30$

7.3.2 What if the lines are perpendicular?

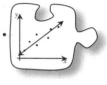

Slopes cf Parallel and Perpendicular Lines

In Lesson 7.1.5, you found that the slopes of parallel lines are equal because lines with the same steepness grow at the same rate. What about the slopes of perpendicular lines (lines that form a right angle)? Today you will answer this question and then use parallel and perpendicular lines to find the equations of other lines.

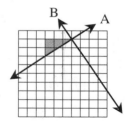

Perpendicular lines form a right angle.

7-91.   SLOPES OF PERPENDICULAR LINES

To investigate the slopes of perpendicular lines, you will need some graph paper and a ruler or straightedge. You will also need a piece of transparency and an overhead pen (or tracing paper).

a.   First place the transparency over the graph paper. Use the grid lines and ruler to draw two perpendicular lines, like the ones shown above. Label one line A and the other line B.

b.   Now turn your transparency so that line A has a slope of $\frac{2}{3}$, as shown in the diagram at right. What is the slope of line B? Verify your results with your teammates and place your results in a table like the one shown at right.

Slope of Line A	Slope of Line B
$\frac{2}{3}$	

c.   Now collect data for at least three more pairs of perpendicular lines. For example, if line A has a slope of 2 , what is the slope of the line perpendicular to it (line B)? What if line A has a slope of $-\frac{1}{4}$? Add each pair to your table from part (a). Share any patterns you find with your teammates.

d.   Use inductive reasoning (using patterns) to find the relationship of the slopes of perpendicular lines. That is, based on your data, how do the slopes of perpendicular lines seem to be related? If you have two perpendicular lines, how can you get the slope of one from the other?

e.   Test your conjecture from part (d). First find the slope of the line perpendicular to a line with slope $\frac{3}{5}$ without using graph paper. Then test it with graph paper.

7-92. Use what you discovered about the slopes of parallel and perpendicular lines to find the equation of each line described below.

    a.   Find the equation of the line that goes through the point (2, –3) and is perpendicular to the line $y = -\frac{2}{5}x + 6$.

    b.   Find the equation of the line that is parallel to the line $-3x + 2y = 10$ and goes through the point (4, 7).

7-93. Line L is perpendicular to the line $6x - y = 7$ and passes through the point (0, 6). Line M is parallel to the line $y = \frac{2}{3}x - 4$ and passes through the point (–3, –1). Where do these lines intersect? Explain how you found your solution.

7-94. EXTENSION

Suppose the rule for line A is $y = \frac{6}{5}x - 10$. Line A is parallel to line B, which is perpendicular to line C. If line D is perpendicular to line C and perpendicular to line E, what is the slope of line E? **Justify** your conclusion.

7-95. In your Learning Log, summarize what you have learned today. Be sure to explain the relationship between the slopes of perpendicular lines and describe how to get the slope of one line when you know the slope of a line perpendicular to it. Title this entry "Slopes of Perpendicular Lines" and include today's date.

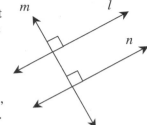

METHODS AND **M**EANINGS

Parallel and Perpendicular Lines

MATH NOTES

Parallel lines lie in the same plane (a flat surface) and never intersect. They have the same steepness, and therefore they grow at the same rate. Lines l and n at right are examples of parallel lines.

On the other hand, **perpendicular lines** are lines that intersect at a right angle. For example, lines m and n at right are perpendicular, as are lines m and l. Note that the small square drawn at the point of intersection indicates a right angle.

The **slopes of parallel lines** are the same. In general, the slope of a line parallel to a line with slope m is m.

The **slopes of perpendicular lines** are opposite reciprocals. For example, if one line has slope $\frac{4}{5}$, then any line perpendicular to it has slope $-\frac{5}{4}$. If a line has slope –3, then any line perpendicular to it has slope $\frac{1}{3}$. In general, the slope of a line perpendicular to a line with slope m is $-\frac{1}{m}$.

7-96.   Dean and Carlos decided to hold their own race. Dean estimates
          that he rides 3 meters every 4 seconds and wants a 5-meter head
          start. Carlos will ride 1 meter per second.

          a.   How many meters does Dean ride each second?

          b.   On one set of axes, graph and label lines to represent each
                rider's distance from the starting line. Find the equation for each rider.

          c.   Use the equations you wrote to determine when Carlos and Dean will be the
                same distance from the starting line.

7-97.   Explain what the slope of each line below represents. Then find the slope.

          a.   b.

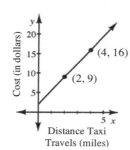   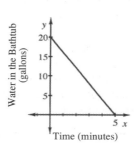

7-98.   In the spring of 2005, there were 30 more Republicans than Democrats in the United
          States House of Representatives. There was also one member from an Independent
          Party. If there were 435 representatives in all, how many Republicans were there?
          Write and solve an equation (or a system of equations) to find your solution.

7-99.   Find the x-intercepts of the parabola $y = x^2 + 2x - 15$ using any representation you
          prefer. Then explain your method.

7-100.   Find the following products.

          a. $(2x-1)(x+3)$ b. $3x(5x-11)$

          c. $(x-5)(5x-2)$ d. $100(3x-0.5)$

7-101.   **Multiple Choice:** What is the slope of the line that goes through the points $(-7, 10)$
          and $(1, 4)$?

          a. $\frac{3}{4}$ b. $-\frac{3}{4}$ c.   1   d. -1

7.3.3 What if I only have two points?

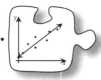

Finding the Equation of a Line through Two Points

So far, you know how to find the equation of a line with a given slope and a *y*-intercept or other point on the line. You have developed tools that help you find the equation using a graph, a table, or an algebraic process. Today you are going to expand your set of tools to include finding the equation of a line through two points. As you work on today's problems, keep these questions in mind:

What do you know about the line?

How can you use that information to find the equation?

How can you verify that your equation is correct?

7-102.   Without graphing, find the equation of the line that goes through the points (14, 52) and (29, 97). Use the questions below to help you organize your work.

a.   What is the slope of the line?

b.   How can you use a point to find the equation? Find the equation of the line.

c.   Once you have the slope, does it matter which point you use to find your equation? Why or why not?

d.   How can you verify that your equation is correct?

7-103.   In your Learning Log, describe the process you used in problem 7-102 to find the equation of a line through two points without graphing. Include an example. Title this entry "How to Find the Equation of a Line through Two Points" and include today's date.

7-104.   WELCOME TO DIZZYLAND!

Finding the equation of a line between two
points can be an effective method for finding
trend lines for data. Trend lines represent linear
data and can be used to make predictions about
an event or situation. In this problem, the
process you used in problem 7-102 will help
you make a prediction.

For over 50 years, Dizzyland has kept track of how many guests pass through its
entrance gates. Below is a table with the names and dates of some significant guests.
Predict when the 1 billionth guest will pass through Dizzyland's gates.

Name	Year	Guest
Elsa Marquez	1955	1 millionth guest
Leigh Woolfenden	1957	10 millionth guest
Dr. Glenn C. Franklin	1961	25 millionth guest
Mary Adams	1965	50 millionth guest
Valerie Suldo	1971	100 millionth guest
Gert Schelvis	1981	200 millionth guest
Brook Charles Arthur Burr	1985	250 millionth guest
Claudine Masson	1989	300 millionth guest
Minnie Pepito	1997	400 millionth guest
Mark Ramirez	2001	450 millionth guest

a.   With your team, represent the data on your grapher or on
graph paper. Let $x = 1955$ represent the year 1955.

b.   Select two points from the data that will make a good trend
line. You should choose your points so that when they are
connected by a line, that line will pass through the middle of
all the data and will resemble the overall trend of the data.
Every member of your team should use the same two points.
Be prepared to explain your choice of points and your
solution to the class.

c.   Use the two points you chose to find an equation for your trend line. Show
your algebraic thinking.

d.   Graph your line on the same axes as your data (either on your graph paper or
on your grapher). Does your line pass through the two points you chose? If
not, go back and check your work. Does the equation seem to do a good job of
fitting the data?

e.   What is the y-intercept of your line? Why does it make sense that it is
negative?

f.   Use your equation to make a prediction: If you want to be Dizzyland's
1 billionth guest, during what year should you go to the park? Remember that
1 billion is 1000 millions.

7-105.   Find the equations of the lines described below.

    a.   The line parallel to the line $y = \frac{1}{5}x - 6$ that goes through the point (–5, 3).

    b.   The line that goes through the points (100, 76) and (106, 58).

7-106.   Find the equation of the line with x-intercept (–4, 0) and y-intercept (0, 9).

7-107.   Find the point of intersection of the system of linear equations below.
$$8 - 3x = y$$
$$2y + 3x = 5$$

7-108.   On graph paper, graph the parabola $y = x^2 - 6x + 10$.

    a.   Label the x- and y-intercepts, if possible.

    b.   The highest or lowest point on a parabola is called the **vertex**. What is the vertex of this parabola?

7-109.   Evaluate the expressions below for the given values.

    a. $-2x^2 - 3x + 1$ for $x = -3$ b. $8 - (3x - 2)^2$ for $x = -2$

    c. $\frac{-3}{k+2}$ for $k = -3$ d. $\frac{15m}{n+1} - m^2 + n$ for $m = 1$, $n = 2$

7-110.   Find the slope of each line below. Which pairs of lines are perpendicular? Which pairs are parallel?

    a. $y = \frac{-5}{6}x + 3$ b. $y = 3$ c. $5x + 6y = 9$ d. $x = -4$

    e. $y = -4x - 5$ f. $y = \frac{1}{4}x - 7$ g. $4x - y = 2$ h. $y = 5 - \frac{6}{5}x$

Algebra Connections

7·3·4 What's the equation of the line?

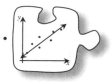

Applying $y = mx + b$ to Find Equations from Graphs

In past lessons, you learned facts about m and b by graphing lines from rules. In today's lesson, you will **reverse** the process used in Lesson 7.1.1 so that you can find the equation of a line when you know its graph.

7-111.   LINE FACTORY LOGO

The Line Factory needs a new logo for its pamphlet. After much work by the design staff, the two logos shown below were proposed.

The only problem is that the staff clerks need to have the equations of the lines in each design to program their pamphlet-production software.

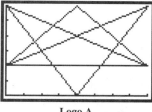

Logo A

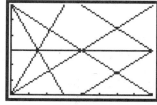

Logo B

Your Task: Find the equations of the lines in Logos A and B and recreate the graphs on your calculators. Split your team into two pairs so that one pair works on Logo A while the other pair works on Logo B.

Find the equations of the lines in your design and then use your grapher to check them. Assume that the axes shown above are scaled by ones. Also, be sure to set your window as shown at right so that the x-axis contains the values between 0 and 8 and the y-axis contains the values between 0 and 6. Once you have found all of the equations, draw all of the lines simultaneously on the same set of axes to recreate the logo on your grapher.

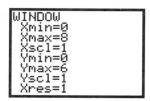

Discussion Points

How many equations should you have for each logo?

What is different about some of the lines? What is the same?

How can you find the equation of a line from its graph?

METHODS AND MEANINGS

Point-Slope Form of a Line

Another method for finding the equation of a line when given its slope and a point on the line uses the **point-slope form** of a line. This form is:

$$y - k = m(x - h)$$

In this form, (h, k) is a point on the line and m is the slope. For example, to find the equation of the line with slope $m = -3$ that goes through the point $(6, 1)$, substitute these values into $y - k = m(x - h)$ as shown below:

$$y - 1 = -3(x - 6)$$

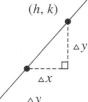

This result can then be changed to $y = mx + b$ form:

$$y - 1 = -3(x - 6)$$
$$y - 1 = -3x + 18$$
$$y = -3x + 19$$

Thus, the equation of the line with slope $m = -3$ that goes through the point $(6, 1)$ can be written as $y - 1 = -3(x - 6)$ or $y = -3x + 19$.

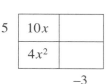
Review & Preview

7-112.   Complete each generic rectangle below and write the area as a sum and as a product.

a.

	10xy
4	

3   5x

b.

5	10x	
	4x²	

−3

7-113.   Peggy decided to sell brownies and cookies to raise
          money for her basketball uniform. She sold
          brownies for $3.00 and cookies for $2.50. If she
          sold 3 fewer cookies than brownies and collected
          $218 in all, then how many brownies did she sell?
          Write and solve an equation (or a system of
          equations) to find your solution.

7-114.   Find the equation of each line below.

          a.   The line with slope $m = -\frac{2}{3}$ that goes through the point $(-6, 5)$.

          b.   A horizontal line that goes through the point $(8, -11)$.

          c.   The line perpendicular to the line in part (a) above but going through the
                origin.

7-115.   Explain what the slope of each line below represents. Then find the slope.

          a.   b.

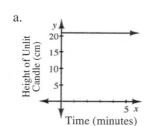   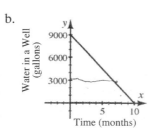

7-116.   Copy and complete each of the Diamond Problems below.
          The pattern used in the Diamond Problems is shown at right.

          a.   b.   c.   d.

7-117.   Simplify each expression below, if possible.

          a. $5x(3x)$ b. $5x + 3x$ c. $6x(x)$ d. $6x + x$

Extension Activity What's the equation of the line?

Finding $y = mx + b$ from Graphs and Tables

In past lessons, you learned facts about m and b by graphing lines from rules. In today's lesson, you will **reverse** the process to find the equation of a line when you know its graph.

7-118.   SAVE THE EARTH

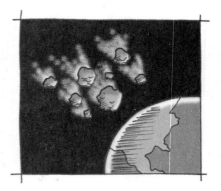

The Earth Protection Service (EPS) has asked your team to defend our planet against dangerous meteors. Luckily, the EPS has developed a very advanced protection system, called the Linear Laser Cannon. This cannon must be programmed with an equation that dictates the path of a laser beam and destroys any meteors in its path. Unfortunately, the cannon uses a huge amount of energy, making it very expensive to fire.

Your Mission: Using the technology (or resource page) provided by your teacher, find equations of lines that will eliminate the meteors as efficiently as possible. The EPS offers big rewards for operators who use the fewest number of lasers possible to eliminate the meteors.

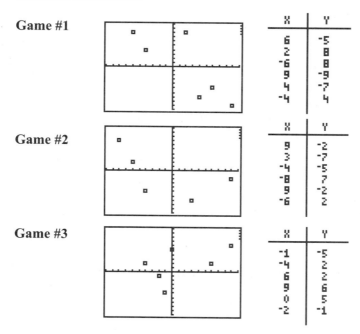

Game #1

X	Y
6	-5
2	8
-6	8
9	-9
4	-7
-4	4

Game #2

X	Y
9	-2
3	-7
-4	-5
-8	7
9	-2
-6	2

Game #3

X	Y
-1	-5
-4	2
6	2
9	6
0	5
-2	-1

Chapter 7 Closure   What have I learned?

Reflection and Synthesis

The activities below offer you a chance to reflect on what you have learned during this chapter. As you work, look for concepts that you feel very comfortable with, ideas that you would like to learn more about, and topics you need more help with. Look for **connections** between ideas as well as **connections** with material you learned previously.

①   TEAM BRAINSTORM

With your team, brainstorm a list for each of the following topics. Be as detailed as you can. How long can you make your list? Challenge yourselves. Be prepared to share your team's ideas with the class.

Topics: What have you studied in this chapter? What ideas and words were important in what you learned? Remember to be as detailed as you can.

Ways of Thinking: What Ways of Thinking did you use in this chapter? When did you use them?

Connections: What topics, ideas, and words that you learned *before* this chapter are **connected** to the new ideas in this chapter? Again, make your list as long as you can.

The following is a list of the vocabulary used in this chapter. The words that appear in bold are new to this chapter. Make sure that you are familiar with all of these words and know what they mean. Refer to the glossary or index for any words that you do not yet understand.

coefficients	graph	growth
linear equation	parallel	**perpendicular**
prediction	**rate of change**	**slope**
slope triangle	solution	**steepness**
trend line	Δx	x-intercept
$y = mx + b$	Δy	y-intercept

Make a concept map showing all of the **connections** you can find among the key words and ideas listed above. To show a **connection** between two words, draw a line between them and explain the **connection**, as shown in the example below. A word can be **connected** to any other word as long as there is a **justified connection**. For each key word or idea, provide a sketch that illustrates the idea (see the following example).

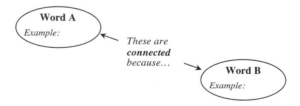

Your teacher may provide you with vocabulary cards to help you get started. If you use the cards to plan your concept map, be sure either to re-draw your concept map on your paper or to glue the vocabulary cards to a poster with all of the **connections** explained for others to see and understand.

While you are making your map, your team may think of related words or ideas that are not listed here. Be sure to include these ideas on your concept map.

③   SUMMARIZING MY UNDERSTANDING

Congratulations! You are now the owner of the city's premiere Line Factory. However, instead of raking in huge profits, you've noticed that you are only breaking even because many customers are ordering the incorrect line. After your company has produced the customer's line (at great expense!), they have refused to pay for it, saying it was not the line that they wanted!

Your Task: To prevent your customers from ordering the wrong lines, you need to produce a pamphlet to explain how to order a line. Carefully determine what information should be in the pamphlet so that customers will know how to write their equation in $y = mx + b$ form to get the line they want.

You can view some examples of fliers to help determine the layout of your pamphlet. A sample is shown at right. Your pamphlet can contain some advertisements, but remember that it needs to include *everything* you know about equations and graphs of lines so that your customers can order wisely. Remember to be specific and show examples!

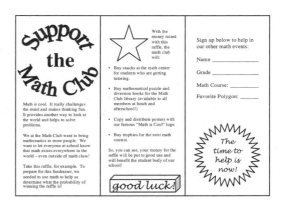

Discussion Points

How do m and b affect the equation of a line?

What information does a customer need to know to order a line correctly?

How could a customer figure out what line to order if he or she only knew two points on the line? One point and the slope?

Does the equation of a line always appear in the same form?

④　　　WHAT HAVE I LEARNED?

This section will help you evaluate which types of problems you have seen with which you feel comfortable and those with which you need more help. Even if your teacher does not assign this section, it is a good idea to try these problems and find out for yourself what you know and what you need to work on.

Solve each problem as completely as you can. The table at the end of the closure section has answers to these problems. It also tells you where you can find additional help and practice on problems like these.

CL 7-119.　For the line graphed at right:

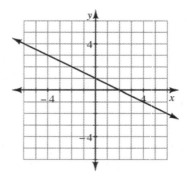

    a.　Find the slope.

    b.　Find the y-intercept.

    c.　Write the equation.

    d.　Find the equation of a line parallel to the one at right that passes through the point $(0, 7)$.

CL 7-120.　Find m and b in the following equations.

    a.　$y = 2x + 1$　　　　b.　$y = \frac{2}{5}x - 4$　　　　c.　$3x + 2y = 4$

CL 7-121.　For each system of equations, find the point of intersection.

    a.　$3x + 4y = 25$　　　　　　　b.　$5x - 2y = 23$
        $y = x + 1$　　　　　　　　　　$-4x + 2y = -18$

CL 7-122.　Shirley starts with \$85 in the bank and saves \$15 every 2 months. Joshua starts with \$212.50 and spends \$20 every 3 months.

    a.　Write equations for the balances of Shirley's and Joshua's bank accounts.

    b.　When will Shirley and Joshua have the same amount of money? How much money will they have then?

CL 7-123. Shannon wants to estimate how many people live in her neighborhood. She knows that there are 56 houses on four blocks and that there are 62 blocks in her neighborhood.

    a.   How many houses are in her neighborhood?

    b.   Shannon estimates that on average, 4 people live in each house. About how many people live in her neighborhood?

CL 7-124. Louis and Max are contestants in a jellybean-eating contest. Louis eats 18 jellybeans in 30 seconds. Max eats 24 jellybeans in 40 seconds.

    a.   Who is eating jellybeans faster?

    b.   Because Max was also in a pie-eating contest today, he gets a 5-jellybean head start. If the contest lasts 3 minutes (180 seconds), who will win?

CL 7-125. Solve for m: $6m - 5 + 8m - (2m + 3) = 3(3m - 8)$.

CL 7-126. Match each situation to its equation and its graph. Explain how you know that all three go together.

Situations for each person:

1. Has $5 after 6 days.
2. Has no money after 7 days.
3. Has $9 after 1 day.
4. Has $10 after 2 days.
5. Started with $15.

Equations:

i. $-x + 2y = 18$

ii. $y = \frac{2}{3}x + 1$

iii. $x + 3y = 45$

iv. $y = 4x + 5$

v. $y = -x + 7$

Graphs:

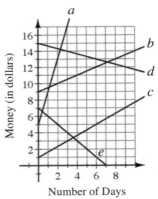

CL 7-127. Rewrite each product below as a sum.

    a. $(x + 3)(2x - 5)$

    b. $(3x - 6)(x - 4)$

CL 7-128. For each equation below, write the equation of a line that is **parallel** and passes through the origin. Then find another that is **perpendicular** and passes through the origin.

    a. $y = \frac{4}{3}x - 7$

    b. $y = 5x - 1$

    c. $y = x + 6$

CL 7-129. Copy and complete the table below for the rule $y = x^2 - 3x - 10$. Then graph the rule on graph paper.

x	-4	-3	-2	-1	0	1	2	3	4	5	6	7
y												

CL 7-130. Each box of tennis balls contains 3 tennis balls, while each box of baseballs only contains 2 baseballs. A sporting-goods store sold 26 boxes of tennis balls and baseballs. If a total of 70 balls were sold, how many boxes of tennis balls were sold? Write and solve an equation (or a system of equations) to find your answer.

CL 7-131. Find the equation of the line that passes through the points $(-5, 7)$ and $(10, 1)$.

CL 7-132. Check your answers using the table at the end of the closure section. Which problems do you feel confident about? Which problems were hard? Use the table to make a list of topics you need help on and a list of topics you need to practice more.

⑤   HOW AM I THINKING?

This course focuses on five different **Ways of Thinking**: reversing thinking, justifying, generalizing, making connections, and applying and extending understanding. These are some of the ways in which you think while trying to make sense of a concept or to solve a problem (even outside of math class). During this chapter, you have probably used each Way of Thinking multiple times without even realizing it!

Choose three of these Ways of Thinking that you remember using while working in this chapter. For each Way of Thinking that you choose, show and explain where you used it and how you used it. Describe why thinking in this way helped you solve a particular problem or understand something new. (For instance, explain why you wanted to **generalize** in this particular case, or why it was useful to see these particular **connections**.) Be sure to include examples to demonstrate your thinking.

Answers and Support for Closure Activity #4
What Have I Learned?

Problem	Solution	Need Help?	More Practice
CL 7-119.	a. The slope is $-\frac{1}{2}$. b. The y-intercept is $(0, 1)$. c. $y = -\frac{1}{2}x + 1$ d. $y = -\frac{1}{2}x + 7$	Lessons 7.1.3, 7.1.5, 7.2.2, 7.2.3, and 7.3.2 Math Notes boxes	Problems 7-59, 7-61, 7-76, 7-92, and 7-105
CL 7-120.	a. $m = 2$, $b = 1$ b. $m = \frac{2}{5}$, $b = -4$ c. $m = -\frac{3}{2}$, $b = 2$	Lesson 7.2.2 Math Notes box	Problems 7-76, 7-82, and 7-90
CL 7-121.	a. $(3, 4)$ b. $(5, 1)$	Lesson 7.1.4 Math Notes box	Problems 7-5, 7-38, 7-48, 7-58, 7-59, 7-73, 7-87, and 7-107
CL 7-122.	a. Let x = # of months that have passed Let y = amount of money in the account For Shirley: $y = \frac{15}{2}x + 85$ For Joshua: $y = -\frac{20}{3}x + 212.5$ b. They will have the same amount of money after 9 months. They will each have $152.50 in their accounts.	Lesson 7.1.4 Math Notes box	Problems 7-9, 7-26, 7-29, 7-47, 7-70, 7-96, 7-98, and 7-113
CL 7-123.	a. There are 868 houses in the neighborhood. b. There are 3472 people in the neighborhood.	Lesson 5.2.1 Math Notes box	Problems 7-6, 7-41, 7-57, and 7-66
CL 7-124.	a. They are eating jellybeans at the same rate (36 jellybeans per minute). b. Max will win. After 3 minutes, Louis will have eaten 108 jellybeans and Max will have eaten 113 jellybeans.	Lesson 7.2.2	Problems 7-65 and 7-96

Problem	Solution	Need Help?	More Practice
CL 7-125.	$m=-\frac{16}{3}$	Lesson 5.1.3 Math Notes box, Lesson 5.1.4	Problems 7-15, 7-28, 7-39, 7-50, and 7-88
CL 7-126.	Situation 1, Equation *ii*, Graph (c) Situation 2, Equation *v*, Graph (e) Situation 3, Equation *iv*, Graph (a) Situation 4, Equation *i*, Graph (b) Situation 5, Equation *iii*, Graph (d)	Lesson 7.2.1, Lessons 7.2.2 and 7.2.3 Math Notes boxes	Problems 7-32, 7-37, 7-64, 7-76, 7-90, 7-97, and 7-115
CL 7-127.	a. $2x^2+x-15$ b. $3x^2-18x+24$	Lesson 5.1.3 Math Notes box	Problems 7-30, 7-68, and 7-100
CL 7-128.	a. parallel: $y=\frac{4}{3}x$ perpendicular: $y=-\frac{3}{4}x$ b. parallel: $y=5x$ perpendicular: $y=-\frac{1}{5}x$ c. parallel: $y=x$ perpendicular: $y=-x$	Lesson 7.3.2 Math Notes box	Problems 7-44, 7-92, 7-93, 7-105, and 7-110
CL 7-129.	*y*-values in table: 18, 8, 0, –6, –10, –12, –12, –10, –6, 0, 8, and 18	Lesson 3.1.4, Lessons 3.1.4 and 4.1.7 Math Notes boxes	Problems 7-25 and 7-108
CL 7-130.	If t = number of boxes of tennis balls and b = number of boxes of baseballs, then $3t+2b=70$ and $t+b=26$; $t=18$, so 18 boxes of tennis balls were sold.	Lesson 7.1.4 Math Notes box	Problems 7-9, 7-26, 7-29, 7-47, 7-70, 7-96, 7-98, and 7-113
CL 7-131.	$y=-\frac{2}{5}x+5$	Lesson 7.3.3, Lesson 7.3.4 Math Notes box	Problems 7-102 and 7-106

CHAPTER 8

In Chapter 4, you used a web to organize the connections you found between each of the different representations of lines. These connections enabled you to use any representation (such as a graph, rule, situation, or table) to find any of the other representations.

In this chapter, a quadratics web will challenge you to find connections between the different representations of a parabola. Through this endeavor, you will learn how to rewrite quadratic equations by using a process called factoring. You will also discover and use a very important property of zero.

Guiding Questions

Think about these questions throughout this chapter:

How can I rewrite it?

What's the connection?

What's special about zero?

What information do I need?

Is there another method?

In this chapter, you will learn:

➢ How to factor a quadratic expression completely.

➢ How to find the roots of a quadratic equation, if they exist.

➢ How to move from all representations of a parabola (rule, graph, table, and situation) to each of the other representations directly.

Chapter Outline

Section 8.1 In this section, you will develop a method to change a quadratic equation written as a sum into its product form (also called its factored form).

Section 8.2 Through a fun application, you will find ways to generate each representation of a parabola from each of the others. You will also develop a method to solve quadratic equations using the Zero Product Property.

Section 8.3 In this section, you will be introduced to another method to solve quadratic equations called the Quadratic Formula.

Algebra Connections

8.1.1 How can I find the product?

Introduction to Factoring Quadratics

In Chapter 5 you learned how to multiply algebraic expressions using algebra tiles and generic rectangles. This section will focus on **reversing** this process: How can you find a product when given a sum?

8-1.   Review what you know about products and sums below.

   a.   Write the area of the rectangle at right as a product and as a sum. Remember that the product represents the area found by multiplying the length by the width, while the sum is the result of adding the areas inside the rectangle.

   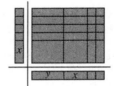

   b.   Use a generic rectangle to multiply $(6x - 1)(3x + 2)$. Write your solution as a sum.

8-2.   The process of changing a sum to a product is called **factoring**. Can every expression be factored? That is, *does every sum have a product that can be represented with tiles?*

   Investigate this question by building rectangles with algebra tiles for the following expressions. For each one, write the area as a sum and as a product. If you cannot build a rectangle, be prepared to convince the class that no rectangle exists (and thus the expression cannot be factored).

   a. $2x^2 + 7x + 6$ b. $6x^2 + 7x + 2$

   c. $x^2 + 4x + 1$ d. $2xy + 6x + y^2 + 3y$

8-3.   Work with your team to find the sum and the product for the following generic rectangles. Are there any special strategies you discovered that can help you determine the dimensions of the rectangle? Be sure to share these strategies with your teammates.

a.

$2x$	5
$6x^2$	$15x$

b.

$-2y$	-6
$5xy$	$15x$

c.

$-9x$	-12
$12x^2$	$16x$

8-4.   While working on problem 8-3, Casey noticed a pattern with the diagonals of each generic rectangle. However, just before she shared her pattern with the rest of her team, she was called out of class! The drawing on her paper looked like the diagram below. Can you figure out what the two diagonals have in common?

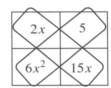

8-5.   Does Casey's pattern always work? Verify that her pattern works for all of the 2-by-2 generic rectangles in problem 8-3. Then describe Casey's pattern for the diagonals of a 2-by-2 generic rectangle in your Learning Log. Be sure to include an example. Title this entry "Diagonals of a Generic Rectangle" and include today's date.

METHODS AND **M**EANINGS

MATH NOTES

New Vocabulary to Describe Algebraic Expressions

Since algebraic expressions come in many different forms, there are special words used to help describe these expressions. For example, if the expression can be written in the form $ax^2 + bx + c$ and if a is not 0, it is called a **quadratic** expression. Study the examples of quadratic expressions below.

Examples of quadratic expressions:
$$x^2 - 15x + 26$$
$$16m^2 - 25$$
$$12 - 3k^2 + 5k$$

The way an expression is written can also be named. When an expression is written in product form, it is described as being **factored**. When factored, each of the expressions being multiplied is called a **factor**. For example, the factored form of $x^2 - 15x + 26$ is $(x - 13)(x - 2)$, so $x - 13$ and $x - 2$ are each factors of the original expression.

Finally, the number of terms in an expression can help you name the expression to others. If the expression has one term, it is called a **monomial**, while an expression with two terms is called a **binomial**. If the expression has three terms, it is called a **trinomial**. Study the examples below.

Examples of monomials: $\quad 15xy^2$ and $-2m$

Examples of binomials: $\quad 16m^2 - 25$ and $7h^9 + \frac{1}{2}h$

Examples of trinomials: $\quad 12 - 3k^2 + 5k$ and $x^2 - 15x + 26$

8-6.   Write the area of the rectangle at right as a sum and as a product.

$-3x$	$-6y$	12
$2x^2$	$4xy$	$-8x$

8-7.   Multiply the expressions below using a generic rectangle. Then verify Casey's pattern (that the product of one diagonal equals the product of the other diagonal).

    a. $(4x - 1)(3x + 5)$ b. $(2x - 7)^2$

8-8.   Remember that a Diamond Problem is a pattern for which the **product** of two numbers is placed on top, while the **sum** of the same two numbers is placed on bottom. (This pattern is demonstrated in the diamond at right.) Copy and complete each Diamond Problem below.

    a.   b.   c.   d.

    e.   f.

8-9.   For each line below, name the slope and y-intercept.

    a. $y = \frac{-1+4x}{2}$ b. $3x + y = -7$

    c. $y = \frac{-2}{3}x + 8$ d. $y = -2$

8-10.   On graph paper, graph $y = x^2 - 2x - 8$.

    a.   Name the y-intercept. What is the connection between the y-intercept and the rule $y = x^2 - 2x - 8$?

    b.   Name the x-intercepts.

    c.   Find the lowest point of the graph, the vertex.

8-11.   Calculate the value of each expression below.

    a. $5 - \sqrt{36}$ b. $1 + \sqrt{39}$ c. $-2 - \sqrt{5}$

8.1.2 Is there a shortcut?

Factoring with Generic Rectangles

Since mathematics is often described as the study of patterns, it is not surprising that generic rectangles have many patterns. You saw one important pattern in Lesson 8.1.1 (Casey's pattern from problem 8-4). Today you will continue to use patterns while you develop a method to factor trinomial expressions.

8-12. Examine the generic rectangle shown at right.

$-35x$	14
$10x^2$	$-4x$

    a. Review what you learned in Lesson 8.1.1 by writing the area of the rectangle at right as a sum and as a product.

    b. Does this generic rectangle fit Casey's pattern for diagonals? Demonstrate that the product of each diagonal is equal.

8-13. FACTORING QUADRATICS

To develop a method for factoring without algebra tiles, first study how to factor with algebra tiles, and then look for connections within a generic rectangle.

    a. Using algebra tiles, factor $2x^2 + 5x + 3$; that is, use the tiles to build a rectangle, and then write its area as a product.

    b. To factor with tiles (like you did in part (a)), you need to determine how the tiles need to be arranged to form a rectangle. Using a generic rectangle to factor requires a different process.

        Miguel wants to use a generic rectangle to factor $3x^2 + 10x + 8$. He knows that $3x^2$ and 8 go into the rectangle in the locations shown at right. Finish the rectangle by deciding how to place the ten x-terms. Then write the area as a product.

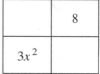

    c. Kelly wants to find a shortcut to factor $2x^2 + 7x + 6$. She knows that $2x^2$ and 6 go into the rectangle in the locations shown at right. She also remembers Casey's pattern for diagonals. Without actually factoring yet, what do you know about the missing two parts of the generic rectangle?

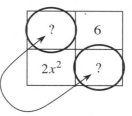

    d. To complete Kelly's generic rectangle, you need two x-terms that have a sum of $7x$ and a product of $12x^2$. Create and solve a Diamond Problem that represents this situation.

product

sum

    e. Use your results from the Diamond Problem to complete the generic rectangle for $2x^2 + 7x + 6$, and then write the area as a product of factors.

8-14.   Factoring with a generic rectangle is especially convenient when algebra tiles are not available or when the number of necessary tiles becomes too large to manage. Using a Diamond Problem helps avoid guessing and checking, which can at times be challenging. Use the process from problem 8-13 to factor $6x^2 + 17x + 12$. The questions below will guide your process.

a. When given a trinomial, such as $6x^2 + 17x + 12$, what two parts of a generic rectangle can you quickly complete?

b. How can you set up a Diamond Problem to help factor a trinomial such as $6x^2 + 17x + 12$? What goes on the top? What goes on the bottom?

product

c. Solve the Diamond Problem for $6x^2 + 17x + 12$ and complete its generic rectangle.

d. Write the area of the rectangle as a product.

sum

8-15.   Use the process you developed in problem 8-13 to factor the following quadratics, if possible. If a quadratic cannot be factored, justify your conclusion.

a. $x^2 + 9x + 18$ b. $4x^2 + 17x - 15$

c. $4x^2 - 8x + 3$ d. $3x^2 + 5x - 3$

METHODS AND MEANINGS

Diagonals of Generic Rectangles

MATH NOTES

Why does Casey's pattern from problem 8-4 work? That is, why does the product of the terms in one diagonal of a 2-by-2 generic rectangle always equal the product of the terms in the other diagonal?

Examine the generic rectangle at right for $(a + b)(c + d)$. Notice that each of the resulting diagonals have a product of $abcd$. Thus, the product of the terms in the diagonals are equal.

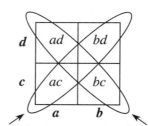

Product = $abcd$ Product = $abcd$

8-16.   Use the process you developed in problem 8-13 to factor the following quadratics, if possible.

   a. $x^2 - 4x - 12$ b. $4x^2 + 4x + 1$

   c. $2x^2 - 9x - 5$ d. $3x^2 + 10x - 8$

8-17.   For each rule represented below, state the x- and y-intercepts, if possible.

   a.   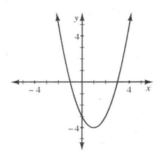   b.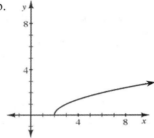

   c.   d. $5x - 2y = 40$

x	-5	-4	-3	-2	-1	0	1	2
y	8	4	0	-4	0	2	0	-4

8-18.   Graph $y = x^2 - 9$ on graph paper.

   a.   Name the y-intercept. What is the connection between the y-intercept and the rule $y = x^2 - 9$?

   b.   Name the x-intercepts. What is the connection between the x-intercepts and the rule $y = x^2 - 9$?

8-19.   Find the point of intersection for each system.

   a. $y = 2x - 3$ b. $3x = y - 2$
        $x + y = 15$ $6x = 4 - 2y$

8-20.   Solve each equation below for the given variable, if possible.

   a. $\frac{4x}{5} = \frac{x-2}{7}$ b. $-3(2b - 7) = -3b + 21 - 3b$ c. $6 - 2(c - 3) = 12$

8-21.   Find the equation of the line that passes through the points (–800, 200) and (–400, 300).

8.1.3 How can I factor this?

Factoring with Special Cases

Practice your new method for factoring quadratic expressions without tiles as you consider special types of quadratic expressions.

8-22. Factor each quadratic below, if possible. Use a Diamond Problem and generic rectangle for each one.

a. $x^2 + 6x + 9$ b. $2x^2 + 5x + 3$

c. $x^2 + 5x - 7$ d. $3m^2 + m - 14$

8-23. SPECIAL CASES

Most quadratics are written in the form $ax^2 + bx + c$. But what if a term is missing? Or what if the terms are in a different order? Consider these questions while you factor the expressions below. Share your ideas with your teammates and be prepared to demonstrate your process for the class.

a. $9x^2 - 4$ b. $12x^2 - 16x$

c. $3 + 8k^2 - 10k$ d. $40 - 100m$

8-24. Now turn your attention to the quadratic below. Use a generic rectangle and Diamond Problem to factor this expression. Compare your answer with your teammates' answers. Is there more than one possible answer?

$$4x^2 - 10x - 6$$

8-25.   The multiplication table below has factors along the top row and left column. Their product is where the row and column intersect. With your team, complete the table with all of the factors and products.

Multiply	$x - 2$	
$x + 7$		
	$3x^2 - 5x - 2$	$6x^2 + 5x + 1$

8-26.   In your Learning Log, explain how to factor a quadratic expression. Be sure to offer examples to demonstrate your understanding. Include an explanation of how to deal with special cases, such as when a term is missing or when the terms are not in standard order. Title this entry "Factoring Quadratics" and include today's date.

METHODS AND MEANINGS

MATH NOTES

Standard Form of a Quadratic

A quadratic expression in the form $ax^2 + bx + c$ is said to be in **standard form**. Notice that the terms are in order from greatest exponent to least.

Examples of quadratic expressions in standard form: $3m^2 + m - 1$, $x^2 - 9$, and $3x^2 + 5x$. Notice that in the second example, $b = 0$, while in the third example, $c = 0$.

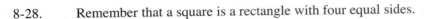

8-27.   The perimeter of a triangle is 51 cm. The longest side is twice the length of the shortest side. The third side is 3 cm longer than the shortest side. How long is each side? Write an equation that represents the problem and then solve it.

8-28.   Remember that a square is a rectangle with four equal sides.

   a.   If a square has an area of 81 square units, how long is each side?

   b.   Find the length of the side of a square with area 225 square units.

   c.   Find the length of the side of a square with area 10 square units.

   d.   Find the area of a square with side 11 units.

8-29.   Factor the following quadratics, if possible.

   a. $k^2 - 12k + 20$ b. $6x^2 + 17x - 14$

   c. $x^2 - 8x + 16$ d. $9m^2 - 1$

8-30.   Examine the two equations below. Where do they intersect?

$$y = 4x - 3$$
$$y = 9x - 13$$

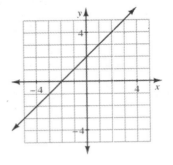

8-31.   Find the equation of a line perpendicular to the one graphed at right that passes through the point (6, 2).

8-32.   Solve each equation below for x. Check each solution.

   a. $2x - 10 = 0$ b. $x + 6 = 0$ c. $(2x - 10)(x + 6) = 0$

   d. $4x + 1 = 0$ e. $x - 8 = 0$ f. $(4x + 1)(x - 8) = 0$

Algebra Connections

8.1.4 Can it still be factored?

Factoring Completely

There are many ways to write the number 12 as a product of factors. For example, 12 can be rewritten as $3 \cdot 4$, as $2 \cdot 6$, as $1 \cdot 12$, or as $2 \cdot 2 \cdot 3$. While each of these products is accurate, only $2 \cdot 2 \cdot 3$ is considered to be **factored completely**, since the factors are prime and cannot be factored themselves.

During this lesson you will learn more about what it means for a quadratic expression to be factored completely.

8-33. Review what you have learned by factoring the following expressions, if possible.

a. $9x^2 - 12x + 4$

b. $81m^2 - 1$

c. $28 + x^2 - 11x$

d. $3n^2 + 9n + 6$

8-34. Compare your solutions for problem 8-33 with the rest of your class.

a. Is there more than one factored form of $3n^2 + 9n + 6$? Why or why not?

b. Why does $3n^2 + 9n + 6$ have more than one factored form while the other quadratics in problem 8-33 only have one possible answer? Look for clues in the original expression ($3n^2 + 9n + 6$) and in the different factored forms.

c. **Without factoring**, predict which quadratic expressions below may have more than one factored form. Be prepared to defend your choice to the rest of the class.

i. $12t^2 - 10t + 2$

ii. $5p^2 - 23p - 10$

iii. $10x^2 + 25x - 15$

iv. $3k^2 + 7k - 6$

8-35.   FACTORING COMPLETELY

In part (c) of problem 8-34, you should have noticed that each term in $12t^2 - 10t + 2$ is divisible by 2. That is, it has a **common factor** of 2.

a.   What is the common factor for $10x^2 + 25x - 15$?

b.   For an expression to be **completely factored**, each factor must have all common factors separated out. Sometimes it is easiest to do this first. Since 5 is a common factor of $10x^2 + 25x - 15$, you can factor $10x^2 + 25x - 15$ using a special generic rectangle, which is shown below. Find the length of this generic rectangle and write its area as a product of its length and width.

$$5 \; \boxed{\;10x^2 \;\big|\; + 25x \;\big|\; - 15\;}$$

c.   Can the result be factored even more? That is, can either factor from the result from part (b) above also be factored? Factor any possible expressions and write your solution as a product of all three factors.

8-36.   Factor each of the following expressions as completely as possible.

a. $5x^2 + 15x - 20$ b. $3x^3 - 6x^2 - 45x$

c. $2x^2 - 50$ d. $x^2y - 3xy - 10y$

MATH NOTES

METHODS AND MEANINGS

Factoring Quadratic Expressions

Review the process of factoring quadratics developed in problem 8-13 and outlined below. This example demonstrates how to factor $3x^2 + 10x + 8$.

1. Place the x^2- and constant terms of the quadratic expression in opposite corners of the generic rectangle. Determine the sum and product of the two remaining corners: The sum is simply the x-term of the quadratic expression, while the product is equal to the product of the x^2- and constant terms.

2. Place this sum and product into a Diamond Problem and solve it.

3. Place the solutions from the Diamond Problem into the generic rectangle and find the dimensions of the generic rectangle.

4. Write your answer as a product: $(3x + 4)(x + 2)$.

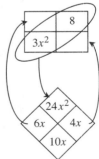

8-37. Factor the quadratic expressions below. If the quadratic is not factorable, explain why not.

    a. $2x^2 + 3x - 5$ b. $x^2 - x - 6$

    c. $3x^2 + 13x + 4$ d. $2x^2 + 5x + 7$

8-38. A line has intercepts (4, 0) and (0, –3). Find the equation of the line.

8-39. As Jhalil and Joman practice for the SAT, their scores on practice tests rise. Jhalil's current score is 850, and it is rising by 10 points per week. On the other hand, Joman's current score is 570 and is growing by 50 points per week.

    a. When will Joman's score catch up to Jhalil's?

    b. If the SAT test is in 12 weeks, who will score highest?

8-40. Mary says that you can find an x-intercept by substituting 0 for x, while Michelle says that you need to substitute 0 for y.

    a. Who, if anyone, is correct and why?

    b. Use the correct approach to find the x-intercept of $-4x + 5y = 16$.

8-41. Find three consecutive numbers whose sum is 138 by writing and solving an equation.

8-42. Match each rule below with its corresponding graph. Can you do this without making any tables? Explain your selections.

    a. $y = -x^2 - 2$ b. $y = x^2 - 2$ c. $y = -x^2 + 2$

    1. 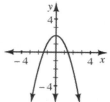   2. 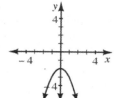   3.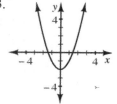

8.2.1 What do I know about a parabola?

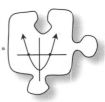

Investigating a Parabola

In previous chapters, you have investigated linear equations. In Section 8.2, you will study parabolas. You will learn all you can about their shape, study different equations used to graph them, and see how they can be used in real-life situations.

8-43. FUNCTIONS OF AMERICA

Congratulations! Your work at the Line Factory was so successful that the small local company grew into a national corporation called Functions of America. Recently your company has had some growing pains, and your new boss has turned to your team for help. See her memo below.

MEMO

To: *Your study team*
From: *Ms. Freda Function, CEO*
Re: *New product line*

I have heard that while lines are very popular, there is a new craze in Europe to have non-linear designs. I recently visited Paris and Milan and discovered that we are behind the times!

Please investigate a new function called a parabola. I'd like a full report at the end of today with any information your team can give me about its shape and equation. Spare no detail! I'd like to know everything you can tell me about how the rule for a parabola affects its shape. I'd also like to know about any special points on a parabola or any patterns that exist in its table.

Remember, the company is only as good as its employees! I need you to uncover the secrets that our competitors do not know.

Sincerely,
Ms. Function, CEO

Problem continues on next page →

8-43.   *Problem continued from previous page.*

Your Task: Your team will be assigned its own parabola to study. Investigate your team's parabola and be ready to describe everything you can about it by using its graph, rule, and table. Answer the questions below to get your investigation started. You may answer them in any order; however, do not limit yourselves to these questions!

- Does your parabola have any **symmetry**? That is, can you fold the graph of your parabola so that each side of the fold exactly matches the other? If so, where would the fold be? Do you think this works for all parabolas? Why or why not?

- Is there a highest or lowest point on the graph of your parabola? If so, where is it? This point is called a **vertex**. How can you describe the parabola at this point?

- Are there any special points on your parabola? Which points do you think are important to know? Are there any special points that you expected but do not exist for your parabola? What connection(s) do these points have with the rule of your parabola?

- How would you describe the shape of your parabola? For example, would you describe your parabola as pointing up or down? Do the sides of the parabola ever go straight up or down (vertically)? Why or why not? Is there anything else special about its shape?

List of Parabolas:

$$y = x^2 - 2x - 8$$

$$y = x^2 - 4x + 5$$

$$y = x^2 - 6x + 5$$

$$y = -x^2 + 2x - 1$$

$$y = -x^2 + 4$$

$$y = x^2 - 2x + 1$$

$$y = -x^2 + 3x + 4$$

$$y = x^2 + 5x + 1$$

8-44.   Prepare a poster for the CEO detailing your findings from your parabola investigation. Include any insights you and your teammates found. Explain your conclusions and justify your statements. Remember to include a complete graph of your parabola with all special points carefully labeled.

OOKING DEEPER

Symmetry

MATH NOTES

When a graph or picture can be folded so that both sides of the fold will perfectly match, it is said to have **symmetry**. The line where the fold would be is called the **line of symmetry**. Some shapes have more than one line of symmetry. See the examples below.

This shape has
one line of
symmetry.

This shape has
two lines of
symmetry.

This shape has
eight lines of
symmetry.

This graph has
two lines of
symmetry.

Review & Preview

8-45.   Calculate the value of each expression below.

a. $\dfrac{2+\sqrt{16}}{3}$

b. $\dfrac{-1+\sqrt{49}}{-2}$

c. $\dfrac{-10-\sqrt{5}}{2}$

8-46.   Find the equation of the line that goes through the points $(-15, 70)$ and $(5, 10)$.

8-47.   Change $6x - 2y = 10$ to slope-intercept ($y = mx + b$) form. Then state the slope (m) and the y-intercept (b).

8-48.   Copy the figure at right onto your paper. Then draw any lines of symmetry.

8-49.   For each rule represented below, state the x- and y-intercepts.

a.

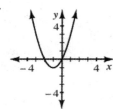

b.

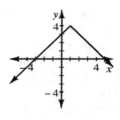

c.

x	-3	-2	-1	0	1	2	3
y	8	3	0	-1	0	3	8

d. $2x + 3y = 18$

8-50.   Use a generic rectangle to multiply each expression below.

a. $(3x - 4)(2x + 3)$

b. $(5x - 2)^2$

8.2.2 What's the connection?

Multiple Representations for Quadratics

In Chapter 4 you completed a web for the different representations of linear equations. You discovered special shortcuts to help you move from one representation to another. For example, given a linear equation, you can now draw the corresponding graph as well as determine an equation from a graph.

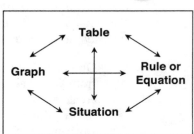

Today you will explore the connections between the different representations for quadratics. As you work, keep in mind the following questions:

What representations are you using?

What is the connection between the various representations?

What do you know about a parabola?

8-51.   WATER-BALLOON CONTEST

Every year Newtown High School holds a water-balloon competition during halftime of their homecoming game. Each contestant uses a catapult to launch a water balloon from the ground on the football field. This year you are the judge! You must decide which contestants win the prizes for *Longest Distance* and *Highest Launch*. Fortunately, you have a computer that will collect data for each throw. The computer uses *x* to represent horizontal distance in yards from the goal line and *y* to represent the height in yards.

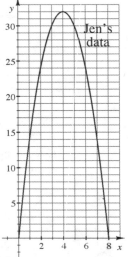

The announcer shouts, "Maggie Nanimos, you're up first!" She runs down and places her catapult at the 3-yard line. After Maggie's launch, the computer reports that the balloon traveled along the parabola $y = -x^2 + 17x - 42$.

Then you hear, "Jen Erus, you're next!" Jen runs down to the field, places her catapult at the goal line, and releases the balloon. The tracking computer reports the path of the balloon with the graph at right.

The third contestant, Imp Ecable, accidentally launches the balloon before you are ready. The balloon launches, you hear a roar from the crowd, turn around, and...SPLAT! The balloon soaks you and your computer! You only have time to write down the following partial information about the balloon's path before your computer fizzles:

x (yards)	2	3	4	5	6	7	8	9
y (yards)	0	9	16	21	24	25	24	21

Finally, the announcer calls for the last contestant, Al Truistic. With your computer broken, you decide to record the balloon's height and distance by hand. Al releases the balloon from the 10-yard line. The balloon reaches a height of 27 yards and lands at the 16-yard line.

a.   Obtain the Lesson 8.2.2 Resource Page from your teacher. For each contestant, create a table and graph using the information provided for each toss. Determine which of these contestants should win the *Longest Distance* and *Highest Throw* contests.

b.   Find the *x*-intercepts of each parabola. What information do the *x*-intercepts tell you about each balloon toss?

c.   Find the vertex of each parabola. What information does the vertex tell you about each balloon throw?

8-52.   Today you have explored the four different representations of
quadratics: table, graph, equation, and a description of a
physical situation involving motion. Draw the representations
of the web as shown below in your Learning Log and label it
"Quadratic Web."

a.   Draw in arrows showing the connections
that you currently know how to make
between different representations. Be
prepared to **justify** a connection for the
class.

b.   What connections are still missing?

```
QUADRATIC WEB

          Table

Graph              Rule or
                   Equation

        Situation
```

8-53.   SITUATION TO RULE

Review how to write a rule from a situation by
examining the tile pattern below.

```
QUADRATIC WEB

          Table

Graph              Rule or
                   Equation

        Situation
```

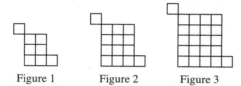

Figure 1   Figure 2   Figure 3

a.   Write a rule to represent the number of tiles in Figure x.

b.   Is the rule from part (a) **quadratic**? Explain how you know.

c.   If you have not done so already, add this pathway to your web from problem
8-52.

8-54.   Graph $y = x^2 - 8x + 7$ and label its vertex, x-intercepts, and y-intercepts.

8-55.   What is special about the number zero? Think about this as you answer the
         questions below.

   a.   Find each sum:

        $0 + 3 =$ $-7 + 0 =$ $0 + 6 =$ $0 + (-2) =$

   b.   What is special about adding zero? Write a
        sentence that begins, "When you add zero to a
        number, ..."

   c.   Julia is thinking of two numbers a and b. When she
        adds them together, she gets a sum of b. Does that
        tell you anything about either of Julia's numbers?

   d.   Find each product:

        $3 \cdot 0 =$ $(-7) \cdot 0 =$ $0 \cdot 6 =$ $0 \cdot (-2) =$

   e.   What is special about multiplying by zero? Write a sentence that begins,
        "When you multiply a number by zero, ..."

8-56.   Based on the tables below, say as much as you can about the x- and y-intercepts of
         the corresponding graphs.

a.

x	y
2	0
0	18
−4	0
−1	−8
6	22
3	0

b.

x	y
7	−4
3	0
10	8
0	−3
8	0
−7	−1

c.

x	y
0	−4
−5	11
3	−2
1	0
13	27
−6	14

8-57.   For the line described by the equation $y = 2x + 6$:

   a.   What is the x-intercept?

   b.   What is the slope of any line perpendicular to the given line?

8-58.   Solve the following systems of equations using any method. Check your solution if
         possible.

   a. $6x - 2y = 10$ b. $x - 3y = 1$
        $3x - y = 2$ $y = 16 - 2x$

8.2.3 How are quadratic rules and graphs connected?

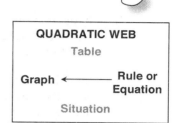

Zero Product Property

You already know a lot about quadratics and parabolas, and you have made several connections between their different representations on the quadratic web. Today you are going to develop a method to sketch a parabola from its equation without a table.

QUADRATIC WEB
Table
Graph ⟵ Rule or Equation
Situation

8-59.   **WHAT DO YOU NEED TO SKETCH A PARABOLA?**

How many points do you need in order to sketch a parabola? 1? 10? 50? Think about this as you answer the questions below. (Note: A sketch does not need to be exact. The parabola merely needs to be reasonably placed with important points clearly labeled.)

a.   Can you sketch a parabola if you only know where its y-intercept is? For example, if the y-intercept of a parabola is at $(0, -15)$, can you sketch its graph? Why or why not?

b.   What about the two x-intercepts of the parabola? If you only know where the x-intercepts are, can you draw the parabola? For example, if the x-intercepts are at $(-3, 0)$ and $(5, 0)$, can you predict the path of the parabola?

c.   Can you sketch a parabola with only its x-intercepts and y-intercept? To test this idea, sketch the graph of a parabola $y = x^2 - 2x - 15$ with x-intercepts $(-3, 0)$ and $(5, 0)$ and y-intercept $(0, -15)$.

8-60.   In problem 8-59, you learned that if you can find the intercepts of a parabola from a rule, then you can sketch its graph without a table.

a.   What is true about the value of y for all x-intercepts? What is true about the value of x for all y-intercepts? Review your knowledge of intercepts and describe it here.

b.   If $x = 0$ at the y-intercept, find the y-intercept of the graph of $y = 2x^2 + 5x - 12$.

c.   Since the x-intercept occurs when $y = 0$, write the equation that you would need to solve to find the x-intercepts of the graph of $y = 2x^2 + 5x - 12$.

d.   The solutions of the equation $2x^2 + 5x - 12 = 0$ are called its **roots** and are the **zeros** of $2x^2 + 5x - 12$. At this point, can you solve $2x^2 + 5x - 12 = 0$ for x? Explain why or why not.

8-61.   ZERO PRODUCT PROPERTY

The equation you wrote in part (c) of problem
8-60 is called a **quadratic equation**. To solve it,
you need to examine what you know about zero.
Study the special properties of zero below.

Nathan, Nancy, and Gaston are playing a
game where Nathan and Nancy each think
of a number and then give Gaston a clue
about their numbers. Using the clue,
Gaston must tell them everything that he
knows about their numbers.

a.   Nathan and Nancy's first clue for Gaston is that when you multiply their
numbers together, the result is zero. What conclusion can Gaston make?

b.   Disappointed that Gaston came so close to figuring out their numbers, Nathan
and Nancy invite Nadia over to make things harder. Nathan, Nancy, and Nadia
all think of secret numbers. This time Gaston is told that when their *three*
secret numbers are multiplied together, the answer is zero. What can Gaston
conclude this time?

c.   Does it matter how many numbers are multiplied? If the
product is zero, what do you know about one of the numbers?
This property is called the **Zero Product Property**. With the
class, write a description of this property in your Learning
Log. Title this entry "Zero Product Property" and include
today's date.

8-62.   How can you use the Zero Product Property to help you solve the quadratic equation
$0 = 2x^2 + 5x - 12$ from part (c) of problem 8-60?

a.   Examine the quadratic equation. Is there a product that equals zero? If not,
how can you rewrite the quadratic expression as a product?

b.   Now that the equation is written as a product of factors equaling zero, you can
use the Zero Product Property to solve it. Since you know that one of the
factors must be zero, you can set up two smaller equations to help you solve for
x. Use one factor at a time and determine what x-value makes it equal to zero.

c.   What do these solutions represent? What do they tell you?

d.   You now know the roots of the equation $0 = 2x^2 + 5x - 12$ (also called the
zeros of $2x^2 + 5x - 12$). Use the roots to find the x-intercepts of the graph of
the parabola $y = 2x^2 + 5x - 12$. Then sketch a graph of the parabola.

8-63.   Use a similar process to sketch the parabola $y = x^2 + x - 6$ by using its intercepts.

8-64.   Sketch the parabola $y = 2x^2 + 6x + 4$ by using its intercepts.

METHODS AND MEANINGS

Zero Product Property

When the product of two or more numbers is zero, one of those numbers must be zero. This is known as the **Zero Product Property**. If the two numbers are a and b, this property can be written as follows:

If a and b are two numbers where $a \cdot b = 0$, then $a = 0$ or $b = 0$.

For example, if $(2x - 3)(x + 5) = 0$, then $2x - 3 = 0$ or $x + 5 = 0$. Solving yields the solutions $x = \frac{3}{2}$ or $x = -5$. This property helps you solve quadratic equations when the equation can be written as a product of factors.

 Review & Preview

8-65.   Compare the two equations below.

$$(x + 2)(x - 1) = 0 \quad \text{and} \quad (x + 2) + (x - 1) = 0$$

   a.   How are the equations different?

   b.   Solve both equations.

8-66.   For each equation below, solve for x.

   a. $(x - 2)(x + 8) = 0$ b. $(3x - 9)(x - 1) = 0$

   c. $(x + 10)(2x - 5) = 0$ d. $(x - 7)^2 = 0$

8-67.   Examine the system of equations below.

$$5x - 2y = 4$$
$$x = 0$$

a.   Before solving this system, Danielle noticed that the point of intersection is also the y-intercept of $5x - 2y = 4$. Explain how she knows this.

b.   Find the point of intersection of the two rules above.

8-68.   The x-intercepts of the graph of $y = 2x^2 - 16x + 30$ are $(3, 0)$ and $(5, 0)$.

a.   What is the x-coordinate of the vertex? How do you know?

b.   Use your answer to part (a) above to find the y-coordinate of the vertex. Then write the vertex as a point (x, y).

8-69.   Factor each quadratic below completely.

a. $2x^2 - 2x - 4$ b. $4x^2 - 24x + 36$

8-70.   The "≤" symbol represents "less than or equal to," while the "<" symbol represents "less than."

a.   Similarly, translate "≥" and ">."

b.   How can you write an expression that states that 5 is greater than 3?

c.   Write another expression that states that x is less than or equal to 9.

d.   Translate the expression $-2 < 7$ into words.

8.2.4   What new connection can I make?
···
Solving Quadratic Equations by Factoring

In Lesson 8.2.3, you developed a method for finding the x-intercepts of a parabola given by $y = ax^2 + bx + c$ by finding the roots of the corresponding quadratic equation, $ax^2 + bx + c = 0$, or the zeros of $ax^2 + bx + c$. Today you will learn how to use that skill to solve a wide variety of quadratic equations.

QUADRATIC WEB
Table
Graph   Rule or Equation
Situation

You will also revisit the quadratic web, make a connection between the table and rule of a parabola, and then apply this connection to the water-balloon competition you analyzed in problem 8-51.

Algebra Connections

8-71.   Review what you learned in Lesson 8.2.3 by sketching the graph of $y = x^2 + 3x + 2$ without a table. Specifically, find the x-intercepts and the y-intercept of the parabola and sketch its graph.

8-72.   Part of finding the x-intercepts of a parabola involves creating a quadratic equation of the form $ax^2 + bx + c = 0$ and finding its roots (which are also the zeros of the expression $ax^2 + bx + c$). Practice using the Zero Product Property to solve the quadratic equations below.

   a. $x^2 + 6x + 8 = 0$ b. $0 = 3x^2 - 7x + 4$

   c. $(x + 5)(-2x + 3) = 0$ d. $x^2 + 6x = 0$

   e. $0 = 3(x - 5)(2x + 3)$ f. $x^2 + 4x - 9 = 3$

8-73.   TABLE TO RULE

   You know how to make a table for a quadratic rule, but how can you write an equation when given the table? Examine this new connection that requires you to **reverse** your understanding of the Zero Product Property as you find a rule for each table below. What clues in the tables helped you find the rule?

   a.

x	−4	−3	−2	−1	0	1	2	3	4
y	6	0	−4	−6	−6	−4	0	6	14

   b.

x	−6	−5	−4	−3	−2	−1	0	1	2	3	4
y	7	0	−5	−8	−9	−8	−5	0	7	16	27

8-74.   WATER-BALLOON CONTEST REVISITED

   Remember Imp's water-balloon toss? Since the water balloon was thrown on the computer, you were given only a table of data, shown again below. Find a rule that represents the height of Imp's balloon as it traveled through the air.

x (yards)	2	3	4	5	6	7	8	9
y (yards)	0	9	16	21	24	25	24	21

8-75.   Find the quadratic web in your Learning Log entry from Lesson 8.2.3. In this entry, add a short explanation for how to find a quadratic equation from its table. Then add an arrow to your web for the connection you made today.

8-76. Jamie was given the problem, "Find the result when the factors of $65x^2 + 212x - 133$ are multiplied together." Before she could answer, her sister, Lauren, said, "I know the answer without factoring or multiplying!" What was Lauren's answer and how did she know?

8-77. Solve the equations below for x. Check your solutions.

    a. $(6x - 18)(3x + 2) = 0$ b. $x^2 - 7x + 10 = 0$

    c. $2x^2 + 2x - 12 = 0$ d. $4x^2 - 1 = 0$

8-78. Sketch each parabola below with the given information.

    a.   A parabola with x-intercepts (2, 0) and (7, 0) and y-intercept (0, –8).

    b.   A parabola with exactly one x-intercept at (–1, 0) and y-intercept (0, 3).

    c.   The parabola represented by the equation $y = (x + 5)(x - 1)$.

8-79. Review the meanings of the inequality symbols in the box at right. Then decide if the statements below are true or false.

<	less than
≤	less than or equal to
>	greater than
≥	greater than or equal to

    a. $5 < 7$ b. $-2 \geq 9$

    c. $0 \leq 0$ d. $-5 > -10$

    e. $16 \leq -16$ f. $1 > 1$

8-80. Calculate the expressions below with a scientific calculator.

    a. $\frac{-10 + \sqrt{25}}{5}$ b. $\frac{8 + \sqrt{40}}{3 \cdot 3}$ c. $\frac{8 + \sqrt{3^2 + 2 \cdot 3 + 1}}{-4}$

8-81. Find the equation of the line through the points (6, –8) and (0, 0).

    a.   What is the slope of the line?

    b.   Is the point (3, –4) on the line? How can you tell?

Algebra Connections

8.2.5 What's the connection?

Completing the Quadratic Web

In just three lessons you have almost completed the quadratic web. Revisit the web posted in your classroom. What connections, if any, still need to be made?

Today you will focus on how to get a quadratic rule from a graph and a situation. As you work, ask yourself the following questions:

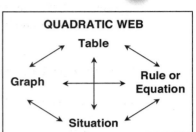

Which representation am I given?
Which representation am I looking for?

How can I **reverse** this process?

Is there another way?

8-82. Several parabolas and quadratic rules are shown below. Match each graph with its rule. Justify your choices and share any shortcuts you find with your teammates. (Note: Not every rule will be matched with a parabola.)

Graphs:

(1)

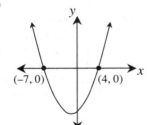

(2)

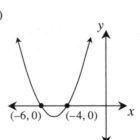

(3)

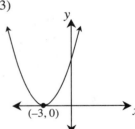

(4)

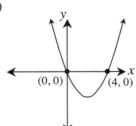

(5)

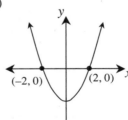

(6)

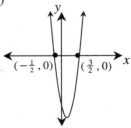

Rules:

a. $y = (x+3)^2$

b. $y = x^2 + 3x - 28$

c. $y = x^2 - 11x + 28$

d. $y = x^2 - 4$

e. $y = x^2 + 10x + 24$

f. $y = 2x^2 + 11x + 5$

g. $y = x^2 - 4x$

h. $y = (x-3)^2$

i. $y = 4x^2 - 4x - 3$

8-83.   QUALITY CONTROL, Part One

Congratulations! With your promotion, you are now the Quality Assurance Representative of the Function Factory. Your job is to make sure your clients are happy. Whenever a client writes to the company, you must reply with clear directions that will solve his or her problem.

Your boss has provided graphing technology and a team of fellow employees to help you fulfill your job description.

Your Task:

1.   Carefully read the complaints below. Study each situation with your grapher. Work with your team to resolve each situation.

2.   Write each customer a friendly response that offers a solution to his or her problem. Remember that the customers are not parabola experts! Do not assume that they know anything about parabolas.

A

Dear Ms. Quadratic,

I followed all of the directions given in your brochure on how to order a parabola. I tried to order a parabola that passed through the points (1, 0) and (–6, 0), only to have you send me the wrong one!

Please tell me how to order the correct parabola. Your immediate reply is appreciated.

Perturbed in Pennsylvania

B

Dear Ms. Quadratic,

I am a very dissatisfied customer. I want a parabola that hits the x-axis only <u>once</u> at (5, 0), yet I see NO mention of this type of parabola in your pamphlet. Your company mission statement assures me that "my needs will be met no matter what." How should I order my special parabola?

Sincerely,

Troubled in Texas

C

Dear Ms. Quadratic,

Please help! I have searched through your entire brochure and did not see a parabola that would fit my needs. All I want is a parabola that looks like this:

Every time I order an equation to give me this parabola you always send me a different one! I refuse to pay for any parabola but the one shown above. Please tell me how I should find the equation of this parabola or I will take my business elsewhere!

Thank you,

Agitated in Alaska

8-84.   EXTRA! EXTRA!

A journalist from the school newspaper wants to publish the results from the water-balloon contest. She wants a rule for each toss so that she can program her computer to create a graph for her article. You already have rules for the tosses made by Maggie and Imp from problems 8-51 and 8-74.

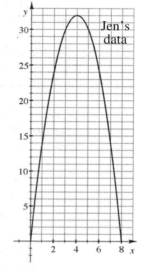

a.   Examine the graph at right that represents the height of Jen's toss. Find the rule for this parabola.

b.   Al released his balloon from the 10-yard line, and it landed at the 16-yard line. If the ball reached a height of 27 yards, what equation represents the path of his toss?

8-85.   QUALITY CONTROL, Part Two

Lots O'Dough, a wealthy customer, would like to order a variety of parabolas. However, he is feeling pressed for time and said that he will pay you *lots* of extra money if you complete his order for him. Of course you agreed! He sent you sketches of each parabola that he would like to receive. Determine a possible equation for each parabola so that you can pass this information on to the Manufacturing Department.

a.

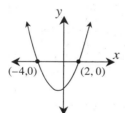

b.

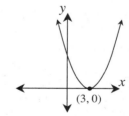

c.

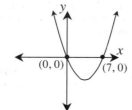

d.

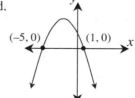

8-86.   Find the slope and y-intercept of the graph of $6y - 3x = 24$.

8-87.   Examine the graph of $y = 2x^2 + 2x - 1$ at right.

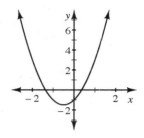

   a.   Estimate the zeros of $2x^2 + 2x - 1$ from the graph.

   b.   What happens if you try to use the Zero Product
         Property to find the roots of $2x^2 + 2x - 1 = 0$?

8-88.   Solve the equations below for x. Check your solutions.

   a. $x^2 + 6x - 40 = 0$ b. $2x^2 + 13x - 24 = 0$

8-89.   Calculate the expressions below. Then compare your answers from (a) and (b) to
         those in problem 8-88. What do you notice?

   a. $\dfrac{-6+\sqrt{6^2-(4)(1)(-40)}}{2\cdot 1}$ b. $\dfrac{-6-\sqrt{6^2-(4)(1)(-40)}}{2\cdot 1}$

   c. $\dfrac{-13-\sqrt{13^2-(4)(2)(-24)}}{2\cdot 2}$ d. $\dfrac{-13+\sqrt{13^2-(4)(2)(-24)}}{2\cdot 2}$

8-90.   Use any method to solve the systems of equations below.

   a. $2x - 3y = 5$ b. $m = -3 + 2n$
         $4x + y = 3$ $4m + 6n = -5$

8.3.1   What if it's not factorable?

• •

Introduction to the Quadratic Formula

In Section 8.2 you developed a method to find the x-intercepts of a parabola by factoring and
using the Zero Product Property. Today you will learn a new method to solve quadratic
equations.

8-91.   Use the Zero Product Property to find the roots of $x^2 - 3x - 7 = 0$.

   a.   What happenėd?

   b.   What does this result tell you about the roots?

   c.   Your teacher will display the graph of $y = x^2 - 3x - 7$ for the class. Did the
         graph confirm your answer to part (b)? Estimate the roots using the graph.

8-92.   QUADRATIC FORMULA

Since a parabola can have x-intercepts even when its
corresponding quadratic equation is not factorable,
another way to find the roots of a quadratic equation is
needed.

a.   One way to find the roots of a quadratic
      equation is by using the **Quadratic Formula**,
      shown below. This formula uses values a, b,
      and c from a quadratic equation written in
      standard form (explained in the next paragraph).

$$x = \frac{-b \pm \sqrt{b^2 - 4ac}}{2a}$$

When the quadratic equation is written in **standard form** (i.e., it looks like
$ax^2 + bx + c = 0$), then a is the number of x^2-terms, b is the number of
x-terms, and c is the constant. If $x^2 - 3x - 7 = 0$, then what are a, b, and c?

b.   The Quadratic Formula calculates *two* possible answers by using the "$\pm$"
      symbol. This symbol (read as "plus or minus") is shorthand notation that tells
      you to calculate the formula twice: once with addition and once with
      subtraction in the numerator. Therefore, every Quadratic Formula problem is
      really two different problems unless the value of $\sqrt{b^2 - 4ac}$ is 0.

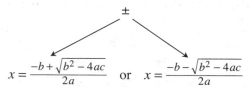

$$x = \frac{-b + \sqrt{b^2 - 4ac}}{2a} \quad \text{or} \quad x = \frac{-b - \sqrt{b^2 - 4ac}}{2a}$$

Carefully substitute a, b, and c from $x^2 - 3x - 7 = 0$ into the Quadratic
Formula. Evaluate each expression (once using addition and once using
subtraction) to solve for x. Do these solutions match those from part (c) of
problem 8-91?

8-93.   The Quadratic Formula is only one of the tools you can use to solve quadratic
         equations.

a.   What are the other methods that you can use?

b.   You may be thinking, "Where did this formula come from? Why does it
      work?" You can find the formula by starting with a generic quadratic
      $ax^2 + bx + c = 0$ and using your algebra skills to solve for x. See the Math
      Notes box for this lesson to learn about one way this formula can be derived.
      Later, in Chapter 12, you will learn another formal method to derive the
      Quadratic Formula.

8-94.   Use the Quadratic Formula to solve the equations below for x, if possible. Check your solutions.

a. $3x^2 + 7x + 2 = 0$ b. $2x^2 - 9x - 35 = 0$

c. $8x^2 + 10x + 3 = 0$ d. $x^2 - 5x + 9 = 0$

8-95.   In your Learning Log, describe how to use the Quadratic Formula. Be sure to include an example. Title this entry "Quadratic Formula" and include today's date.

LOOKING DEEPER

Deriving the Quadratic Formula

Why is $x = \frac{-b \pm \sqrt{b^2 - 4ac}}{2a}$ a solution of $ax^2 + bx + c = 0$? One way to derive this formula is shown below.

1. Begin with the quadratic equation in standard form.

$$ax^2 + bx + c = 0$$

2. Multiply each side by $4a$.

$$4a(ax^2 + bx + c) = 0$$

3. Add $b^2 - 4ac$ to each side in order to get a factorable quadratic on the left.

$$4a^2x^2 + 4abx + 4ac = 0$$

$$4a^2x^2 + 4abx + b^2 = b^2 - 4ac$$

4. The left side can be factored as $(2ax + b)^2$, which is demonstrated in the generic rectangle shown at right.

	$2abx$	b^2
b		
$2ax$	$4a^2x^2$	$2abx$

(column labels: b | top: $2abx$, b^2; $2ax$ | $4a^2x^2$, $2abx$; bottom: $2ax$, b)

5. Take the square root of each side. Since both the positive and negative values of a number can be squared to give the same result (for example, 4^2 and $(-4)^2$ both equal 16), then there are two possible square root values: $\sqrt{b^2 - 4ac}$ and $-\sqrt{b^2 - 4ac}$.

$$(2ax + b)^2 = b^2 - 4ac$$

6. Now continue to solve for x by subtracting b from both sides and dividing by $2a$. Notice that a cannot equal zero or else you will get an error! However, if $a = 0$, then this equation would not be quadratic and you would not use this formula.

$$2ax + b = \pm\sqrt{b^2 - 4ac}$$

$$2ax = -b \pm \sqrt{b^2 - 4ac}$$

$$x = \frac{-b \pm \sqrt{b^2 - 4ac}}{2a}$$

7. Thus, $x = \frac{-b \pm \sqrt{b^2 - 4ac}}{2a}$ are solutions of the equation $ax^2 + bx + c = 0$.

8-96.   Solve the following quadratic equations by factoring and using the Zero Product Property. Be sure to check your solutions.

    a. $x^2 - 13x + 42 = 0$ b. $0 = 3x^2 + 10x - 8$

    c. $2x^2 - 10x = 0$ d. $4x^2 + 8x - 60 = 0$

8-97.   Use the Quadratic Formula to solve $x^2 - 13x + 42 = 0$. Did your solution match the solution from part (a) of problem 8-96?

8-98.   Does a quadratic equation always have two solutions? That is, does a parabola always intersect the x-axis twice?

    a.   If possible, draw an example of a parabola that only intersects the x-axis once.

    b.   What does it mean if the quadratic equation has no solution? Draw a possible parabola that would cause this to happen.

8-99.   Find the equation of the line through the point (–2, 8) with slope $\frac{1}{2}$.

8-100.   For each of the following equations, indicate whether its graph would be a line or a parabola.

    a. $5x + 2y = 7$ b. $y = 3x^2$

    c. $y = 3$ d. $4x^2 + 3x = 7 + y$

8-101.   **Multiple Choice:** Which equations below are equivalent to:

$$\tfrac{1}{2}(6x - 14) + 5x = 2 - 3x + 8 ?$$

    a. $3x - 7 + 5x = 10 - 3x$ b. $3x - 14 + 5x = 2 - 3x + 8$

    c. $8x - 14 = 10 - 3x$ d. $6x - 14 + 10x = 4 - 6x + 16$

8-102.   Review the descriptions for the inequality symbols $<$, $\leq$, $>$, and $\geq$ in problem 8-79. Then decide if the statements below are true or false.

    a. $11 < -13$ b. $5 \cdot 2 \geq 10$ c. $13 > -3(2 - 6)$ d. $4 \leq 4$

    e. $9 \geq -9$ f. $-2 > -2$ g. $-16 < -15$ h. $0 > 6$

8.3.2 What if the equation is not in standard form?

More Solving Quadratic Equations

Today you will **apply** and **extend** what you know about solving quadratic equations.

8-103.   For the quadratic equation $6x^2 + 11x - 10 = 0$:

 a.   Solve it using the Zero Product Property.

 b.   Solve it using the Quadratic Formula.

 c.   Did the solutions from parts (a) and (b) match? If not, why not?

8-104.   As the Math Notes box from Lesson 8.3.1 demonstrated, the Quadratic Formula can solve any quadratic equation $ax^2 + bx + c = 0$ if $a \neq 0$. But what if the equation is not in standard form? What if terms are missing? Consider these questions as you solve the quadratic equations below. Share your ideas with your teammates and be prepared to demonstrate your process for the class.

 a. $4x^2 - 121 = 0$ b. $2x^2 - 2 - 3x = 0$

 c. $15x^2 - 165x = 630$ d. $36x^2 + 25 = 60x$

8-105.   THE SAINT LOUIS GATEWAY ARCH

The Saint Louis Gateway Arch (pictured at right) has a shape much like a parabola. Suppose the Gateway Arch can be approximated by $y = 630 - 0.00635x^2$, where both x and y represent distances in feet and the origin is the point on the ground directly below the arch's apex (its highest point).

 a.   Find the x-intercepts of the Gateway Arch. What does this information tell you? Use a calculator to evaluate your answers.

 b.   How wide is the arch at its base?

 c.   How tall is the arch? How did you find your solution?

 d.   Draw a quick sketch of the arch on graph paper, labeling the axes with all of the values you know.

METHODS AND MEANINGS

Solving a Quadratic Equation

So far in this course, you have learned two algebraic methods to solve a quadratic equation of the form $ax^2 + bx + c = 0$.

One of these methods, the Zero Product Property, requires the equation to be a product of factors that equal zero. In this case, the quadratic equation must be factored, as shown in Example 1 below. Another strategy uses the Quadratic Formula, as demonstrated in Example 2 below. Notice that each strategy results in the same answer.

Example 1: Solve $3x^2 + x - 14 = 0$ for x using the Zero Product Property.

Solution: First, factor the quadratic so it is written as a product: $(3x + 7)(x - 2) = 0$. The Zero Product Property states that if the product of two terms is 0, then at least one of the factors must be 0. Thus, $3x + 7 = 0$ or $x - 2 = 0$.

Solving these equations for x reveals that $x = -\frac{7}{3}$ or that $x = 2$.

Example 2: Solve $3x^2 + x - 14 = 0$ for x using the Quadratic Formula.

Solution: First, identify a, b, and c. a equals the number of x^2-terms, b equals the number of x terms, and c equals the constant. For $3x^2 + x - 14 = 0$, $a = 3$, $b = 1$, and $c = -14$. Substitute the values of a, b, and c into the Quadratic Formula and evaluate the expression twice: once with addition and once with subtraction. Examine this method below:

$$x = \frac{-1 + \sqrt{1^2 - 4(3)(-14)}}{2 \cdot 3} \qquad x = \frac{-1 - \sqrt{1^2 - 4(3)(-14)}}{2 \cdot 3}$$

$$= \frac{-1 + \sqrt{169}}{6} \qquad\qquad = \frac{-1 - \sqrt{169}}{6}$$

$$= \frac{-1 + 13}{6} \qquad \text{or} \qquad = \frac{-1 - 13}{6}$$

$$= \frac{12}{6} \qquad\qquad\qquad = \frac{-14}{6}$$

$$= 2 \qquad\qquad\qquad\quad = -\frac{7}{3}$$

8-106.   Solve the following quadratic equations by factoring and using the Zero Product Property. Then check your solutions.

a. $x^2 - 10x + 25 = 0$ b. $0 = 3x^2 + 17x - 6$

c. $3x^2 - 2x = 5$ d. $16x^2 - 9 = 0$

8-107.   Use the Quadratic Formula to solve part (b) of problem 8-106 above. Did your solution match the solution you got by factoring and using the Zero Product Property (in part (b) of problem 8-106)?

8-108.   Find the equation of each parabola below based on the given information.

a.
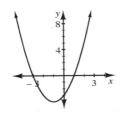

b.

x	-4	-3	-2	-1	0	1	2	3	4
y	12	5	0	-3	-4	-3	0	5	12

8-109.   Solve the following problem using any method. Write your solution as a sentence.

The length of a rectangle is 5 cm longer than twice the length of the width. If the area of the rectangle is 403 square centimeters, what is the width?

8-110.   Which of the points below is a solution to $4x - 3y = 10$? Note: More than one point may make this equation true.

a.   (1, 2)   b.   (4, 2)   c.   (7, 6)   d.   (4, -3)

8-111.   Kristen loves shortcuts. She figured out that she can find x- and y-intercepts for any line without graphing! For example, she knows that the x-intercept for $5x - 3y = 15$ is (3, 0) just by examining the rule.

a.   What is her shortcut?

b.   Does this shortcut work for the y-intercept? Try it and then test your result by changing $5x - 3y = 15$ into $y = mx + b$ form.

c.   Use this shortcut to find the x- and y-intercepts of $3x - 2y = 24$.

8.3.3 Which method should I use?

Choosing a Strategy

You now have two algebraic methods to solve quadratic equations: using the Zero Product Property and using the Quadratic Formula. How can you decide which strategy is best to try first? By the end of this lesson, you should have some strategies to help you determine which method to try first when solving a quadratic equation.

8-112. Examine the quadratic equations below with your team. For each equation:

- Decide which strategy is best to try first.

- Solve the equation. If your first strategy does not work, switch to the other strategy.

- Check your solution(s).

Be prepared to share your process with the class.

a. $x^2 + 12x + 27 = 0$ b. $0.5x^2 + 9x + 3.2 = 0$

c. $(3x + 4)(2x - 1) = 0$ d. $x^2 + 16 = 8x$

e. $x^2 + 5 - 2x = 0$ f. $20x^2 - 30x = 2x + 45$

8-113.   With the class, decide when it is best to solve a quadratic by factoring and when you should go directly to the Quadratic Formula. Copy your observations in your Learning Log. Title this entry "Choosing a Strategy to Solve Quadratics" and include today's date.

8-114.   While solving $(x-5)(x+2)=-6$, Kyle decided that x must
          equal 5 or –2. "Not so fast!" exclaimed Stanton, "The product
          does not equal zero. We need to change the equation first."

    a.   What is Stanton talking about?

    b.   How can the equation be rewritten?
          Discuss this with your team and use
          your algebraic tools to rewrite the
          equation so that it can be solved.

    c.   Solve the resulting equation from
          part (b) for x. Do your solutions
          match Kyle's?

8-115.   MOE'S YO

          Moe is playing with a yo-yo. He throws the yo-yo down and then pulls it back up.
          The motion of the yo-yo is represented by the equation $y = 2x^2 - 4.8x$, where
          x represents the number of seconds since the yo-yo left Moe's hand, and y represents
          the vertical height in inches of the yo-yo with respect to Moe's hand. Note that
          when the yo-yo is in Moe's hand, $y = 0$, and when the yo-yo is below his hand,
          y is negative.

    a.   How long is Moe's yo-yo in the air
          before it comes back to Moe's hand?
          Write and solve a quadratic equation to
          find the times that the yo-yo is in
          Moe's hand.

    b.   At what time does the yo-yo turn
          around? Use what you know about
          parabolas to help you.

    c.   How long is the yo-yo's string? That is,
          what is y when the yo-yo changes
          direction?

    d.   Draw a sketch of the graph representing
          the motion of Moe's yo-yo. On the sketch, label the important points: when
          the yo-yo is in Moe's hand and when it changes direction.

LOOKING DEEPER

Simplifying Square Roots

Before calculators were universally available, people who wanted to use approximate decimal values for numbers like $\sqrt{45}$ had a few options:

1. Carry around copies of long square-root tables.

2. Use Guess and Check repeatedly to get desired accuracy.

3. "Simplify" the square roots. A square root is **simplified** when there are no more perfect square factors (square numbers such as 4, 25, and 81) under the radical sign.

Simplifying square roots was by far the fastest method. People factored the number as the product of integers hoping to find at least one perfect square number. They memorized approximations of the square roots of the integers from one to ten. Then they could figure out the decimal value by multiplying these memorized facts with the roots of the square numbers. Here are some examples of this method.

Example 1: Simplify $\sqrt{45}$.

First rewrite $\sqrt{45}$ in an equivalent factored form so that one of the factors is a perfect square. Simplify the square root of the perfect square. Verify with your calculator that both $3\sqrt{5}$ and $\sqrt{45} \approx 6.71$.

Example 1

$$\sqrt{45} = \sqrt{9 \cdot 5}$$
$$= \sqrt{9} \cdot \sqrt{5}$$
$$= 3\sqrt{5}$$

Examine **Example 2** and **Example 3** at right. Note that in Example 3, $\sqrt{72}$ was rewritten as $\sqrt{36} \cdot \sqrt{2}$, rather than as $\sqrt{9} \cdot \sqrt{8}$ or $\sqrt{4} \cdot \sqrt{18}$, because 36 is the largest perfect square factor of 72. However, since

Example 2

$$\sqrt{27}$$
$$= \sqrt{9} \cdot \sqrt{3}$$
$$= 3\sqrt{3}$$

Example 3

$$\sqrt{72}$$
$$= \sqrt{36} \cdot \sqrt{2}$$
$$= 6\sqrt{2}$$

$$\sqrt{4} \cdot \sqrt{18} = 2\sqrt{9 \cdot 2} = 2\sqrt{9} \cdot \sqrt{2} = 2 \cdot 3\sqrt{2} = 6\sqrt{2} \quad \text{and}$$
$$\sqrt{9} \cdot \sqrt{8} = 3\sqrt{4 \cdot 2} = 3\sqrt{4} \cdot \sqrt{2} = 3 \cdot 2\sqrt{2} = 6\sqrt{2},$$

you can still get the same answer if you simplify it using different methods.

When you take the square root of an integer that is not a perfect square, the result is a decimal that never repeats itself and never ends. This result is called an **irrational number**. The irrational numbers and the rational numbers together form the numbers we use in this course, which are called **real numbers**.

Generally, since it is now the age of technology, when a decimal approximation of an irrational square root is desired, a calculator is used. However, for an exact answer, the number must be written using the $\sqrt{}$ symbol.

8-116.   Write and solve an equation (or system of equations) for the situation described
          below. Define your variable(s) and write your solution as a sentence.

          Daria has 18 coins that are all nickels and quarters. The number of nickels is 3 more
          than twice the number of quarters. If she has $1.90 in all, how many nickels does
          Daria have?

8-117.   Solve the following quadratic equations using any method.

          a. $10000x^2 - 64 = 0$ b. $9x^2 - 8 = -34x$

          c. $2x^2 - 4x + 7 = 0$ d. $3.2x + 0.2x^2 - 5 = 0$

8-118.   Find a rule that represents the
          number of tiles in Figure x for
          the tile pattern at right.

                                Figure 1   Figure 2   Figure 3

8-119.   Solve the equations below for x. Check your solutions.

          a. $3x^2 + 3x = 6 + 3x^2$ b. $\frac{5}{x} = \frac{1}{3}$

          c. $5 - (2x - 3) = -3x + 6$ d. $6(x - 3) + 2x = 4(2x + 1) - 22$

8-120.   Line L passes through the points $(-44, 42)$ and $(-31, 94)$, while line M has the rule
          $y = 6 + 3x$. Which line is steeper? **Justify** your answer.

8-121.   **Multiple Choice:** Which line below is perpendicular to the line $2x - 5y = 3$?

          a. $2x + 5y = 7$ b. $-2x + 5y = 4$

          c. $5x - 2y = -1$ d. $5x + 2y = 3$

Chapter 8 Closure What have I learned?

Reflection and Synthesis

The activities below offer you a chance to reflect on what you have learned during this chapter. As you work, look for concepts that you feel very comfortable with, ideas that you would like to learn more about, and topics you need more help with. Look for **connections** between ideas as well as **connections** with material you learned previously.

①   TEAM BRAINSTORM

With your team, brainstorm a list for each of the following topics. Be as detailed as you can. How long can you make your list? Challenge yourselves. Be prepared to share your team's ideas with the class.

Topics: What have you studied in this chapter? What ideas and words were important in what you learned? Remember to be as detailed as you can.

Ways of Thinking: What Ways of Thinking did you use in this chapter? When did you use them?

Connections: What topics, ideas, and words that you learned *before* this chapter are **connected** to the new ideas in this chapter? Again, make your list as long as you can.

② MAKING CONNECTIONS

The following is a list of the vocabulary used in this chapter. The words that appear in bold are new to this chapter. Make sure that you are familiar with all of these words and know what they mean. Refer to the glossary or index for any words that you do not yet understand.

binomial	**factor**	generic rectangle
graph	**monomial**	parabola
product	**quadratic equation**	**Quadratic Formula**
root	solution	**standard form for quadratics**
sum	**symmetry**	**trinomial**
vertex	x-intercept	$x \rightarrow y$ table
y-intercept	**Zero Product Property**	

Make a concept map showing all of the **connections** you can find among the key words and ideas listed above. To show a **connection** between two words, draw a line between them and explain the **connection**, as shown in the example below. A word can be **connected** to any other word as long as there is a **justified connection**. For each key word or idea, provide a sketch that illustrates the idea (see the example below).

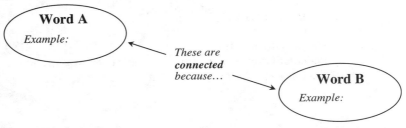

Your teacher may provide you with vocabulary cards to help you get started. If you use the cards to plan your concept map, be sure either to re-draw your concept map on your paper or to glue the vocabulary cards to a poster with all of the **connections** explained for others to see and understand.

While you are making your map, your team may think of related words or ideas that are not listed above. Be sure to include these ideas on your concept map.

③ SUMMARIZING MY UNDERSTANDING

This section gives you an opportunity to show what you know about certain math topics or ideas. Your teacher will give you directions for exactly how to do this. Your teacher may also provide a "GO" page to work on. The "GO" stands for "Graphic Organizer," a tool you can use to organize your thoughts and communicate your ideas clearly.

WHAT HAVE I LEARNED?

This section will help you evaluate which
types of problems you have seen with
which you feel comfortable and those with
which you need more help. Even if your
teacher does not assign this section, it is a
good idea to try these problems and find
out for yourself what you know and what
you need to work on.

Solve each problem as completely as you
can. The table at the end of the closure
section has answers to these problems. It
also tells you where you can find additional
help and practice on problems like these.

CL 8-122. For the graph of the line at right:

   a.   Find the slope.

   b.   Find the y-intercept.

   c.   Find the equation.

   d.   Find the equation of a line
         perpendicular to this one that
         passes through $(0,7)$.

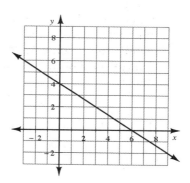

CL 8-123. Factor and use the Zero Product Property to find the roots of the following quadratic
equations.

   a. $0 = x^2 - 7x + 12$ b. $0 = 6x^2 - 23x + 20$

   c. $0 = x^2 - 9$ d. $0 = x^2 + 12x + 36$

CL 8-124. Use the Quadratic Formula to solve these equations.

   a. $0 = x^2 - 7x + 3$ b. $3x^2 + 5x + 1 = 0$

CL 8-125. Use the graph at right to answer the
questions below.

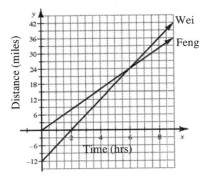

a. One of these lines represents Feng, and
one represents Wai. Write an equation
for each girl's line.

b. The two girls are riding bikes. How
fast does each girl ride?

c. When do Feng and Wai meet? At that
point, how far are they from school?

CL 8-126. Factor each expression below completely.

a. $3x^2 + 21x + 30$

b. $7x^2 - 63$

CL 8-127. Find the coordinates of the y-intercept, x-intercepts, and vertex of $y = x^2 - 2x - 15$.
Show all of the work that you do to find these points.

CL 8-128. Solve for x using the method of your choice.

a. $0 = 2x^2 - 5x - 33$

b. $0 = 3x^2 - 4x - 1$

CL 8-129. Quinn started off with twice as
much candy as Denali, but then
he ate 4 pieces. When Quinn and
Denali put their candy together,
they now have a total of 50
pieces. How many pieces of
candy did Denali start with?

CL 8-130. Check your answers using the table at the end of the closure section. Which
problems do you feel confident about? Which problems were hard? Use the table to
make a list of topics you need help on and a list of topics you need to practice more.

HOW AM I THINKING?

This course focuses on five different **Ways of Thinking**: reversing thinking, justifying, generalizing, making connections, and applying and extending understanding. These are some of the ways in which you think while trying to make sense of a concept or to solve a problem (even outside of math class). During this chapter, you have probably used each Way of Thinking multiple times without even realizing it!

Choose three of these Ways of Thinking that you remember using while working in this chapter. For each Way of Thinking that you choose, show and explain where you used it and how you used it. Describe why thinking in this way helped you solve a particular problem or understand something new. (For instance, explain why you wanted to **generalize** in this particular case, or why it was useful to see these particular **connections**.) Be sure to include examples to demonstrate your thinking.

Answers and Support for Closure Activity #4
What Have I Learned?

Problem	Solution	Need Help?	More Practice
CL 8-122.	a. $m = -\frac{2}{3}$ b. y-intercept: 4 c. $y = -\frac{2}{3}x + 4$ d. $y = \frac{3}{2}x + 7$	Lessons 7.1.3, 7.1.5, 7.2.2, 7.2.3, and 7.3.2 Math Notes boxes	Problems 8-9, 8-31, 8-57, 8-86, 8-99, and 8-121
CL 8-123.	a. $x = 4$ or $x = 3$ b. $x = \frac{5}{2}$ or $x = \frac{4}{3}$ c. $x = -3$ or $x = 3$ d. $x = -6$	Lessons 8.1.4, 8.2.3, and 8.3.2 Math Notes boxes	Problems 8-66, 8-72, 8-77, 8-88, 8-96, and 8-106
CL 8-124.	a. $x = \frac{7 \pm \sqrt{37}}{2}$ ($x \approx 6.54$ or 0.46) b. $x = \frac{-5 \pm \sqrt{13}}{6}$ ($x \approx -0.23$ or -1.43)	Problem 8-92, Lessons 8.3.1 and 8.3.2 Math Notes boxes	Problems 8-94, 8-97, 8-104, and 8-107

Problem	Solution	Need Help?	More Practice
CL 8-125.	a. Feng: $y = 4x$ Wai: $y = 6x - 12$ b. Feng rides at 4 miles per hour; Wai rides at 6 miles per hour. c. Feng and Wai meet after 6 hours. At that point, they are 24 miles from school.	Lessons 7.1.5 and 7.2.2 Math Notes boxes	See Lessons 7.2.2 and 7.2.3
CL 8-126.	a. $3(x+2)(x+5)$ b. $7(x+3)(x-3)$	Problems 8-13, 8-14, and 8-35; Lesson 8.1.5 Math Notes box	Problems 8-15, 8-16, 8-22, 8-23, 8-24, 8-29, 8-33, 8-36, 8-37, and 8-69
CL 8-127.	y-intercept: -15 x-intercepts: 5 and -3 vertex: $(1, -16)$	Problems 8-43, 8-51, 8-59, 8-60, 8-61, and 8-62	Problems 8-10, 8-54, 8-68, and 8-82
CL 8-128.	a. $x = \frac{11}{2}$ or $x = -3$ b. $x = \frac{4 \pm \sqrt{28}}{6} = \frac{4 \pm 2\sqrt{7}}{6} = \frac{2 \pm \sqrt{7}}{3}$ $(x \approx 1.55$ or $x \approx -0.22)$	Lessons 8.1.4, 8.2.3, 8.3.1, 8.3.2	Problems 8-112 and 8-117
CL 8-129.	Denali has 18 pieces of candy.	Lesson 7.1.4 Math Notes box	Problem 8-116

INEQUALITIES

9

CHAPTER 9   Inequalities

So far in this course you have focused on what you can determine when two expressions are equal. By using what you know about balancing equations, you can now solve linear and quadratic equations for a given variable.

However, what if the two expressions are not equal? If you know that one expression is always larger than the other, what does that tell you about the variable? In this chapter you will learn how to deal with these types of relationships, called *inequalities*, and will develop ways to represent solutions to inequalities both algebraically and graphically.

In addition, you will extend your ability to work with mathematical sentences by learning how to write inequalities from word problems.

In this chapter, you will learn:

➤ How to write an inequality to represent a word problem.

➤ How to solve linear inequalities and represent the solutions on a number line.

➤ How to represent the solutions of linear and nonlinear inequalities with two variables on a graph.

➤ How to graph a system of inequalities.

Guiding Questions

Think about these questions throughout this chapter:

How can I represent it algebraically?

How can I solve it?

What is a solution?

What is the connection?

Chapter Outline

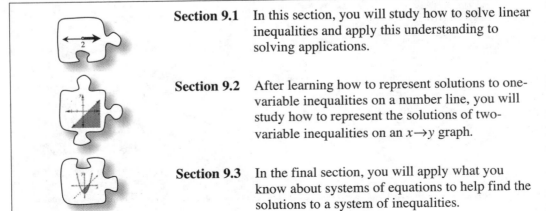

Section 9.1 In this section, you will study how to solve linear inequalities and apply this understanding to solving applications.

Section 9.2 After learning how to represent solutions to one-variable inequalities on a number line, you will study how to represent the solutions of two-variable inequalities on an $x \rightarrow y$ graph.

Section 9.3 In the final section, you will apply what you know about systems of equations to help find the solutions to a system of inequalities.

Algebra Connections

9.1.1 What if the quantities are not equal?

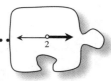

Solving Linear, One-Variable Inequalities

In this course, you have developed a variety of skills to find solutions to different kinds of equations. Now you will **apply** these equation-solving skills to solve inequalities.

9-1.   As a class, create a "human number line" for each of the following mathematical sentences. You will be assigned a number to represent on the number line. When your number makes the equation or inequality true, stand up to show that your number is a solution. If your number does not make the equation or inequality true, remain seated.

   a. $x \geq -2$ b. $x \leq 1$ c. $x = 3$ d. $x \geq 0$

   e. $x = -2$ f. $-1 \leq x \leq 4$ g. $x^2 \geq 4$ h. $x < -3$

9-2.   Based on your observations from problem 9-1, discuss the following questions with your class. Be sure to **justify** your responses.

   a.   Compare the solutions to an inequality (like $x \geq -2$) with that of an equation (like $x = 3$). What is different? What causes this to happen?

   b.   How many solutions does an inequality such as $x \leq 1$ have?

   c.   How is the result of $-1 \leq x \leq 4$ different from the other inequalities? What about the result of $x^2 \geq 4$?

9-3. Write an inequality that represents the solutions on each number line below.

a.
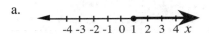

b.
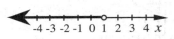

c.

$$\longleftarrow \!\!\!\!\begin{array}{ccccccccc} + & + & + & + & + & + & \bullet & + & + \\ -4 & -3 & -2 & -1 & 0 & 1 & 2 & 3 & 4 \ x \end{array}\!\!\!\!\longrightarrow$$

d.

$$\longleftarrow \!\!\!\!\begin{array}{ccccccccc} + & \circ & + & + & + & + & \bullet & + & + \\ -4 & -3 & -2 & -1 & 0 & 1 & 2 & 3 & 4 \ x \end{array}\!\!\!\!\longrightarrow$$

9-4. SOLUTIONS TO A LINEAR INEQUALITY

With your study team, find at least <u>five</u> x-values that make the inequality below true:

$$2x - 5 \geq 3$$

a. How many solutions are there?

b. What is the smallest solution for x? This point is called a **boundary point**.

c. What is the significance of the boundary point? What is its relationship with the inequality $2x - 5 \geq 3$?

d. Write an inequality that represents the solutions for x. On a number line, highlight the solutions for x. Be ready to share your number line with the class.

9-5. SOLVING LINEAR INEQUALITIES WITH ONE VARIABLE

Analyze the process for solving an inequality, such as $3 - 2x < 1$, by addressing the questions below.

a. The key point to start with is the **boundary point**. How can you quickly solve for this point? Once you have determined your strategy, find the boundary point for $3 - 2x < 1$.

b. Decide if the boundary point is part of the solution to the inequality. If it <u>is</u> part of the solution, indicate this on a number line with a solid point. If it is <u>not</u> a solution, show this by using an **unfilled circle** as a boundary.

c. Finally, to determine on which side of the boundary the solutions lie, choose a point to test in the inequality. If the point <u>is</u> a solution, then all points on that side of the boundary are part of the solution. If the point is <u>not</u> a solution, what does that tell you about the solutions? Write your solutions to $3 - 2x < 1$ as an inequality and represent the solutions on a number line.

9-6. With your study team, find all of the solutions to the inequality $3x + 1 < 7$. Decide how to represent these solutions on a number line and be prepared to **justify** your decisions to the class.

METHODS AND MEANINGS

MATH NOTES

Inequality Symbols

Just as the symbol "=" is used to represent that two quantities are equal in mathematics, the **inequality symbols** at right are used when describing the relationships between quantities that are not necessarily equal.

$<$ less than
$\leq$ less than or equal to
$>$ greater than
$\geq$ greater than or equal to

When graphing an inequality on a number line, such as $x \geq 4$, a solid point indicates that the value is a solution of the inequality. However, an unfilled circle indicates that the value is not part of the solution.

9-7.   Solve the problem below by writing and solving an equation. A Guess and Check table may help you write the equation. Be sure to define your variable.

There are a total of 122 countries in Africa, Europe, and North America (as of 2003). Europe has twice as many countries as North America, and Africa has seven more than Europe. How many countries are in each of these three continents? Write an equation and solve it to answer this question.

9-8.   Solve each of the following inequalities for the given variable. Represent your solutions on a number line.

a. $2(3p+1) > -4$ b. $9k - 2 < 3k + 10$ c. $5 - h \geq 4$

9-9.   Solve the following quadratic equations. Check your solutions, if possible.

a. $2k^2 + k - 6 = 0$ b. $m^2 = 9$

c. $w(2w + 8) = 24$ d. $3n^2 - 4n = 5$

9-10.   Identify the statements below as sometimes true, always true, or never true.

<	less than
≤	less than or equal to
>	greater than
≥	greater than or equal to

a. $-4 \le 9$ b. $x < 1$

c. $-5 > -2$ d. $3x + 5 = 2$ e. $61 = 61$ f. $-6 < -6$

9-11.   Assuming that x does not equal zero, what is $\frac{x}{x}$? Explain how you know.

9-12.   Robbie builds model rockets. One day he sets up a rocket, backs away from the launch pad, and then shoots the rocket off into the air. The rocket's path is represented by the equation $y = -10x^2 + 130x - 400$, where y is the height in meters off the ground and x is the horizontal distance in meters from Robbie.

a.   Use either the Zero Product Property or the Quadratic Formula to find the x-intercepts of the path of Robbie's rocket. What do the x-intercepts tell you?

b.   When Robbie's rocket lands, how far is it from the launch pad?

9-13.   For each parabola graphed below, visually estimate the x-intercepts. Then use the Quadratic Formula to confirm your estimates.

a. $y = x^2 - 5x + 3$ b. $y = x^2 + 2x - 6$

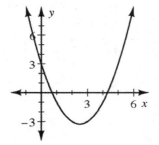   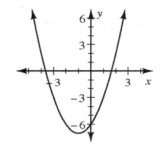

Algebra Connections

9.1.2 How can I use inequalities?

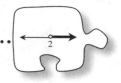

More Solving Inequalities

In Lesson 9.1.1 you learned how to solve inequalities with one variable. Today you will focus on special inequalities and learn how you can use inequalities to solve an application problem.

9-14.   Review what you learned in Lesson 9.1.1 to solve the inequalities below. Represent your solutions both as an inequality and on a number line.

   a. $x - 7 < -2$ b. $3m + 2 \le 8m - 8$ c. $\frac{2}{3}p - 2 > -4$

   d. $2 - 3(x - 1) \ge x - 7$ e. $9k - 4 + 1 \le 2k - 3 + 7k$ f. $3y + 1 < 3y + 1$

9-15.   THE UNITED NATIONS

At the end of this chapter, your team will have the exciting responsibility of representing a country at a special meeting of the United Nations (U.N.). The U.N. needs your help preparing for future large-scale disasters. You will need to help find a solution that not only works best for the country you represent, but that also accommodates the needs of each of the other countries. To prepare you for this task, this chapter will present daily problems to familiarize you with the important issues and concerns of other countries.

Start by writing and solving an equation (or system of equations) that represents the problem below. Be sure to define any variables you use.

Turkey has a population of 66 million people and is made up almost entirely of two ethnic groups: Turks and Kurds. There are four times more Turks than Kurds. Write an equation and solve it to find out how many Kurds live in Turkey.

9-16. In 1912, Japan gave the United States several thousand flowering cherry trees as a symbol of friendship. Similarly, the nation of Cameroon plans to give flowering Satta trees to other countries this year. When asked how to decide which Satta trees make good gifts, Cameroon's chief arborist explained:

"We plant Satta trees when they are 6 cm tall, and they grow 9 cm every year. The trees only flower when they are taller than 150 cm."

It is very important that the trees Cameroon gives flower this year! It would be considered an insult to receive a tree that did not bloom. Luckily, Cameroon has many groves of Satta trees from which to select its gifts. How old must the trees be so that they will flower within the year?

a. Discuss with your study team whether an inequality or an equation is appropriate for this situation. Be prepared to share your reasoning.

b. Write and solve a mathematical sentence to determine how old the trees can be so that they flower this year.

c. Later, the arborist added:

"I almost forgot to tell you! When the trees become very old, they stop flowering. Make sure you choose trees that are no more than 240 cm tall!"

Discuss with your team how you can use this additional information to make sure you choose trees that will flower. Be prepared to share your answer with the class.

9-17.   Solve the inequalities below for the given variables. Represent your solutions on a number line.

   a. $3(2k-1)<9$ b. $\frac{2p}{5}\le 6$

   c. $-2+8n>2$ d. $7t-4\ge 2t-4$

9-18.   Use your graphing shortcuts to graph $y=-2x+3$. Identify the x- and y-intercepts.

9-19.   Find the equation of the line with slope $-\frac{3}{5}$ passing through the point $(-6, 2)$.

9-20.   Use a generic rectangle to multiply $(x+2)(3x-5)$.

   a.   What is $(3x^2+x-10)\div(x+2)$? How do you know?

   b.   Likewise, determine $(3x^2+x-10)\div(3x-5)$.

9-21.   Solve the quadratic equation below. Check your solutions with a calculator.

$$3x^2+2.5x=12.5$$

9-22.   Factor the expressions below completely, if possible.

   a. $4x^2-20x+25$ b. $x^2+11x-2$

   c. $3x^2-12x$ d. $10x^2-35x-20$

9.2.1 What if the inequality has two variables?

Graphing Two-Variable Inequalities

In Section 9.1, you learned how to use an inequality with one variable to help solve a word problem. You also discovered that a one-variable inequality can have zero, one, or more solutions and that these solutions can be represented on a number line. But what if an inequality has two variables? What is a solution to a two-variable inequality? And how could these solutions be represented graphically?

9-23.   EXAMINING THE SOLUTIONS OF A LINEAR EQUATION

Find your graph of $y = -2x + 3$ from problem 9-18. Compare your graph with the poster graph provided by your teacher.

a.   Is the point (–1, 5) a solution to the equation $y = -2x + 3$? How can you tell by looking at the graph? How can you tell by using the equation?

b.   Is the point (2, –1) a solution? What about the point (0, 0)? **Justify** each conclusion with both the graph and the equation.

c.   What determines if a point lies on the line? What is the difference between the points on the line and the points not on the line?

9-24.   GRAPHING A LINEAR INEQUALITY

In problem 9-23, you found that the points on the line are the *only* points that make the equation $y = -2x + 3$ true. But what if you want to graph the solutions for the inequality $y \geq -2x + 3$? How will that graph differ from the graph of $y = -2x + 3$? Consider this question as you follow the steps below.

a.   Your team will be given a list of points to test in the inequality $y \geq -2x + 3$. For each point that makes the inequality true, place a sticky dot on that point on the class graph.

b.   Now examine the solutions shown on the graph. With your team, discuss the questions below. Be ready to share your discoveries with the class.

- Are there any points on the graph that you suspect are solutions but do not have a sticker?

- Are there any stickers that you think may be misplaced? If so, verify these points so that you can have a complete graph of the solutions.

- What about the points on the line? Are they all solutions to the inequality $y \geq -2x + 3$? Why or why not?

- How many solutions are there?

- Why aren't any of the solutions located below the line?

Algebra Connections

9-25.   What else can you learn about solutions of linear
         inequalities? Think about this as you answer the
         questions below with your team.

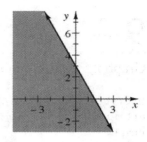

    a.   What if the graph were shaded like the one at
          right? What inequality would correspond with
          this graph?

                        b.   Heidi asks, "What if I changed the inequality
                              to be $y < -2x + 3$? Now what would the
                              graph look like?" Discuss this with your
                              teammates and decide the best way to
                              represent the solutions to the inequality
                              $y < -2x + 3$. Be prepared to share your
                              graph with the class.

9-26.   Graph the inequalities below on graph paper. For each inequality:

         •   Graph the boundary as either a solid or a dashed line.

         •   Shade the region that makes the inequality true.

    a. $y > -\frac{1}{3}x - 1$ b. $y \le 4x + 2$

    c. $y < \frac{5}{2}x + 3$ d. $2x - y \le 5$

9-27.   In your Learning Log, explain how to graph a linear inequality.
         Be sure to address the questions below. Title this entry "Graphing
         Linear Inequalities" and include today's date.

         •   How can you determine if the line is part of the solution?

         •   How can you determine which side of the line the solution belongs to?

         •   What point(s) is (are) easiest to test?

         •   How many points do you need to test?

9-28.   Represent the solutions to the inequalities below on a number line.

   a. $3x - 2 < 10$ b. $5x - 1 - 3x \geq 4x + 5$

   c. $2(x + 2) > 10 - x$ d. $4(x - 3) + 5 \geq -7$

9-29.   Algeria has decided to take out an advertisement in
         the U.N newspaper, *Liberty Daily*. The newspaper
         charges a base fee of $1200 for an ad. There is an
         additional fee of $300 for every inch in height. If
         Algeria is willing to spend any amount up to (and
         including) $2700, what choices does the country
         have for the height of the ad?

9-30.   Solve the problem below by writing and solving one or two equations. A Guess and
         Check table may help you get started. Be sure to define your variable(s) and write
         your solution as a sentence.

         Rowan received 3 points for each question he answered correctly on Part 1 of a test
         and 2 points for each question he answered correctly on Part 2. If he answered 33
         questions correctly and received a total of 85 points, how many questions did he
         answer correctly on Part 1?

9-31.   Line *m* has intercepts (–7, 0) and (0, –2).

   a.   Find the equation of line *m*.

   b.   Is the point (49, –16) also on line *m*? How do you know?

   c.   Write the equation of a line that is perpendicular to line *m* and passes through
         the point (6, –1).

9-32.   Thui made the following hypotheses: $2n - 1 < 5$ and $n + 1 \leq 2n$. Which of the
         following conclusions can she make?

   a. $1 \leq n \leq 3$ b. $1 \leq n < 3$ c. $1 < n \leq 3$ d. $1 < n < 3$

9-33.   **Multiple Choice:** Which of the expressions below is a factor of $6m^2 + 7m - 5$?

   a. $2m + 1$ b. $m + 5$ c. $2m - 5$ d. $3m + 5$

9.2.2 What if the inequality is not linear?

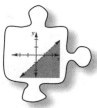

Graphing Linear and Non-Linear Inequalities

In Lesson 9.2.1, you discovered that the solutions of a linear inequality with two variables can be represented by a shaded region on one side of the line. But how can the graph of an inequality help solve a problem? And what happens when the inequality is not linear? Consider these questions as you complete the following problems with your study team.

9-34.   Review what you learned about graphing inequalities in Lesson 9.2.1 by graphing the inequality below on graph paper.

$$y \geq -\tfrac{5}{3}x - 3$$

a.   What is the minimum number of points you need to test in order to know which side of the line the solution falls on?

b.   Orville thinks that using the point (0, 0) to test this inequality is a great idea. Why is using this point so convenient?

c.   Anita decided to use the point (–3, 2) to test the inequality. Test the inequality with her point. Does this point help her decide which side to shade? Why or why not?

9-35.   FOREIGN AID

One of the purposes of the United Nations is to have nations work together to help each other. Recently, the members of the U. N. decided to give grants to poor countries to help reduce poverty. However, the United Nations only has the resources to help those countries in the greatest need. Therefore, it was decided that only countries in which the number of people in poverty is **more than** one-half of its total population would receive foreign aid.

a.   Write an inequality that represents the criteria to receive foreign aid. Let *x* represent the population and *y* represent the number of people in poverty.

b.   On the Lesson 9.2.2 Resource Page provided by your teacher (also available at www.cpm.org), find the graph that shows the number of people in poverty per the population for each of the countries being considered for foreign aid. Carefully graph your inequality from part (a) on this data graph. Which countries should receive foreign aid?

9-36.   What if an inequality is non-linear? Decide with your team how to graph the inequality $y < x^2 - 4x + 3$ on graph paper. Your graphing shortcuts can help.

9-37. With your team, graph the following inequalities on graph paper.

a. $y < -\frac{2}{3}x + 4$ b. $y \geq x^2$ c. $x < 2$

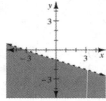

9-38. Write the inequality for the solution graphed at right.
Be prepared to explain how you found your rule.

$\mathbf{M}$ETHODS AND $\mathbf{M}$EANINGS

MATH NOTES

Solving One-Variable Inequalities

To solve a one-variable inequality, first treat the problem as if it were an equality. The solution to the equality is called the **boundary point**. For example, $x = 12$ is the boundary point for the inequality $10 - 2(x - 3) \geq -8$, as shown below.

Problem: $10 - 2(x - 3) \geq -8$

$$10 - 2(x - 3) = -8$$
$$10 - 2x + 6 = -8$$
$$-2x + 16 = -8$$
$$-2x = -24$$
$$x = 12$$

First change the problem to an equality and solve for x:

Since the original inequality is true when $x = 12$, place your boundary point on the number line as a solid point. Then test one value on either side in the *original* inequality to determine which set of numbers makes the inequality true.

Therefore, the solution is $x \leq 12$.

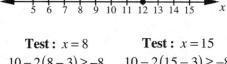

Test: $x = 8$	Test: $x = 15$
$10 - 2(8 - 3) \geq -8$	$10 - 2(15 - 3) \geq -8$
$10 - 2(5) \geq -8$	$10 - 2(12) \geq -8$
$0 \geq -8$	$-14 \geq 17$
TRUE!	FALSE!

When the inequality is $<$ or $>$, the boundary point is *not* included in the answer. On a number line, this would be indicated with an open circle at the boundary point.

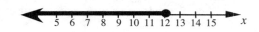

386

Algebra Connections

9-39.   **Multiple Choice:** Which of the expressions below is a factor of $6x^2 + 7x - 20$?

    a. $3x - 4$ b. $2x - 5$ c. $3x + 4$ d. $4x - 3$

9-40.   **Multiple Choice:** Which of the following expressions is the product of $(4y - 3x)(2y + x)$?

    a. $8y^2 - 2xy - 3x^2$ b. $6y^2 - 2xy - 2x^2$

    c. $8y^2 + 10xy - 3x^2$ d. $6y^2 - 2x$

9-41.   WHAT'S THE DIFFERENCE?

Examine the following situations in which you need to find the difference between two amounts.

    a.   Rocio has $298 saved in the bank, while Thomas has $314. What is the difference between their bank balances? How did you get your answer?

    b.   The temperature in Minneapolis on January 10 ranged between $-23°$ and $19°$ Fahrenheit. What was the difference between the high and low temperatures for this date? How did you get your answer?

    c.   Urban High School has 1850 students, while Metro High School has 1490 students. What is the difference of their student populations?

    d.   Explain why these differences in (a) through (c) are all positive.

9-42.   Solve the following equations and inequalities for x. Check your solution(s), if possible.

    a. $\frac{3}{x} = 9$ b. $\sqrt{x} = 4$ c. $x^2 = 25$ d. $2(x - 3) > 4$

9-43.   During a race, Bernie ran 9 meters every 4 seconds, while Barnaby ran 2 meters every second and got a 10-meter head start. If the race was 70 meters long, did Bernie ever catch up with Barnaby? If so, when? **Justify** your answer.

9-44.   Find the x-intercepts of the graph of $y = 5x^2 + 7x - 6$ using *two different methods*. The answers from each method should match.

9.2.3 What's the difference?

Introduction to Absolute Value

In the past few lessons, you learned what inequalities are and learned how to graph linear and non-linear inequalities with two variables. Today you will learn a new operation and will learn how you can use it to create new and interesting inequality graphs.

9-45.   ABSOLUTE-VALUE OPERATION

Your teacher will present you with information about an operation called **absolute value**. As your teacher finds the absolute values of numbers such as –11 and 4, record the results on your paper. Look for a pattern!

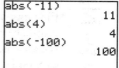

a.   Study the relationship between the number entered in the parentheses and the results shown. Write a statement describing this operation.

b.   Why would you ever need an absolute value?

9-46.   While some graphing calculators, like the one shown in problem 9-45, display the absolute value as "abs(–100) = 100," the written notation is $|-100| = 100$. This notation consists of two vertical lines on each side of the input value.

a.   The expression $|-3|+1$ can be translated as, "*Change –3 to a positive value and then add 1.*" Translate the expression $|-5+1|-3$ into words and then find its value.

b.   Evaluate these expressions:

　　　　i.　　$|-100|-98$　　　　　　*ii.*　　$5|2-8|$

　　　　iii.　　$|-13|+|0|$　　　　　　*iv.*　　$14-|-10+3|$

c.   Now create your own expression using the absolute value that has a result of 10. Be creative and be ready to share your expression with the class.

9-47.   Mr. Guo is thinking of a number. When he takes the absolute value of his number, he gets 15. What could his number be? Is there more than one possible answer?

9-48.   Riley wants to know what an absolute value might look like on a graph.

a.   Set up a table and graph $y = |x|$.

b.   Describe for Riley what the graph looks like. Be as detailed as you can.

9-49.   Dorinae is confused. She is making a table for $y = |x + 1|$. She is trying to find y when $x = -3$, but she is not sure if she should find the absolute value first, or if she should first add 1. Explain to Dorinae what she should do first. **Justify** your reasoning.

9-50.   Graph the inequality $y < |2x - 1|$. Be ready to share your graph with the class.

ⓂETHODS AND MEANINGS

MATH NOTES

Definition of Absolute Value

An **absolute value**, represented by two vertical bars, | |, determines the positive value of a number. Numerically, it represents a distance on a number line between a number and zero. Since a distance is always positive, the absolute value is *always* either a positive value or zero. The absolute value of a number is *never* negative.

For example, the number –3 is 3 units away from 0, as shown on the number line at right. Therefore, the absolute value of –3 is 3. This is written $|-3| = 3$.

distance of 3

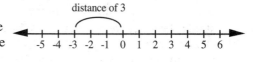

Likewise, the number 5 is 5 units away from 0. The absolute value of 5 is 5, written $|5| = 5$.

distance of 5

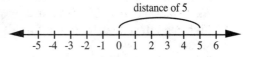

Review & Preview

9-51.   Brazil's rain forests currently cover about 1,400,000 square miles, but are becoming smaller every year because of deforestation. Realizing that the rain forests are a great resource, Brazil has decided to control how quickly the forests are cleared.

In 50 years Brazil would like the rain forests to cover more than 1,200,000 square miles. If x represents the forest area that is cleared each year, write and solve an inequality that would help determine acceptable values of x.

9-52.   Calculate the value of each expression below. You may want to refer to the Math
         Notes box for this lesson for help.

   a. $\left|-4\right|-3$ b. $\left|6-11+3\right|$ c. $-9-\left|-2\right|$ d. $5\left|6\right|-2$

9-53.   Clifford thinks that $x = 7$ is a solution to $3(x-2) \le 4$. Is he correct? Show why or
         why not.

9-54.   Graph the inequalities below on graph paper.

   a. $y \le -x + 5$ b. $y > \frac{2}{3}x - 1$

9-55.   Zachary has $718 in his bank account and automatically withdraws (subtracts) $14
         every month to pay for his computer service. Christian has $212 in his bank account
         and deposits (adds) $32 each month from his newspaper-delivery tips. Assuming
         they make no other deposits or withdrawals, when will Zachary and Christian have
         the same amount of money in their bank accounts?

9-56.   Stacey is the star of the basketball team. She makes
         many baskets during each game and could break the
         record for the most baskets made in one season at her
         high school. The data for the first five games of this
         season is below.

Game Number	Total Number of Baskets
1	6
2	11
3	18
4	25
5	31

   a.   Plot a graph with these data points.

   b.   Draw a trend line for this data using two carefully selected points that best
        represent the data.

   c.   Use the equation of your line to predict how many baskets Stacey will make by
        the end of the season if the season has 15 games.

9.3.1 How can I represent it?

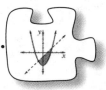

Systems of Inequalities

In Chapter 6 you learned that the solution to a system of equations is a point that makes both equations true. But what about the solution of a system of two inequalities? How can you represent these solutions on a graph? How many solutions can a system of inequalities have?

Consider these questions as you learn how to graph a system of inequalities.

9-57.   Find your graphs for problem 9-54.

    a.   Compare your solution graphs for $y \leq -x + 5$ and $y > \frac{2}{3}x - 1$ with those of your teammates. Correct any errors. Be sure to focus on whether the boundary line should be included in each graph.

    b.   What would the graph of the system of inequalities look like? Consider the system of inequalities below. Which points are solutions to this system (that is, which points make *both* inequalities true)?

$$y \leq -x + 5$$
$$y > \frac{2}{3}x - 1$$

    c.   If you have not done so already, verify your solution region from part (b) algebraically by substituting the coordinates of a point from your solution region into each inequality.

    d.   How can you be sure that this region is the only set of points that makes both inequalities true?

9-58.   Draw a graph of the region satisfying both inequalities at right. Start by graphing the boundary lines and then test points to find the region that makes both inequalities true.

$$y < x + 2$$
$$y \leq 10 - \frac{3}{4}x$$

9-59.   HOW MANY REGIONS?

When graphing the system of inequalities
below, Reyna started with the boundary graph
of each inequality shown at right.

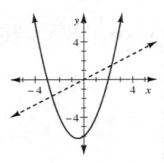

$$y \le x^2 + x - 6$$
$$y > \tfrac{2}{3}x$$

a.   Why is the line dashed while the parabola is
     not?

b.   Find a copy of Reyna's graph on the Lesson 9.3.1B
     Resource Page provided by your teacher. How many possible solution regions
     are there? Carefully count each region with your teammates.

c.   Pick a point in each region and test it in the system of inequalities. Shade any
     regions that contain solutions to both inequalities. How many regions make up
     the solution to this system?

d.   Why is (0, 0) not a good point to use to test for this solution?

9-60.   How does changing the inequality affect the solution graph? Notice that each
         system of inequalities below uses the same boundary graphs as Reyna's graph
         from problem 9-59. However, notice that this time the inequalities are slightly
         altered.

With your teammates, devise a method to determine which region (or regions) are
solutions for each system. Shade the appropriate regions on your resource page.

a. $y \ge x^2 + x - 6$ b. $y \ge x^2 + x - 6$ c. $y \le x^2 + x - 6$
     $y > \tfrac{2}{3}x$ $y < \tfrac{2}{3}x$ $y < \tfrac{2}{3}x$

9-61. The United Nations asked every nation to write a system of inequalities that best approximates its country's shape (the U.N. thinks this will help find each country's area). Honduras sent in its inequalities by fax, but some of the information is unreadable. With your study team, determine the missing parts of the inequalities and rewrite them on your paper.

 $x + 3$ $y \geq \frac{1}{2}x - $

 2 y  $-\frac{2}{3}x + 4$

y  $-\frac{2}{3}x - 1$

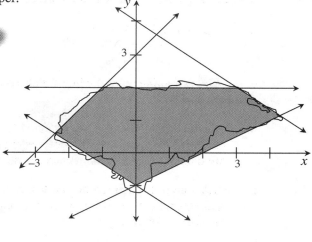

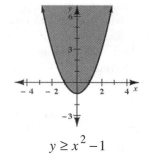

METHODS AND MEANINGS

MATH NOTES

Graphing Inequalities with Two Variables

To graph an inequality with two variables, first graph the boundary line or curve. If the inequality does not include an equality (that is, if it is > or < rather than ≥ or ≤), then the graph of the boundary is dashed to indicate that it is not included in the solution. Otherwise, the boundary is a solid line or curve.

Once the boundary is graphed, choose a point that does not lie on the boundary to test in the inequality. If that point makes the inequality true, then the entire region in which that point lies is a solution. Examine the two examples below.

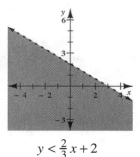

$$y < \frac{2}{3}x + 2$$

$$y \geq x^2 - 1$$

9-62. Match each graph below with the correct inequality.

   a. $y > -x + 2$ b. $y < 2x - 3$ c. $y \geq \frac{1}{2}x$ d. $y \leq -\frac{2}{3}x + 2$

   1) 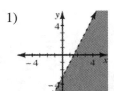   2) 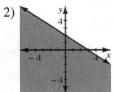   3) 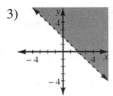   4)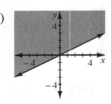

9-63. Solve each inequality below. Represent the solutions on number lines.

   a. $7x - 2 < 3 + 2x$ b. $\frac{1}{3}x \geq 2$

   c. $3(2m - 1) - 5m \leq -1$ d. $2k + 3 \leq 2k + 1$

9-64. Which of the following expressions are equal to 1? (Note: More than one expression may be equal to 1!)

   a. $\frac{114}{114}$ b. $\frac{2}{3} \cdot \frac{3}{2}$ c. $\frac{m+4}{m+4}$ d. $\frac{p^2}{p \cdot p}$

9-65. Factor the following quadratics completely.

   a. $5x^2 + 13x - 6$ b. $6t^2 - 26t + 8$ c. $6x^2 - 24$

9-66. When a family with two adults and three children bought tickets for a movie, they paid a total of $27.75. The next family in line, with two children and three adults, paid $32.25 for the same movie. Find the adult and child ticket prices by writing a system of equations with two variables.

9-67. **Multiple Choice:** Which of the points below is a solution of $y < |x - 3|$?

   a. (2, 1)   b. (−4, 5)   c. (−2, 8)   d. (0, 3)

9.3.2 How can I apply it?

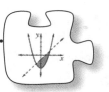

More Systems of Inequalities

9-68. Review what you learned about systems of inequalities in Lesson 9.3.1 by graphing the system of inequalities at right on graph paper. Carefully shade the region of points that make *both* inequalities true.

$$y \le |x| + 4$$
$$-x + 4y \ge 4$$

9-69. SEARCH AND RESCUE

"I'm completely lost… water everywhere I can see… both engines have failed… Wait! I see land. I'm going to try to land. I think it's…"

Those were the last words heard from Harold in his hot-air balloon. The last time the balloon showed up on radar, it was near the Solomon Islands in the Pacific Ocean.

Your Task: Your team must determine where to send the search-and-rescue teams! Use the following reports along with the map on the Lesson 9.3.2 Resource Page (also available at www.cpm.org) and look carefully for information that will help you draw boundary lines. Write a system of inequalities to give to the search-and-rescue team. Be sure to identify the probable landing site on the map.

Basic facts of the case:

The balloon departed from the airport at the very northern tip of the Philippines. The flight was supposed to follow a straight path *directly* to an airport in French Polynesia.

The balloon's last known location was at (−1000, 1000) near the Solomon Islands.

Pilot's report from a nearby airplane:

"We were on our way from Australia, when we saw a hot-air balloon sinking rapidly. I am certain that it crashed south of our flight path. When we left Australia, we traveled 2000 km north for every 3000 km east that we flew."

Phone call received today:

"I was a passenger on a flight that flew directly from French Polynesia to Indonesia. I was looking out my window when I saw the balloon going down to the north of where we were flying."

9-70.   Notice that each system of inequalities below contains the same boundary lines. On graph paper, graph the boundaries for the system on one set of axes. Then, for each pair of inequalities, work with your teammates to decide which region is the solution, if a solution exists. Be ready to share your conclusions with the class.

a. $y \leq \frac{2}{3}x + 3$ b. $y \leq \frac{2}{3}x + 3$ c. $y \geq \frac{2}{3}x + 3$

     $y \geq \frac{2}{3}x$ $y \leq \frac{2}{3}x$ $y \leq \frac{2}{3}x$

9-71.   In your Learning Log, describe your method for graphing systems of inequalities for a student who has missed class for the last couple of days. Be sure to include examples and important details. Title this entry "Graphing Systems of Inequalities" and include today's date.

9-72.   Graph and shade the solution for the inequality below.

$$y \leq x^2 + 2x - 8$$

9-73.   Graph and shade the solution for the system of inequalities below.

$$y \geq \frac{3}{4}x - 2$$
$$y < -\frac{1}{2}x + 3$$

9-74.   Write the inequality that represents the x-values highlighted on each number line below.

a.      b.

c.      d.

9-75.   Determine if the following statements are true or false.

a. $|-6| < 4$ b. $|-3+5| > 2.5$ c. $4 \geq |0|$ d. $|-4+3| > 1$

9-76.   **Multiple Choice:** Which equation below is perpendicular to the line $y = \frac{1}{3}x + 7$?

   a. $x + 3y = 4$ b. $x - 3y = 4$ c. $3x + y = 4$ d. $3x - y = 4$

9-77.   For the Spring Festival, the Math Club is selling rulers for $1 and compasses for $2.50.

   a.   While the club would like to sell as many items as they can to raise funds, they need to make at least $15.00 to break even. Write an inequality to represent this situation. Let r = the number of rulers sold and c = the number of compasses sold.

   b.   School rules state that the club can sell a maximum of 25 items for the festival. Write an inequality for this constraint (limitation).

   c.   Graph the inequalities from parts (a) and (b) on the same set of axes so that compasses are represented on the x-axis and rulers are represented on the y-axis. Find the region of points that are solutions to each of them. Can this region fall below the x-axis or to the left of the y-axis? Why or why not?

   d.   What do the points in the solution region represent?

9.3.3 How can I use inequalities to solve problems?
••
Applying Inequalities to Solve Problems

Today you will pull together all of the mathematics you have studied in this chapter and **apply** it to solve an application problem.

9-78.   UNITED NATIONS TO THE RESCUE

As a representative of your country, you have been sent the following letter and given an important task:

Dear Representative to the United Nations:

A critical matter has come to the attention of the United Nations. In the past, when a catastrophe struck a part of the world, the U. N. gathered supplies to give to people in need. Unfortunately, because the U. N. had to collect supplies from each country at the time of the catastrophe, it was always quite a few days before the supplies could be sent to the areas that needed them the most.

A recommendation has come before the U. N. to create a supply of food and medicine packages for future emergencies. Each food package will be able to feed several hundred people, while each medicine package will supply one first-aid station. I am asking each country to donate the same number of packages so each country shares the burden equally.

I am asking each country to determine how many food and medicine packages they are able to give. You will present your findings at today's United Nations meeting. Please be certain to use the information that your country's Budget Committee has prepared to help you decide how many packages you can afford.

Best of luck, and may our efforts make our world a better place!

Sincerely,
The Secretary General of the United Nations

After consulting with your country's Budget Committee, your teacher will supply you with some information that will help decide how many food and medicine packets your country can afford.

Your Task: To communicate your country's budget constraints, write an inequality expressing how many food and medicine packages your country is able to give. Let x equal the number of food packages and y equal the number of medicine packages.

On the Lesson 9.3.3B Resource Page provided by your teacher (also available at www.cpm.org), graph the solution region representing the number of medicine and food packets that can be donated by your country. Be prepared to share your graph with the other countries of the United Nations.

9-79.   As a member of the United Nations, you must consider each of the following
         proposals. In each case, assume that the United Nations would like to receive as
         many emergency supplies as possible, while still having each nation give equally.

   a.   One proposal is that each country gives 185 medicine packages. How many
         food packages should the United Nations require from each country in this
         case? Explain how you made your decision.

   b.   Another proposal is to get the largest number of medicine packages possible.
         What is the largest number of medicine packages that each country can offer?
         How did you find your answer?

9-80.   EXTENSION

         A last-minute proposal suggests balancing the number of food and medicine
         supplies. For instance, if a country gives 150 food packages, then they would also
         give 150 medicine packages. How many food and medicine packages should the
         United Nations require from each country in this case? Explain how you determined
         your solution.

9-81.   While setting up a mathematical sentence to solve a problem, Paulina and Aliya
         came up with the equations below. Since the equations did not look alike, the girls
         turned to you for help.

$$\text{Paulina:}\quad 4x + 2y = 6$$

$$\text{Aliya:}\quad 12x + 6y = 18$$

   a.   Are these equations equivalent? That is, will the graph of each line be the
         same? Explain how you know.

   b.   Find another equation that is equivalent to both of these. How did you find
         your equation?

9-82.   The town you live in has decided to limit the
         amount of trash thrown out each month. Your
         town, which has 3280 homes, has asked each
         household to keep track of how many pounds
         of trash they produce during a month. In
         addition, the town council has found that other
         sources of trash, such as local businesses,
         combine to create 1500 lbs of trash each
         month. If the town has a goal of creating **less
         than** 50,000 lbs of trash, how much trash
         should a household be limited to? Write an
         inequality for this situation and solve it.

9-83.   Solve the following inequalities for the given variable and represent the solutions on
         a number line.

   a. $2 < 2m - 8$ b. $\frac{1}{3}x - 1 \le -3$

   c. $5(2x - 8) + 24 > 3(4 + 2x)$ d. $5 + 2k < k - 2 + k$

9-84.   Graph the system of inequalities below.

$$y \ge x(x - 4)$$
$$y < x$$

   a.   Carefully shade the solution region.

   b.   Is (0, 0) a solution to this system? How can you tell?

9-85.   Solve the quadratic equation below *twice*, once using the Zero Product Property and
         once using the Quadratic Formula. Verify that the solutions from both methods are
         the same.

$$2x^2 - 19x + 9 = 0$$

9-86.   Read the following problem. Then decide which system of equations below can
         represent this situation.

         Multiple Choice: The length of a rectangle is 4 units longer than twice its width. If
         the area is 126 square units, find the length and width.

   a. $w = 2l + 4$ b. $l = 2w + 4$ c. $w = 2l + 4$ d. $l = 2w + 4$
         $wl = 126$ $l + w = 126$ $l + w = 126$ $wl = 126$

Algebra Connections

Chapter 9 Closure What have I learned?

Reflection and Synthesis

The activities below offer you a chance to reflect on what you have learned during this chapter. As you work, look for concepts that you feel very comfortable with, ideas that you would like to learn more about, and topics you need more help with. Look for **connections** between ideas as well as **connections** with material you learned previously.

①   TEAM BRAINSTORM

With your team, brainstorm a list for each of the following topics. Be as detailed as you can. How long can you make your list? Challenge yourselves. Be prepared to share your team's ideas with the class.

Topics: What have you studied in this chapter? What ideas and words were important in what you learned? Remember to be as detailed as you can.

Ways of Thinking: What Ways of Thinking did you use in this chapter? When did you use them?

Connections: What topics, ideas, and words that you learned *before* this chapter are **connected** to the new ideas in this chapter? Again, make your list as long as you can.

②   MAKING CONNECTIONS

The following is a list of the vocabulary used in this chapter. The words that appear in bold are new to this chapter. Make sure that you are familiar with all of these words and know what they mean. Refer to the glossary or index for any words that you do not yet understand.

absolute value	**boundary**	coordinates
equation	graph	**inequality**
number line	**region**	solution
system of inequalities		

Make a concept map showing all of the **connections** you can find among the key words and ideas listed above. To show a **connection** between two words, draw a line between them and explain the **connection**, as shown in the example on the following page. A word can be **connected** to any other word as long as there is a **justified connection**. For each key word or idea, provide a sketch that illustrates the idea (see the example on the following page).

Continues on next page →

②   *Continued from previous page.*

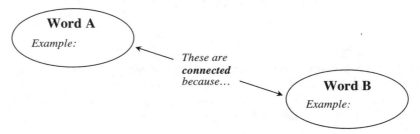

Your teacher may provide you with vocabulary cards to help you get started. If you use the cards to plan your concept map, be sure either to re-draw your concept map on your paper or to glue the vocabulary cards to a poster with all of the **connections** explained for others to see and understand.

While you are making your map, your team may think of related words or ideas that are not listed here. Be sure to include these ideas on your concept map.

③   SUMMARIZING MY UNDERSTANDING

This section gives you the opportunity to show what you know about certain math topics or ideas. Your teacher will give you directions for exactly how to do this.

④   WHAT HAVE I LEARNED?

This section will help you evaluate which types of problems you have seen with which you feel comfortable and those with which you need more help. This section appears at the end of every chapter to help you check your understanding. Even if your teacher does not assign this section, it is a good idea to try the problems and find out for yourself what you know and what you need to work on.

Solve each problem as completely as you can. The table at the end of the closure section has answers to these problems. It also tells you where you can find additional help and practice on problems like these.

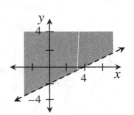

CL 9-87.   Write an inequality that represents the graph at right.

CL 9-88.   Find the equation of the line that passes through the points $(-3, 13)$ and $(4, -1)$.

CL 9-89. Is the point $(0, 4)$ a solution to the system of inequalities at right? **Justify** your answer.

$$y \leq -3x + 4$$
$$y > x^2 + 3x - 2$$

CL 9-90. Factor these quadratic expressions completely, if possible.

a. $x^2 + x - 30$

b. $-3x^2 + 23x - 14$

c. $2x^2 - 5x + 4$

d. $6x^2 + 10x - 24$

CL 9-91. Solve each inequality below for the given variable. Then represent each solution on a number line.

a. $4x - 3 \geq 9$

b. $3(t + 4) < 5$

c. $\frac{2y}{7} < 8$

d. $5x + 4 > -3(x - 8)$

CL 9-92. Brian was holding a ballroom dance. He wanted to make sure girls would come, so he charged boys \$5 to get in but girls only \$3. The 45 people who came paid a total of \$175. How many girls came to the dance?

CL 9-93. Solve these quadratic equations using any method.

a. $0 = 3x^2 + 4x - 7$

b. $x^2 - 3x + 18 = 0$

CL 9-94. Write equations for lines (a) through (e) shown in the graph at right.

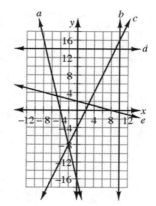

CL 9-95. Graph the system of inequalities below on graph paper.

$$y < x^2$$
$$y \geq x + 2$$

CL 9-96. Lew says to his granddaughter Audrey, "Even if you tripled your age and added 9, you still wouldn't be as old as I am." Lew is 60 years old. Write and solve an inequality to determine the possible ages Audrey could be.

CL 9-97. Graph the solutions of $y \geq |x + 2|$ on graph paper.

CL 9-98. The hare leaps 500 centimeters every 20 seconds. The tortoise crawls 250 centimeters every 50 seconds, but gets a 1000-centimeter head start. Use any method you know to determine how long it takes the hare to catch up to the tortoise.

CL 9-99. Check your answers using the table at the end of the closure section. Which problems do you feel confident about? Which problems were hard? Use the table to make a list of topics you need help on and a list of topics you need to practice more.

⑤ HOW AM I THINKING?

This course focuses on five different **Ways of Thinking**: reversing thinking, justifying, generalizing, making connections, and applying and extending understanding. These are some of the ways in which you think while trying to make sense of a concept or to solve a problem (even outside of math class). During this chapter, you have probably used each Way of Thinking multiple times without even realizing it!

Review each of the Ways of Thinking that are described in the closure sections of Chapters 1 through 5. Then choose three of these Ways of Thinking that you remember using while working in this chapter. For each Way of Thinking that you choose, show and explain where you used it and how you used it. Describe why thinking in this way helped you solve a particular problem or understand something new. (For instance, explain why you wanted to **generalize** in this particular case, or why it was useful to see particular **connections**.) Be sure to include examples to demonstrate your thinking.

Answers and Support for Closure Activity #4
What Have I Learned?

Problem	Solution	Need Help?	More Practice
CL 9-87.	$y > \frac{1}{2}x - 2$	Lesson 9.3.1 Math Notes box	Problems 9-38 and 9-62
CL 9-88.	$y = -2x + 7$	Lesson 7.3.3 and Lesson 7.3.4 Math Notes box	Problems 9-19 and 9-31
CL 9-89.	Yes; the point (0, 4) lies on the graph $x^2 + 3x - 2 < y \le -3x + 4$. Therefore, it is a solution to the system of inequalities. 	Problems 9-57 and 9-59	Problems 9-58, 9-60, 9-68, 9-70, 9-73, and 9-84
CL 9-90.	a. $(x+6)(x-5)$ b. $(-3x+2)(x-7)$ c. not factorable d. $2(x+3)(3x-4)$	Problems 8-13, 8-14, and 8-35; Lesson 8.1.4 Math Notes box	Problems 9-22, 9-33, 9-39, and 9-65
CL 9-91.	a. $x \ge 3$ b. $t < -\frac{7}{3}$ c. $y < 28$ d. $x > 2.5$	Lesson 9.2.2 Math Notes box	Problems 9-6, 9-8, 9-14, 9-17, 9-28, 9-63, and 9-83
CL 9-92.	25 girls came to the dance.	Lesson 7.1.4 Math Notes box	Problems 9-7, 9-30, 9-66, and 9-86

Problem	Solution	Need Help?	More Practice
CL 9-93.	a. $x = 1$ or $x = -\frac{7}{3}$ b. no solution	Lessons 8.1.4, 8.2.3, 8.3.1, and 8.3.2	Problems 9-9, 9-21, and 9-85
CL 9-94.	a. $y = -4x - 16$ b. $x = 10$ c. $y = 2x - 4$ d. $y = 14$ e. $y = -\frac{1}{4}x + 2$	Lesson 7.2.2 Math Notes box	Problems 9-18, 9-19, and 9-31
CL 9-95.		Problems 9-57 and 9-59	Problems 9-58, 9-60, 9-68, 9-70, 9-73, and 9-84
CL 9-96.	Audrey is less than 17 years old.	Lessons 9.1.1 and 9.2.2 Math Notes boxes	Problems 9-29, 9-51, 9-77, and 9-82
CL 9-97.		Lessons 9.2.3 and 9.3.1 Math Notes boxes	Problems 9-25, 9-26, 9-50, 9-54, 9-62, 9-62, and 9-72
CL 9-98.	The hare catches up to the tortoise after 50 seconds.	Lesson 7.1.4 Math Notes box	Problems 9-43 and 9-55

SIMPLIFYING AND SOLVING

10

CHAPTER 10   Simplifying and Solving

Since the beginning of this course, you have studied several different types of equations and have developed successful methods to solve them. For example, you have learned how to solve linear equations, systems of linear equations, and quadratic equations.

In Chapter 10, you will **extend** your solving skills to include other types of equations, including equations with square roots, absolute values, and messy fractions.

Another focus of this chapter is on learning how to simplify algebraic fractions (called "rational expressions") and expressions with exponents. By using the special properties of the number 1 and the meaning of exponents, you will be able to simplify large, complicated expressions.

In this chapter, you will learn how to:

➢ Simplify expressions involving exponents and fractions.

➢ Solve quadratic equations by completing the square.

➢ Use multiple methods to solve new types of equations and inequalities, such as those with square roots, rational expressions, and absolute values.

Guiding Questions

Think about these questions throughout this chapter:

How can I rewrite it?

How can I solve it?

Is there another method?

What is special about the number 1?

Chapter Outline

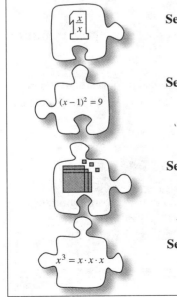

Section 10.1   In this section, you will study the properties of the number 1 and use them to simplify rational expressions and solve equations with fractions.

Section 10.2   Using the skills you learned in Section 10.1, you will develop new ways to solve unfamiliar, complicated equations involving square roots and absolute values.

Section 10.3   In this section, you will learn how to rewrite quadratics in perfect square form using a process called "completing the square."

Section 10.4   At the end of this chapter, you will use the meaning of an exponent to develop strategies to simplify exponential expressions.

10.1.1 How can I simplify?

Simplifying Expressions

In Chapter 8, you used the special qualities of the number zero to develop a powerful way to solve factorable quadratics. In Section 10.1, you will focus on another important number: the number 1. What is special about 1? What can you do with the number 1 that you cannot do with any other number? You will use your understanding of the number 1 to simplify algebraic fractions, which are also known as **rational expressions**.

10-1.   What do you know about the number 1? Brainstorm with your team and be ready to report your ideas to the class. Create examples to help show what you mean.

10-2.   Mr. Wonder claims that anything divided by itself equals 1 (as long as you do not divide by zero). For example, he says that $\frac{16x}{16x} = 1$ if x is not zero.

   a.   Is Mr. Wonder correct?

   b.   Why can't x be zero?

   c.   Next he considers $\frac{x-3}{x-3}$. Does this equal 1? What value of x must be excluded in this fraction?

   d.   Create your own rational expression (algebraic fraction) that equals 1. **Justify** that it equals 1.

   e.   Mr. Wonder also says that when you multiply any number by 1, the number stays the same. For example, he says that the product below equals $\frac{x}{y}$. Is he correct?

$$\boxed{1\,\frac{z}{z}} \cdot \frac{x}{y} = \frac{x}{y}$$

10-3.   Use what you know about the number 1 to simplify each expression below, if possible. State any values of the variables that would make the denominator zero.

   a. $\frac{x^2}{x^2}$ b. $\frac{x}{x} \cdot \frac{x}{x} \cdot \frac{x}{3}$ c. $\frac{x-2}{x-2} \cdot \frac{x+5}{x-1}$ d. $\frac{9}{x} \cdot \frac{x}{9}$

   e. $\frac{h \cdot h \cdot k}{h}$ f. $\frac{(2m-5)(m+6)}{(m+6)(3m+1)}$ g. $\frac{6(n-2)^2}{3(n-2)}$ h. $\frac{3-2x}{(4x-1)(3-2x)}$

10-4.   Mr. Wonder now tries to simplify $\frac{4x}{x}$ and $\frac{4+x}{x}$.

a.   Mr. Wonder thinks that since $\frac{x}{x} = 1$, then $\frac{4x}{x} = 4$.
      Is he correct? Substitute three values of x to **justify**
      your answer.

b.   He also wonders if $\frac{4+x}{x} = 5$. Is this simplification correct?
      Substitute three values of x to **justify** your answer. Remember
      that $\frac{4+x}{x}$ is the same as $(4+x) \div x$.

c.   Compare the results of parts (a) and (b). When can a rational expression be
      simplified in this manner?

d.   Which of the following expressions below is simplified correctly? Explain
      how you know.

i. $\frac{x^2+x+3}{x+3} = x^2$ ii. $\frac{(x+2)(x+3)}{x+3} = x+2$

10-5.   In problem 10-4, you may have noticed that the numerator and denominator of an
          algebraic fraction must both be written as a product before any terms create a 1.
          Examine the expressions below. Factor the numerator and denominator of each
          fraction, if necessary. That is, rewrite each one as a product. Then look for "ones"
          and simplify. For each expression, assume the denominator is not zero.

a. $\frac{x^2+6x+9}{x^2-9}$ b. $\frac{2x^2-x-10}{3x^2+7x+2}$ c. $\frac{28x^2-x-15}{28x^2-x-15}$ d. $\frac{x^2+4x}{2x+8}$

10-6.   In your Learning Log, explain how to simplify rational expressions
          such as those in problem 10-5. Be sure to include an example. Title
          this entry "Simplifying Rational Expressions" and include today's date.

LOOKING DEEPER

Multiplicative Identity Property

MATH NOTES

When any number is multiplied by 1, its value stays the same.

For example:

$142 \cdot 1 = 142$ $1 \cdot k^2 = k^2$ $\frac{4}{4} \cdot \frac{2}{3} = \frac{2}{3}$

10-7.   How many solutions does each equation below have?

   a. $4x + 3 = 3x + 3$ b. $3(x - 4) - x = 5 + 2x$

   c. $(5x - 2)(x + 4) = 0$ d. $x^2 - 4x + 4 = 0$

10-8.   While David was solving the equation $100x + 300 = 500$, he wondered if he could first change the equation to $x + 3 = 5$. What do you think?

   a.   Solve both equations and verify that they have the same solution.

   b.   What could you do to the equation $100x + 300 = 500$ to change it into $x + 3 = 5$?

10-9.   Solve each of the following inequalities for the given variable. Represent your solutions on a number line.

   a. $5 + 3x < 5$ b. $-3x \geq 8 - x$

10-10.   For each rational expression below, state any values of the variables that would make the denominator zero. Then complete each part.

   a.   Use the fact that $(x + 4)^2 = (x + 4)(x + 4)$ to rewrite $\frac{(x+4)^2}{(x+4)(x-2)}$. Then look for "ones" and simplify.

   b.   Use the strategy you used in part (a) to simplify the expression $\frac{8(x+2)^3(x-3)^3}{4(x+2)^2(x-3)^5}$.

10-11.   In Lesson 10.1.2 you will focus on multiplying and dividing rational expressions. Recall what you learned about multiplying and dividing fractions in a previous course as you answer the questions below. To help you, the following examples have been provided.

$$\frac{9}{16} \cdot \frac{4}{6} = \frac{36}{96} = \frac{3}{8}$$

$$\frac{5}{6} \div \frac{20}{12} = \frac{5}{6} \cdot \frac{12}{20} = \frac{60}{120} = \frac{1}{2}$$

   a.   Without a calculator, multiply $\frac{2}{3} \cdot \frac{9}{14}$ and reduce the result. Then use a calculator to check your answer. Describe your method for multiplying fractions.

   b.   Without a calculator, divide $\frac{3}{5} \div \frac{12}{25}$ and reduce the result. Then use a calculator to check your answer. Describe your method for dividing fractions.

10-12.   **Multiple Choice:** Which of the points below is a solution to $y < |x - 3|$?

   a.   (2, 1)   b.   (−4, 5)   c.   (−2, 8)   d.   (0, 3)

Chapter 10: Simplifying and Solving

10.1.2 How can I rewrite it?

Multiplying and Dividing Rational Expressions

In a previous course you learned how to multiply and divide fractions. But what if the fractions have variables in them? (That is, what if they are rational expressions?) Is the process the same? Today you will learn how to multiply and divide rational expressions and will continue to practice simplifying rational expressions.

10-13.   Review what you learned yesterday as you simplify the rational expression at right. What are the excluded values of x? (That is, what values can x <u>not</u> be?)

$$\frac{3x^2+11x-4}{2x^2+11x+12}$$

10-14.   With your team, review your responses to homework problem 10-11. Verify that everyone obtained the same answers and be prepared to share with the class how you multiplied and divided the fractions below.

$$\frac{2}{3} \cdot \frac{9}{14} \qquad\qquad \frac{3}{5} \div \frac{12}{25}$$

10-15.   Use your understanding of multiplying and dividing fractions to rewrite the expressions below. Then look for "ones" and simplify. For each rational expression, also state any values of the variables that would make the denominator zero.

a. $\frac{4x+3}{x-5} \cdot \frac{x-5}{x+3}$

b. $\frac{x+2}{9x-1} \div \frac{2x+1}{9x-1}$

c. $\frac{2m+3}{3m-2} \cdot \frac{7+4m}{3+2m}$

d. $\frac{(y-2)^3}{3y} \cdot \frac{y+5}{(y+2)(y-2)}$

e. $\frac{15x^3}{3y} \div \frac{10x^2y}{4y^2}$

f. $\frac{(5x-2)(3x+1)}{(2x-3)^2} \div \frac{(5x-2)(x-4)}{(x-4)(2x-3)}$

10-16.   PUTTING IT ALL TOGETHER

Multiply or divide the expressions below. Leave your answers as simplified as possible. For each rational expression, assume the denominator is not zero.

a. $\frac{20}{22} \cdot \frac{14}{35}$

b. $\frac{12}{40} \div \frac{15}{6}$

c. $\frac{5x-15}{3x^2+10x-8} \div \frac{x^2+x-12}{3x^2-8x+4}$

d. $\frac{12x-18}{x^2-2x-15} \cdot \frac{x^2-x-12}{3x^2-9x-12}$

e. $\frac{5x^2+34x-7}{10x} \cdot \frac{5x}{x^2+4x-21}$

f. $\frac{2x^2+x-10}{x^2+2x-8} \div \frac{4x^2+20x+25}{x+4}$

10-17.   In your Learning Log, explain how to multiply and divide rational expressions. Include an example of each. Title this entry "Multiplying and Dividing Rational Expressions" and include today's date.

Algebra Connections

METHODS AND MEANINGS

MATH NOTES

Rewriting Rational Expressions

To simplify a rational expression, both the numerator and denominator must be written in factored form. Then look for factors that make 1 and simplify. Study Examples 1 and 2 below.

Example 1: $\dfrac{x^2+5x+4}{x^2+x-12} = \dfrac{(x+4)(x+1)}{(x+4)(x-3)} = 1 \cdot \dfrac{x+1}{x-3} = \dfrac{x+1}{x-3}$ for $x \neq -4$ or 3

Example 2: $\dfrac{2x-7}{2x^2+3x-35} = \dfrac{(2x-7)(1)}{(2x-7)(x+5)} = 1 \cdot \dfrac{1}{x+5} = \dfrac{1}{x+5}$ for $x \neq -5$ or $\dfrac{7}{2}$

Just as you can multiply and divide fractions, you can multiply and divide rational expressions.

Example 3: Multiply $\dfrac{x^2+6x}{(x+6)^2} \cdot \dfrac{x^2+7x+6}{x^2-1}$ and simplify for $x \neq -6$ or 1.

After factoring, this expression becomes: $\dfrac{x(x+6)}{(x+6)(x+6)} \cdot \dfrac{(x+1)(x+6)}{(x+1)(x-1)}$

After multiplying, reorder the factors: $\dfrac{(x+6)}{(x+6)} \cdot \dfrac{(x+6)}{(x+6)} \cdot \dfrac{x}{(x-1)} \cdot \dfrac{(x+1)}{(x+1)}$

Since $\dfrac{(x+6)}{(x+6)} = 1$ and $\dfrac{(x+1)}{(x+1)} = 1$, simplify: $1 \cdot 1 \cdot \dfrac{x}{(x-1)} \cdot 1 \Rightarrow \dfrac{x}{(x-1)}$

Example 4: Divide $\dfrac{x^2-4x-5}{x^2-4x+4} \div \dfrac{x^2-2x-15}{x^2+4x-12}$ and simplify for $x \neq 2, 5, -3,$ or -6.

First, change to a multiplication expression: $\dfrac{x^2-4x-5}{x^2-4x+4} \cdot \dfrac{x^2+4x-12}{x^2-2x-15}$

Then factor each expression: $\dfrac{(x-5)(x+1)}{(x-2)(x-2)} \cdot \dfrac{(x-2)(x+6)}{(x-5)(x+3)}$

After multiplying, reorder the factors: $\dfrac{(x-5)}{(x-5)} \cdot \dfrac{(x-2)}{(x-2)} \cdot \dfrac{(x+1)}{(x-2)} \cdot \dfrac{(x+6)}{(x+3)}$

Since $\dfrac{(x-5)}{(x-5)} = 1$ and $\dfrac{(x-2)}{(x-2)} = 1$, simplify to get: $\dfrac{(x+1)(x+6)}{(x-2)(x+3)} \Rightarrow \dfrac{x^2+7x+6}{x^2+x-6}$

Note: From this point forward in the course, you may assume that all values of x that would make a denominator zero are excluded.

10-18.   Now David wants to solve the equation $4000x - 8000 = 16,000$.

    a.   What easier equation could he solve instead that would give him the same solution? (In other words, what equivalent equation has easier numbers to work with?)

    b.   **Justify** that your equation in part (a) is equivalent to $4000x - 8000 = 16,000$ by showing that they have the same solution.

    c.   David's last equation to solve is $\frac{x}{100} + \frac{3}{100} = \frac{8}{100}$. Write and solve an equivalent equation with easier numbers that would give him the same answer.

10-19.   Find the slope and y-intercept of each line below.

    a. $y = -\frac{6}{5}x - 7$ b. $3x - 2y = 10$

    c.   The line that goes through the points $(5, -2)$ and $(8, 4)$.

10-20.   Solve the systems of equations below using any method.

    a. $3x - 3 = y$ b. $3x - 2y = 30$
        $6x - 5y = 12$ $2x + 3y = -19$

10-21.   Simplify the expressions below.

    a. $\frac{x^2 - 8x + 16}{3x^2 - 10x - 8}$ for $x \neq -\frac{2}{3}$ or 4   b. $\frac{10x + 25}{2x^2 - x - 15}$ for $x \neq -\frac{5}{2}$ or 3

    c. $\frac{(k-4)(2k+1)}{5(2k+1)} \div \frac{(k-3)(k-4)}{10(k-3)}$ for $k \neq 3$, 4, or $-\frac{1}{2}$

10-22.   Solve the equations below. Check your solution(s).

    a. $\frac{m}{6} = \frac{m+1}{5}$ b. $\frac{3x-5}{2} = \frac{4x+1}{4}$ c. $\frac{8}{k} = \frac{14}{k+3}$ d. $\frac{x}{9} = 10$

10-23.   A piece of metal at 20°C is warmed at a steady rate of 2 degrees per minute. At the same time, another piece of metal at 240°C is cooled at a steady rate of 3 degrees per minute. After how many minutes is the temperature of each piece of metal the same? Explain how you found your answer.

10.1.3 How can I solve it?

Solving by Rewriting

Lessons 10.1.1 and 10.1.2 focused on how to multiply, divide, and simplify rational expressions. How can you use these skills to solve problems?

10-24. Review what you learned in Lessons 10.1.1 and 10.1.2 by multiplying or dividing the expressions below. Simplify your results.

a. $\dfrac{x-7}{9(2x-1)} \div \dfrac{(x+5)(x-7)}{6x(x+5)}$

b. $\dfrac{6x^2-x-1}{3x^2+25x+8} \cdot \dfrac{x^2+4x-32}{2x^2+7x-4}$

10-25. Cassie wants to solve the quadratic equation $x^2 + 1.5x - 2.5 = 0$. "I think I need to use the Quadratic Formula because of the decimals," she told Claudia. Suddenly, Claudia blurted out, "No, Cassie! I think there is another way. Can't you first rewrite this equation so it has no decimals?"

a. What is Claudia talking about? Explain what she means. Then rewrite the equation so that it has no decimals.

b. Now solve the new equation (the one without decimals). Check your solution(s).

10-26. SOLVING BY REWRITING

Rewriting $x^2 + 1.5x - 2.5 = 0$ in problem 10-25 gave you a new, **equivalent** equation that was much easier to solve. If needed, refer to the Math Notes box for this lesson for more information about equivalent equations.

How can each equation below be rewritten so that it is easier to solve? With your team, find an equivalent equation for each equation below. Be sure your equivalent equation has no fractions or decimals and has numbers that are reasonably small. Strive to find the *simplest* equation. Then solve the new equation and check your answer(s).

a. $32(3x) - 32(5) = 32(7)$

b. $9000x^2 - 6000x - 15000 = 0$

c. $\frac{1}{3} + \frac{x}{3} = \frac{10}{3}$

d. $2x^2 + 4x - 2.5 = 0$

10-27.   Examine the equation below.

$$\frac{x}{6} - \frac{5}{8} = 4$$

  a.   Multiply each term by 6. What happened? Do any fractions remain?

  b.   If you have not already done so, decide how you can change your result from part (a) so that no fractions remain. Then solve the resulting equation.

  c.   Multiplying $\frac{x}{6} - \frac{5}{8} = 4$ by 6 did not eliminate all the fractions. What could you have multiplied by to get rid of all the fractions? Explain how you got your answer and write the equivalent equation that has no fractions.

  d.   Solve the resulting equation from part (c) and check your solution in the original equation.

10-28.   Now you are going to **reverse** the process. Your teacher will give your team a simple equation that you need to "complicate." Change the equation to make it seem harder (although you know it is still equivalent to the easy equation).

  a.   Verify that your new equation is equivalent to the one assigned by your teacher.

  b.   Share your new equation with the class by posting it on the overhead projector or chalkboard.

  c.   Copy down the equations generated by your class on another piece of paper. You will need these equations for homework problem 10-29.

METHODS AND MEANINGS

Equivalent Equations

MATH NOTES

        Two equations are **equivalent** if they have all the same solutions. There are many ways to change one equation into a different, equivalent equation. Common ways include: *adding* the same number to both sides, *subtracting* the same number from both sides, *multiplying* both sides by the same number, *dividing* both sides by the same (non-zero) number, and *rewriting* one or both sides of the equation.

        For example, the equations below are all equivalent to $2x + 1 = 3$:

$20x + 10 = 30$	$2(x + 0.5) = 3$
$\frac{2x}{3} + \frac{1}{3} = 1$	$0.002x + 0.001 = 0.003$

10-29.   Solve the equations generated by your class in
         problem 10-28. Be sure to check each solution
         and show all work.

10-30.   Multiply or divide the expressions below.
         Leave your answers as simplified as possible.

a. $\dfrac{(3x-1)(x+7)}{4(2x-5)} \cdot \dfrac{10(2x-5)}{(4x+1)(x+7)}$

b. $\dfrac{(m-3)(m+11)}{(2m+5)(m-3)} \div \dfrac{(4m-3)(m+11)}{(4m-3)(2m+5)}$

c. $\dfrac{2p^2+5p-12}{2p^2-5p+3} \cdot \dfrac{p^2+8p-9}{3p^2+10p-8}$

d. $\dfrac{4x-12}{x^2+3x-10} \div \dfrac{2x^2-13x+21}{2x^2+3x-35}$

10-31.   Find the equation of the line parallel to $y=-\frac{1}{3}x+5$ that goes through the
         point $(9, -1)$.

10-32.   Write the inequality represented by the graph at right.

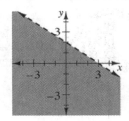

10-33.   Jessica has three fewer candies than twice the
         number Dante has.

a.   If Dante has d candies, write an expression to represent how many candies
      Jessica has.

b.   If Jessica has 19 candies, write and solve an equation to find out how many
      candies Dante has.

10.1.4 How can I solve it?

Fraction Busters

In Lesson 10.1.3, you learned a powerful new method to help solve complicated equations: rewriting the equation first to create a simpler, equivalent equation. Today you will continue to solve new, complicated equations and will focus specifically on equations with fractions. As you solve these new problems, look for ways to **connect** today's work with what you have learned previously.

10-34.   Examine the equation below.

$$\frac{5x}{3} + \frac{15}{2} = \frac{5}{2}$$

a.   Solve the equation by first finding an equivalent equation without fractions. Check your solution(s).

b.   Often, this method of eliminating fractions from an equation is called the **Fraction Busters Method** because the multiplication of the equation by a common denominator or several of the denominators eliminates ("busts") the fractions. The result is an equation with no fractions.

By what number (or numbers) did you multiply both sides of the equation in part (a) to eliminate the fractions? How did you choose that number? Is it the smallest number that would eliminate all of the fractions?

10-35.   Work with your team to solve each of the equations below by first finding an equivalent equation that contains no fractions. Each problem presents new challenges and situations. Be ready to **justify** how you solved each problem and share why you did what you did with the class. Remember to check each solution.

a. $\frac{x}{4} - \frac{x}{6} = \frac{2}{3}$

b. $\frac{5}{x} - 2x = 3$

c. $\frac{-2x+1}{3} - \frac{x+3}{7} = 8$

d. $\frac{x+3}{x-2} + 2 = \frac{x+5}{x-2}$

10-36.   Now examine the equation below.

$$\frac{4+p}{p^2+2p-8} + 3 = \frac{4}{p-2}$$

a.   What values of p are not allowed? Show how you know.

b.   Use your new skills to rewrite the equation above so that it has no fractions. Then solve the new equation. Check your solution(s). What happened?

10-37.   Solve the equations below by first changing each equation to a simpler, equivalent
         equation. Check your solution(s).

   a. $50x^2 + 200x = -150$ b. $\frac{a}{9} + \frac{1}{a} = \frac{2}{3}$

   c. $1.2m - 0.2 = 3.8 + m$ d. $\frac{2}{x+5} + \frac{3x}{x^2+2x-15} = \frac{4}{x-3}$

ᒪOOKING DEEPER

MATH NOTES

Solving Equations with Algebraic Fractions (also known as Fraction Busters)

Example: Solve $\frac{x}{3} + \frac{x}{5} = 2$ for x.

This equation would be much easier to
solve if it had no fractions. Therefore, the
first goal is to find an equivalent equation
that has no fractions.

$$\frac{x}{3} + \frac{x}{5} = 2$$

*The lowest common
denominator of $\frac{x}{3}$ and $\frac{x}{5}$ is 15.*

To eliminate the denominators, multiply
both sides of the equation by the common
denominator. In this example, the lowest
common denominator is 15, so multiplying
both sides of the equation by 15 eliminates
the fractions. Another approach is to
multiply both sides of the equation by one
denominator and then by the other.

$$15 \cdot \left(\frac{x}{3} + \frac{x}{5}\right) = 15 \cdot 2$$

$$15 \cdot \frac{x}{3} + 15 \cdot \frac{x}{5} = 15 \cdot 2$$

Either way, the result is an equivalent
equation without fractions:

$$5x + 3x = 30$$
$$8x = 30$$

The number used to eliminate the
denominators is called a **fraction buster**.
Now the equation looks like many you have
seen before, and it can be solved in the usual
way.

$$x = \frac{30}{8} = \frac{15}{4} = 3.75$$

$$\frac{3.75}{3} + \frac{3.75}{5} = 2$$

Once you have found the solution, remember to
check your answer.

$$1.25 + 0.75 = 2$$

10-38. Solve the equations below by first changing each equation to a simpler equivalent equation. Check your solutions.

a. $3000x - 2000 = 10{,}000$

b. $\frac{x^2}{2} + \frac{3x}{2} - 5 = 0$

c. $\frac{5}{2}x - \frac{1}{3} = 13$

d. $\frac{3}{10} + \frac{2x}{5} = \frac{1}{2}$

10-39. Multiply or divide the expressions below. Express your answers as simply as possible.

a. $\frac{5x^2-11x+2}{x^2+8x+16} \cdot \frac{x^2+10x+24}{10x^2+13x-3}$

b. $\frac{6x+3}{2x-3} \div \frac{3x^2-12x-15}{2x^2-x-3}$

10-40. To avoid a sand trap, a golfer hits a ball so that its height is represented by the equation $h = -16t^2 + 80t$, where h is the height measured in feet and t is the time measured in seconds.

a. When does the ball land on the ground?

b. What is the maximum height of the ball during its flight?

10-41. Write and solve an equation (or a system of equations) for the following situation. Be sure to define your variables.

Each morning, Jerry delivers two different newspapers: the *Times* and the *Star*. The *Times* weighs $\frac{1}{2}$ a pound and the *Star* weighs $\frac{1}{4}$ a pound. If he delivers a total of 27 newspapers that weigh a total of $11\frac{1}{2}$ pounds, how many *Times* newspapers does he deliver?

10-42. Graph the system of inequalities below on graph paper. Shade the region that represents the solution.

$$y \geq x^2 - 4$$
$$y \leq -x^2 + 4$$

10-43. **Multiple Choice:** $x = 2$ is a solution to which of the equations or inequalities below?

a. $\frac{x-4}{3} = \frac{x}{15}$ b. $(x-2)^2 < 0$ c. $|3x-8| \geq -1$ d. $\sqrt{x+2} = 16$

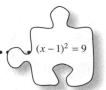
$(x-1)^2 = 9$

Multiple Methods for Solving Equations

So far in this course you have developed many different methods for solving equations, such as adding things to both sides of the equation or multiplying each term by a number to eliminate fractions. But how would you solve a complicated equation such as the one shown below?

$$(\sqrt{|x+5|} - 6)^2 + 4 = 20$$

By looking at equations in different ways, you will be able to solve some equations much more quickly and easily. These new approaches will also allow you to solve new kinds of equations you have not studied before. As you solve equations in today's lesson, ask your teammates these questions:

How can you see it?

Is there another way?

10-44.   DIFFERENT METHODS TO SOLVE AN EQUATION

By the end of this section you will be able to solve the equation $(\sqrt{|x+5|} - 6)^2 + 4 = 20$. This equation is very complex and will require you to look at solving equations in new ways. To be prepared for other strange and unfamiliar equations, you will first examine all of the solving tools you currently have by solving a comparatively easier equation:

$$4(x + 3) = 20$$

Your Task: With your team, solve $4(x + 3) = 20$ for x in *at least* two different ways. Explain how you found x in each case and be prepared to share your explanations with the class.

10-45.   SOLVING BY REWRITING

David wants to find x in the equation $4(x+3) = 20$. He said, "*I can rewrite this equation by distributing the 4 on the left-hand side.*" After distributing, what should his new equation be? Solve this equation using David's method.

10-46.   SOLVING BY UNDOING

Juan says, "I see the whole thing a different way." Here is how he explains his approach to solving $4(x+3) = 20$, which he calls "undoing": "*Instead of distributing first, I want to eliminate the 4 from the left side by undoing the multiplication.*"

a.   What can Juan do to both sides of the equation to remove the 4? Why does this work?

b.   Solve the equation using Juan's method. Did you get the same result as David?

c.   Why is it appropriate for this method to be called "undoing"?

10-47.   SOLVING BY LOOKING INSIDE

Kenya said, "I solved David's equation in a much quicker way!" She solved the equation $4(x+3) = 20$ with an approach that she calls "looking inside." Here is how she described her thinking: "*I think about everything inside the parentheses as a group. After all, the parentheses group all that stuff together. I think the contents of the parentheses must be 5.*"

a.   Why must the expression inside the parentheses equal 5?

b.   Write an equation that states that the contents of the parentheses must equal 5. Then solve this equation. Did you get the same result as with David's method?

———————   *Further Guidance*   ———————
                section ends here.

10-48.   THE THREE METHODS

   a.   Find the Math Notes box for this lesson and read it with your team.

   b.   Match the names of approaches on the left with the examples on the right.

   1. Rewriting   i.   "If $3+(4n-4)=12$, then $(4n-4)$ must
   2. Looking inside   equal 9..."
   3. Undoing   ii. "Subtracting is the opposite of adding, so for
                              the equation $3(x-7)+4=23$, I can start by
                              subtracting 4 from both sides..."

                         iii. "This problem might be easier if I turned
                              $4(2x-3)$ into $8x-12$..."

10-49.   For each equation below, decide whether it would be best to rewrite, look inside, or
          undo. Then solve the equation, showing your work and writing down the name of
          the approach you used. Check your solutions, if possible.

   a. $\frac{2x-8}{10}=6$ b. $4+(x \div 3)=9$

   c. $\sqrt{3x+3}=6$ d. $8-(2x+1)=3$

   e. $\sqrt{x}+4=9$ f. $\frac{x}{3}-\frac{x}{9}=6$

10-50.   Consider the equation $(x-7)^2=9$.

   a.   Solve this equation using *all three* approaches studied in this lesson. Make
          sure each team member solves the equation using all three approaches.

   b.   Did you get the same solution using all three approaches? If not, why not?

   c.   Of the three methods, which do you think was the most efficient method for
          this problem? Why?

METHODS AND MEANINGS

Methods to Solve One-Variable Equations

Here are three different approaches you can take to solve a one-variable equation:

Rewriting: Use algebraic techniques to rewrite the equation. This will often involve using the Distributive Property to get rid of parentheses. Then solve the equation using solution methods you know.

$$5(x-1)=15$$
$$5x-5=15$$
$$5x=20$$
$$x=4$$

Looking inside: Choose a part of the equation that includes the variable and is grouped together by parentheses or another symbol. (Make sure it includes *all* occurrences of the variable!) Ask yourself, "What must this part of the equation equal to make the equation true?" Use that information to write and solve a new, simpler equation.

$$5(x-1)=15$$
$$5(\ 3\ )=15$$
$$x-1=3$$
$$x=4$$

Undoing: Start by undoing the *last* operation that was done to the variable. This will give you a simpler equation, which you can solve either by undoing again or with some other approach.

$$\frac{5(x-1)}{5}=\frac{15}{5}$$
$$x-1=3$$
$$+1=+1$$
$$x=4$$

Review & Preview

10-51. Read the statements made by Hank and Frank below.

Hank says, "The absolute value of 5 is 5."

Frank says, "The absolute value of –5 is 5."

a.   Is Hank correct? Is Frank correct?

b.   How many different values for x make the equation $|x|=5$ true?

Algebra Connections

10-52.   Use the results from problem 10-51 to help you find all possible values for x in each of the following equations.

   a. $|x| = 4$ b. $|x| = 100$

   c. $|x| = -3$ d. $|x - 2| = 5$

10-53.   Which of the expressions below are equal to 1? (Note: More than one answer is possible!)

   a. $\frac{2x+3}{3+2x}$ b. $\frac{6x-12}{6(x-2)}$

   c. $\frac{(2x-3)(x+2)}{2x^2+x-6}$ d. $\frac{x}{2} \div \frac{2}{x}$

10-54.   Solve the inequalities below. Write each solution as an inequality.

   a. $8 + 3x > 2$ b. $\frac{2}{3}x - 6 \le 2$

   c. $-2x - 1 < -3$ d. $\frac{5}{x} \le \frac{1}{3}$

10-55.   For the equation $\frac{3}{200} + \frac{x}{50} = \frac{7}{100}$:

   a.   Find a simpler equivalent equation (i.e., an equivalent equation with no fractions) and solve for x.

   b.   Which method listed in this lesson's Math Notes box did you use in part (a)?

10-56.   Mr. Nguyen has decided to divide $775 among his three daughters. If the oldest gets twice as much as the youngest, and the middle daughter gets $35 more than the youngest, how much does each child get? Write an equation and solve it. Be sure to identify your variables.

10.2.2 How many solutions?

Determining the Number of Solutions

$(x-1)^2 = 9$

So far in this course you have seen many types of equations – some with no solution, some with one solution, others with two solutions, and still others with an infinite number of solutions! Is there any way to predict how many solutions an equation will have without solving it? Today you will focus on this question as you study quadratic equations written in perfect square form and equations with an absolute value. As you work with your team, ask the following questions:

Is there another way?

How do you see it?

Did you find all possible solutions?

10-57.   The quadratic equation below is written in **perfect square form**. It is called this because the term $(x-3)^2$ forms a square when built with tiles. Solve this quadratic equation using one of the methods you studied in Lesson 10.2.1.

$$(x-3)^2 = 12$$

a.   How many solutions did you find?

b.   Write your answer in **exact** form. That is, write it in a form that is precise and does not have any rounded decimals.

c.   Write your answer in **approximate** form. Round your answers to the nearest hundredth (0.01).

10-58.   THE NUMBER OF SOLUTIONS

The equation in problem 10-57 had two solutions. However, from your prior experience you know that some quadratic equations have no solutions and some have only one solution. How can you quickly determine how many solutions a quadratic equation has?

With your team, solve the equations below. Express your answers in both **exact form** and **approximate form**. Look for patterns among those with no solution and those with only one solution. Be ready to report your patterns to the class.

a. $(x+4)^2 = 20$ b. $(7x-5)^2 = -2$ c. $(2x-3)^2 = 49$

d. $(5-10x)^2 = 0$ e. $(x+2)^2 = -10$ f. $(x+11)^2 + 5 = 5$

10-59.   Use the patterns you found in problem 10-58 to determine quickly how many solutions each quadratic below has. You do not need to solve the equations.

a. $(5m-2)^2 + 6 = 0$ b. $(4+2n)^2 = 0$ c. $11 = (7+2x)^2$

10-60.   Consider the equation $|2x-5|=9$.

      a.   How many solutions do you think this equation has? Why?

      b.   Which of the three solution approaches do you think will work best for this equation?

      c.   With your team, solve $|2x-5|=9$. Record your work carefully as you go. Check your solution(s).

10-61.   The equation $|2x-5|=9$ from problem 10-60 had two solutions. Do you think all absolute-value equations must have two solutions? Consider this as you answer the questions below.

      a.   Can an absolute-value equation have no solution? With your team, create an absolute-value equation that has no solution. How can you be sure there is no solution?

      b.   Likewise, create an equation with an absolute value that will have only one solution. **Justify** why it will have only one solution.

10-62.   Is there a **connection** between how to determine the number of solutions of a quadratic in perfect square form and how to determine the number of solutions of an equation with an absolute value? In your Learning Log, describe this connection and explain how you can determine how many solutions both types of equations have. Be sure to include examples for each. Title this entry "Number of Solutions" and include today's date.

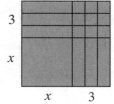

Perfect Square Form of a Quadratic

When a quadratic equation is written in the form $(x-a)^2 = b^2$, such as the one below, we say it is in **perfect square form**. Notice that when the quadratic expression on the left side of the equation below is built with tiles, it forms a square, as shown at right.

$$(x+3)^2 = 25$$

10-63. Solve these equations, if possible. Each time, be sure you have found all possible solutions. Check your work and write down the name of the method(s) you used.

    a. $(x+4)^2 = 49$ b. $3\sqrt{x+2} = 12$

    c. $\frac{2}{x} + \frac{3}{10} = \frac{13}{10}$ d. $5(2x-1) - 2 = 13$

10-64. Is $x = -4$ a solution to $\frac{1}{3}(2x+5) > -1$? Explain how you know.

10-65. Multiply or divide the rational expressions below. Leave your answer in simplified form.

    a. $\frac{(x+4)(2x-1)(x-7)}{(x+8)(2x-1)(3x-4)} \div \frac{(4x-3)(x-7)}{(x+8)(3x-4)}$ b. $\frac{2m^2+7m-15}{m^2-16} \cdot \frac{m^2-6m+8}{2m^2-7m+6}$

10-66. An **exponent** is shorthand for repeated multiplication. For example, $x^3 = x \cdot x \cdot x$. Use the meaning of an exponent to rewrite each of the expressions below.

    a. $(3x-1)^2$ b. 7^4 c. m^3 d. w^{10}

10-67. Factor each of the following expressions completely. Be sure to look for any common factors.

    a. $4x^2 - 12x$ b. $3y^2 + 6y + 3$

    c. $2m^2 + 7m + 3$ d. $3x^2 + 4x - 4$

10-68. Write and solve an equation to answer the question below. Remember to define any variables you use.

Pierre's Ice Cream Shoppe charges $1.19 for a scoop of ice cream and $0.49 for each topping. Gordon paid $4.55 for a three-scoop sundae. How many toppings did he get?

10.2.3 Which method is best?

More Solving and an Application

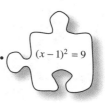

$(x-1)^2 = 9$

Recently you investigated three different approaches to solving one-variable equations: rewriting, looking inside, and undoing. Today you will use those approaches to solve new kinds of equations you have not solved before. You will also use your equation-writing skills to write an inequality for an application. As you work today, ask yourself these questions:

> How can I represent it?

> What is the best approach for this equation?

> Have I found all of the solutions?

10-69. Solve these equations. Each time, be sure you have found all possible solutions. Check your work and write down the name of the method(s) you used.

a. $|x+1| = 5$

b. $(x-13)^3 = 8$

c. $2\sqrt{x-4} = 14$

d. $|4x+20| = 8$

e. $3(x+12)^2 = 27$

f. $6|x-8| = 18$

10-70. RUB A DUB DUB

Ernie is thinking of installing a new hot tub in his backyard. The company he will order it from makes square hot tubs, and the smallest tub he can order is 4 feet by 4 feet. He plans to add a 3-foot-wide deck on two adjacent sides, as shown in the diagram below. If Ernie's backyard (which is also a square) has 169 square feet of space, what are the possible dimensions that his hot tub can be? Write and solve an inequality that represents this situation. Be sure to define your variable.

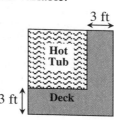

METHODS AND MEANINGS

Solving Absolute-Value Equations

To solve an equation with an absolute value algebraically, first determine the possible values of the quantity inside the absolute value.

For example, if $|2x+3| = 7$, then the quantity $(2x+3)$ must equal 7 or –7.

With these two values, set up new equations and solve as shown below.

$$|2x+3| = 7$$

$$2x+3 = 7 \quad \text{or} \quad 2x+3 = -7$$
$$2x = 4 \qquad\qquad 2x = -10$$
$$x = 2 \qquad\qquad x = -5$$

Always check your solutions by substituting them into the original equation:

Test $x = 2$: $\qquad\qquad |2(2)+3| = 7$ ✓ True

Test $x = -5$: $\qquad\qquad |2(-5)+3| = 7$ ✓ True

10-71.   Sketch a graph of the inequality below. Shade the region containing the solutions of the inequality.

$$y > (x-4)(x+3)$$

10-72.   Jessie looked at the equation $(x-11)^2 = -4$ and stated, "This quadratic has no solutions!" How did she know?

10-73.   Solve these equations, if possible. Be sure to find all possible solutions. Check your work and write down the name of the method(s) you used.

a. $9(x-4)^2 = 81$

b. $|x-6| = 2$

c. $5 = 2 + \sqrt{3x}$

d. $2|x+1| = -4$

Algebra Connections

10-74.   Review what you know about solving inequalities by solving the inequalities below. Show your solutions on a number line.

   a. $6x - 1 < 11$

   b. $\frac{1}{3}x \geq 2$

   c. $9(x - 2) > 18$

   d. $5 - \frac{x}{4} \leq \frac{1}{2}$

10-75.   Multiply or divide the rational expressions below. Leave each answer in simplified form.

   a. $\frac{(x-3)^2}{2x-1} \cdot \frac{2x-1}{(3x-14)(x+6)} \cdot \frac{x+6}{x-3}$

   b. $\frac{4x^2+5x-6}{3x^2+5x-2} \div \frac{4x^2+x-3}{6x^2-5x+1}$

10-76.   Use the meaning of an exponent to rewrite the expression $5x^3y^2$. Review the meaning of an exponent in problem 10-66 if necessary.

10.2.4   How can I solve the inequality?

$(x-1)^2 = 9$

Solving Inequalities with Absolute Value

The three approaches you have for solving equations can also be used to solve inequalities. While the one-variable inequalities you solve today look different than the ones in Chapter 9, the basic process for solving them is similar. As you solve equations and inequalities in today's lesson, ask yourself these questions:

How can I represent it?

What **connection** can I make?

10-77.   Solve the inequality $2x + 7 < 12$. Represent the solution on a number line.

   a.   What is the boundary point? Is it part of the solution? Why or why not?

   b.   In general, how do you find a boundary point? How do you find the solutions of an inequality after you have found the boundary point? Briefly review the process with your team.

10-78.   Now consider the inequality $|x-2|>3$.

   a.   Can you use the process from problem 10-77 to solve this inequality? How is it different from solving $|x-2|=3$? Solve the inequality and represent your solution on a number line.

   b.   How was solving $|x-2|>3$ different from solving $2x+7<12$?

10-79.   Examine the graph of $y=|x-2|$ and $y=3$ at right.

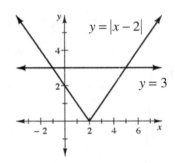

   a.   How does this graph confirm your solution to $|x-2|>3$ from problem 10-78? Be prepared to explain your thinking.

   b.   How would the solution change for the inequality $|x-2|\le 3$? Draw this solution on a number line. Explain how the graph at right also confirms this solution.

   c.   Now use the graph to predict the x-values that make $|x-2|\ge -1$ true. **Justify** your answer.

10-80.   Consider the quadratic inequality $x^2+2x+1<4$.

   a.   Solve for the boundary point(s). How many boundary points are there?

   b.   Place the boundary point(s) on a number line. How many regions do you need to test?

   c.   Test each region and determine which one(s) make the inequality true. Identify the solution region(s) on the number line.

   d.   Confirm your solution by graphing $y=x^2+2x+1$ and $y=4$ on the same set of axes on graph paper. Highlight the portion of the parabola that lies below the line $y=4$. Does this confirm your solution to part (c)?

10-81.   Revisit the graph from problem 10-79. Use it to write an inequality involving $|x-2|$ that has no solution.

10-82.   In your Learning Log, explain how you can solve an inequality that has an absolute value. You may include an explanation of the graphical process if you choose. Then make up your own example problem and show how that problem is solved. Title this entry "Solving Inequalities with Absolute Value" and include today's date.

Algebra Connections

10-83.   Examine the rectangle formed by the tiles shown at
          right. Write the area of the rectangle as a product and
          as a sum.

10-84.   How many solutions does each quadratic equation below have?

          a. $6x^2 + 7x - 20 = 0$ b. $m^2 - 8m + 16 = 0$

          c. $2r^2 + r + 3 = 0$ d. $(2k + 1)^2 = 0$

10-85.   Find the equation of the line perpendicular to $y = -\frac{2}{3}x - 7$ that goes through the
          point (–6, 9).

10-86.   On graph paper, graph the system of inequalities below. Carefully shade the region
          that represents the solution to both inequalities.

          $$y \le -|x - 2| + 3$$
          $$y \ge -1$$

10-87.   Multiply or divide the expressions below. Leave your answer as simplified as
          possible.

          a. $\frac{8x^2-12x-8}{2x^2-5x-3} \cdot \frac{x^2+2x-15}{6x-12}$ b. $\frac{7x^2+5x-2}{x^2+2x-8} \div \frac{3x^2-2x-5}{3x^2-11x+10}$

10-88.   Solve the equations and inequalities below. Check your solution(s), if possible.

          a. $300x - 1500 = 2400$ b. $\frac{3}{2}x = \frac{5}{6}x + 2$

          c. $x^2 - 25 \le 0$ d. $|3x - 2| > 4$

10.2.5   How can I solve this inequality?

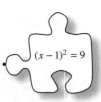

Solving Absolute-Value and Quadratic Inequalities

Today you will finish your focus on solving equations and inequalities. By the end of the lesson today, you will have the tools to solve complex equations and inequalities.

10-89.   At right is a graph showing $y = x^2 + x - 6$ and $y = 3x + 2$. Use the graph to find the solutions for $x^2 + x - 6 \geq 3x + 2$. Indicate your answer on a number line.

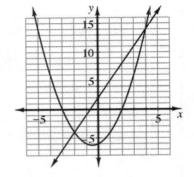

10-90.   Solve the inequalities below, if possible, and represent your solution on a number line.

a. $|x+2| > 1$ b. $x^2 + x - 12 < 0$

c. $|2(x-1)| \geq 0$ d. $9x - 4 \leq 6 - x$

e. $|3x - 11| < -2$ f. $(x-2)^2 > 7$

10-91.   FOG CITY

San Francisco is well known for its fog: very thick, low-lying clouds that hide its hills. One foggy day, Penelope was practicing kicking a football on the football field of her school. Once she kicked the football so high that it disappeared into the fog! If the height h of the ball (in feet) could be represented at time t (in seconds) by the equation $h = -16t^2 + 96t$, and if the fog was 140 feet off the ground, during what times of its flight was the ball not visible? Explain how you got your answer.

Algebra Connections

10-92.   PULLING IT TOGETHER

Now that you have the skills necessary to solve
many interesting equations and inequalities,
work with your team to solve the equation
below. (This equation was first introduced in
Lesson 10.2.1.) Show your solutions on a
number line and be prepared to share your
solving process with the class.

$$(\sqrt{|x+5|} - 6)^2 + 4 = 20$$

10-93.   Review the meaning of an exponent in problem 10-66. Then use its meaning to
rewrite the expression $(y-2)^3$.

10-94.   How many solutions does the equation $|7-3x|+1=0$ have? Explain how you
know.

10-95.   Solve the equations and inequalities below, if possible.

a. $\sqrt{x-1}+13=13$ b. $6|x|>18$ c. $|3x-2|\leq 2$

d. $\frac{4}{5}-\frac{2x}{3}=\frac{3}{10}$ e. $(4x-2)^2 \leq 100$ f. $(x-1)^3 = 8$

10-96.   On graph paper, graph a line with slope $-\frac{2}{3}$ that goes through the point $(4, -3)$.

a.   Find the equation of the line.

b.   Is this line perpendicular to the line $6x-4y=8$? Explain how you know.

10-97.   Simplify the rational expressions below as much as possible.

a. $\frac{(x-4)^3(2x-1)}{(2x-1)(x-4)^2}$ b. $\frac{7m^2-22m+3}{3m^2-7m-6}$

c. $\frac{(z+2)^9(4z-1)^7}{(z+2)^{10}(4z-1)^5}$ d. $\frac{(x+2)(x^2-6x+9)}{(x-3)(x^2-4)}$

10-98.   **Multiple Choice:** Which of the graphs below shows the solutions for $y < -\frac{2}{5}x + 1$?

a.
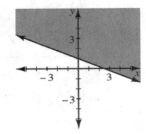

b.
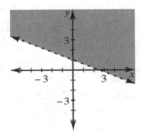

c.
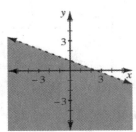

d.
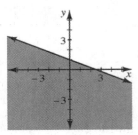

10.3.1   How can I make it a perfect square?

Completing the Square

You have learned many ways to solve quadratic equations so far in this course. Sometimes, using the Quadratic Formula can be complicated and messy, while solving equations in perfect square form (such as $(x+2)^2 = 3$) can be very straightforward. Therefore, it is sometimes convenient to change a quadratic equation from standard form into perfect square form. One method that you will investigate in this lesson is called **completing the square**.

10-99.   Review what you know about solving quadratic equations as you solve the two equations below. Be ready to share your method(s) with the class.

a. $x^2 + 4x + 1 = 0$ b. $(x+2)^2 = 3$

10-100.   With your team, and then with the class, discuss the following questions.

a.   Examine the solutions to $x^2 + 4x + 1 = 0$ and $(x+2)^2 = 3$. What do you notice? What does this tell you about the two equations? Verify your conclusion algebraically.

b.   Of the methods used in problem 10-99, which do you think was most efficient and straightforward?

10-101.   COMPLETING THE SQUARE

With your team, examine how the two different equations from
problem 10-99 can be represented using tiles on an equation mat,
shown below. Then answer questions (a) and (b) below.

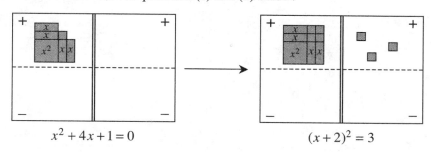

$$x^2 + 4x + 1 = 0$$ $$(x+2)^2 = 3$$

a.   What "legal" move can be done to the equation $x^2 + 4x + 1 = 0$ that will result
in the equation $(x+2)^2 = 3$?

b.   Changing a quadratic equation into perfect square form is also known as
"completing the square." Why is this name appropriate?

10-102.   Use the process from problem 10-101 to change the quadratics below
into perfect square form. Then solve the resulting quadratics. Building
the squares with algebra tiles may be useful. Record your work on the
resource page provided by your teacher.

a.
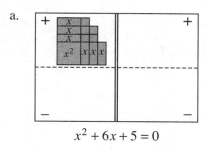

$$x^2 + 6x + 5 = 0$$

b.
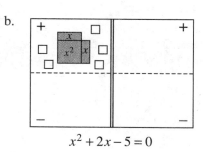

$$x^2 + 2x - 5 = 0$$

10-103. The problems below introduce different situations that can arise while completing the square. Carefully choose what to add to both sides of each equation below to change the quadratics into perfect square form. Then solve the resulting quadratic. Again, building the equations with algebra tiles may be useful. Record your work on the resource page provided by your teacher.

■ = +1
□ = −1

a.

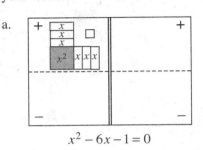

$$x^2 - 6x - 1 = 0$$

b.

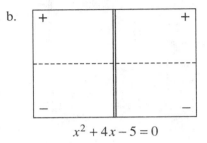

$$x^2 + 4x - 5 = 0$$

c.

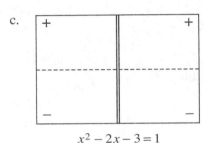

$$x^2 - 2x - 3 = 1$$

10-104. Use algebra tiles to change $4x^2 + 12x + 3 = 10$ into perfect square form. Then solve the resulting quadratic equation.

10-105.   Use your understanding of the number 1 to simplify the rational expressions below.

a. $\dfrac{(x-3)(2x+9)(4x-3)}{(2x+9)(5x+1)(x-3)}$

b. $\dfrac{25x^2+20x+4}{25x^2-4}$

c. $\dfrac{16x^2+24x+8}{2x^2-2x-4}$

d. $\dfrac{24xy^2}{36x^2y}$

10-106.   Solve the quadratic equation below *twice*: once using the Quadratic Formula and once by completing the square and solving the quadratic in perfect square form. You should get the same result using both methods. What happened?

$$x^2 + 6x + 11 = 0$$

10-107.   Solve the inequalities and equations below, if possible. Represent your solution on a number line.

a. $|x|+3<5$

b. $5(2x+1) \geq 30$

c. $\dfrac{1}{x}-\dfrac{5}{2}=\dfrac{3}{2}$

d. $-5-x>3-x$

e. $3\sqrt{4-x}+1=13$

f. $|x+1| \leq 4$

10-108.   Verify your solution to part (f) of problem 10-107 by graphing the functions below on the same set of axes. Highlight the portion(s) of the graph for which $|x+1| \leq 4$.

$$y = |x+1|$$
$$y = 4$$

10-109.   Write and solve an equation to solve the problem below. State your solution as a sentence.

Shu Min currently has 18 CDs, and her music club sends her three more CDs each month. Her brother, Wei, currently has 22 CDs and buys two more CDs each month with his allowance. Their CD holder can only hold 80 CDs. After how many months will their CD holder be full?

10.3.2 How can I generalize?

More Completing the Square

Today you will learn more about completing the square and will **generalize** how to complete the square for any quadratic in standard form.

10-110. Determine the number of solutions for each quadratic equation below by first completing the square (using algebra tiles or drawing a diagram). Then explain how you can quickly determine how many solutions a quadratic equation has once it is written in perfect square form.

   a. $x^2 - 6x + 7 = 0$

   b. $m^2 + 12m + 37 = 0$

   c. $p^2 + 2p + 1 = 0$

   d. $k^2 - 4k + 9 = 0$

10-111. Examine the results of your work in problem 10-110 and look for ways to **generalize** the process of completing the square. In other words, how can you change a quadratic into perfect square form without using tiles or drawing a diagram? It may help to make a table like the one started below. Then answer the questions that follow.

Standard Form	Perfect Square Form
$x^2 - 6x + 7 = 0$	

   a.   Describe any patterns you found when comparing a quadratic written in standard form with its corresponding equation in perfect square form.

   b.   When a quadratic is changed to perfect square form, how can you predict what will be in the parentheses? For example, if you want to change $x^2 + 10x - 3 = 0$ into perfect square form, what will be the dimensions of the square?

   c.   To complete the square, you often need to add some unit tiles to both sides of the equation. How can you predict how many tiles will need to be added or removed?

10-112. Use your generalized process of completing the square to rewrite and solve each quadratic equation below.

   a. $w^2 + 28w + 52 = 0$

   b. $x^2 + 5x + 4 = 0$

   c. $k^2 - 16k - 17 = 0$

   d. $z^2 - 1000z + 60775 = 0$

10-113.   What is the slope of the line passing through the points (4, –8) and (–3, 12)?

10-114.   Use your generalized process of completing the square to rewrite and solve each quadratic equation below.

    a. $x^2 + 4x = -3$ b. $x^2 - 8x + 7 = 0$ c. $x^2 - 24x + 129 = 0$

10-115.   Multiply or divide the rational expressions below. Leave your answers in simplified form.

    a. $\dfrac{4x^2 + x - 14}{3x^2 - 11x + 6} \div \dfrac{4x - 7}{x - 3}$ b. $\dfrac{5x^2 - 8x - 4}{x^2 - 9x - 22} \cdot \dfrac{x^2 - 4}{5x^2 + 22x + 8}$

10-116.   Solve the following equations and inequalities, if possible. Represent each solution on a number line.

    a. $\dfrac{3}{9} - \dfrac{x}{3} = \dfrac{x}{5}$ b. $(3 + x)^2 < 9$ c. $8|x + 1| \geq 64$

    d. $11 - \sqrt{x + 3} = 13$ e. $\dfrac{x}{8} = \dfrac{2}{x}$ f. $|x - 5| + 1 > 0$

10-117.   On graph paper, graph the inequality $y \leq |x| + 2$.

10-118.   Aura currently pays $800 each month to rent her apartment. Due to inflation, however, her rent is increasing by $50 each year. Meanwhile, her monthly take-home pay is $1500 and she predicts that her monthly pay will only increase by $15 each year. Assuming that her rent and take-home pay will continue to grow linearly, will her rent ever equal her take-home pay? If so, when? And how much will rent be that year?

10.4.1 How can I rewrite it?

$x^3 = x \cdot x \cdot x$

Simplifying Exponential Expressions

In Section 10.1, you used the property of the number 1 to simplify rational expressions. Today you will examine how to simplify expressions with exponents. Using patterns, you will develop strategies to simplify expressions when the exponents are too large to expand on paper.

10-119. You have seen that you can rewrite expressions using the number 1. You can also simplify using the meaning of an exponent.

An **exponent** is shorthand for repeated multiplication. For example, $n^4 = n \cdot n \cdot n \cdot n$.

a. Expand each of the expressions below. For example, to expand x^3, you would write: $x \cdot x \cdot x$.

i. y^7 ii. $5(2m)^3$ iii. $(x^3)^2$ iv. $4x^5y^2$

b. Simplify each of the expressions below using what you know about exponents and the number 1. Start by expanding the exponents, and then simplify your results.

i. $\dfrac{x \cdot x \cdot x}{x}$ ii. $\dfrac{x^5}{x^2}$ iii. $x^2 \cdot x^3$ iv. $k^3 \cdot k^5$

v. $\dfrac{16k^3}{8k^2}$ vi. $m^6 \cdot m$ vii. $x^4 \cdot x^5 \cdot x^3$ viii. $\dfrac{6x^3y}{2y}$

challenge: $\dfrac{5x^{50}}{10x^{15}}$

10-120. Simplify each of the expressions below. Start by expanding the exponents, and then simplify your results. Look for patterns or possible shortcuts that will help you simplify more quickly. Be prepared to **justify** your patterns or shortcuts to the class.

a. $y^5 \cdot y^2$

b. $\frac{w^5}{w^2}$

c. $(x^2)^4$

d. $x^{10} \cdot x^{12}$

e. $\frac{13p^4q^5}{p^2q^2}$

f. $\left(\frac{x^2}{y}\right)^3$

g. $5h \cdot 2h^{24}$

h. $\frac{10m^{30}}{2m^8}$

i. $(3k^{20})^4$

j. $\frac{24hg^2}{3hg^9}$

k. $\left(\frac{m^3}{n^{10}}\right)^4$

l. $w^4 \cdot p \cdot w^3$

10-121. Work with your team to write four exponent problems, each having a simplification of x^{12}. At least one problem must involve multiplication, one must involve grouping, and one must involve division. Be creative!

10-122. Gerardo is simplifying expressions with very large exponents. He arrives at each of the results below. For each result, decide if he is correct and **justify** your answer using the meaning of exponents.

a. $\frac{x^{150}}{x^{50}} \Rightarrow x^3$

b. $y^{20} \cdot y^{41} \Rightarrow y^{61}$

c. $(2m^2n^{15})^3 \Rightarrow 2m^6n^{45}$

MΞΤHODS AND MΞANINGS

MATH NOTES

Completing the Square

Previously in this course, you have learned to solve quadratic equations by graphing, factoring, and using the Quadratic Formula. Another way to solve a quadratic equation is by **completing the square**. See the example below.

Example: Solve for x by completing the square: $x^2 + 6x + 7 = 14$

First, use algebra tiles or a generic rectangle to determine if $x^2 + 6x + 7$ is already a perfect square.

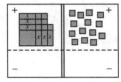

Using algebra tiles (shown at right), you can see that there are not enough tiles to build a complete square. Therefore, two unit tiles must be added to both sides of the equation to complete the square.

$$x^2 + 6x + 7 = 14$$

Add 2 unit tiles to complete the square.

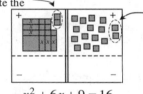

Notice that the square has side length $x + 3$. Any quadratic of the form $x^2 + bx + c$ will be converted to a square of side length $x + \frac{b}{2}$.

$$x^2 + 6x + 9 = 16$$

Now rewrite the expressions on each side of the equation so that the equation is in perfect square form. Then solve this equation by undoing the square and subtracting 3 from both sides.

$$(x + 3)^2 = 16$$
$$x + 3 = \pm 4$$
$$x = -3 \pm 4$$
$$x = 1 \text{ or } -7$$

As always, be sure to check your solutions in the original equation.

$$(1)^2 + 6(1) + 7 = 14$$
$$(-7)^2 + 6(-7) + 7 = 14$$

10-123. Use what you have learned about exponents to rewrite each of the expressions below.

a. $\frac{h^9}{h^{11}}$

b. $x^3 \cdot x^4$

c. $(3k^5)^2$

d. $n^7 \cdot n$

e. $\frac{16x^4y^3}{2x^4}$

f. $4xy^3 \cdot 7x^2y^3$

10-124. Lacey and Haley are simplifying expressions.

a. Haley simplified $x^3 \cdot x^2$ and gets x^5. Lacey simplified $x^3 + x^2$ and got the same result! However, their teacher told them that only one simplification is correct. Who simplified correctly and how do you know?

b. Haley simplifies $3^5 \cdot 4^5$ and gets the result 12^{10}, but Lacey is not sure. Is Haley correct? Be sure to **justify** your answer.

10-125. On your paper, draw the algebra tiles to represent the equation $x^2 + 2x = 8$ on an equation mat.

a. How many tiles do you need to add or remove from each side of the equation to complete the square?

b. Write the equation in perfect square form.

10-126. Find a rule that represents the number of tiles in the tile pattern at right.

Figure 0   Figure 1   Figure 2

10-127. Solve the equations and inequalities below. If necessary, write your solutions in approximate form.

a. $900x - 200 = 500x + 600$

b. $3k^2 - 15k + 14 = 0$

c. $|x - 4| < 6$

d. $\frac{7}{3} + \frac{x}{2} = \frac{6x-1}{6}$

10.4.2 How can I rewrite it?

$$x^3 = x \cdot x \cdot x$$

Zero and Negative Exponents

In Lesson 10.4.1, you used the meaning of an exponent to rewrite expressions such as $y^4 \cdot y^2$ and $(x^2 y)^3$. Today you will use the patterns you discovered to learn how to interpret expressions with exponents that are negative or zero.

10-128. Review what you learned about exponents in Lesson 10.4.1 to rewrite each expression below as simply as possible. If you see a pattern or know of a shortcut, be sure to share it with your teammates.

a. $x^7 \cdot x^4$

b. $(x^3)^3$

c. $\dfrac{m^{14}}{m^2}$

d. $(x^2 y^2)^4$

e. $\dfrac{x^2 y^{11}}{x^5 y^3}$

f. $\dfrac{2x^{12}}{8x^2}$

10-129. With your study team, summarize the patterns you found in problem 10-128. For each one, simplify the given expression and write an expression that represents its **generalization**. Then, in your own words, explain why the pattern works.

	Expression	Generalization	Why is this true?
a.	$x^{25} \cdot x^{40} = ?$	$x^m \cdot x^n = ?$	
b.	$\dfrac{x^{36}}{x^{13}} = ?$	$\dfrac{x^m}{x^n} = ?$	
c.	$(x^5)^{12} = ?$	$(x^m)^n = ?$	

10-130. Describe everything you know about $\dfrac{x^m}{x^m}$. What is its value? How can you rewrite it using a single exponent? What new conclusions can you draw? Be prepared to explain your findings to the class.

10-131. Problem 10-130 helped you recognize that
$x^0 = 1$. Now you will similarly use division to
explore the meaning of x^{-1}, x^{-2}, etc. Simplify
each of the expressions below *twice*:

- Once by expanding the terms and
  simplifying.

- Again by using your new pattern for
  division with exponents.

Be ready to discuss the meaning of negative
exponents with the class.

a. $\dfrac{x^4}{x^5}$ b. $\dfrac{x^2}{x^4}$ c. $\dfrac{x^7}{x^{10}}$

10-132. Use your exponent patterns to rewrite each of the expressions below. For example,
if the original expression has a negative exponent, then rewrite the expression so that
it has no negative exponents – and vice versa. Also, if the expression contains
multiplication or division, then use your exponent rules to simplify the expression.

a. k^{-5} b. m^0 c. $x^{-2} \cdot x^5$ d. $\dfrac{1}{p^2}$

e. $\dfrac{y^{-2}}{y^{-3}}$ f. $(x^{-2})^3$ g. $(a^2b)^{-1}$ h. $\dfrac{1}{x^{-1}}$

10-133. EXPONENT CONCENTRATION

Split your team into two pairs and decide which is Team A and which is Team B.
Your teacher will distribute a set of cards for a game described below.

- Arrange the cards face down in a rectangular grid.

- Team A selects and turns over two cards.

- If Team A thinks the values on the cards are equivalent, they must **justify**
  this claim to Team B. If everyone in Team B agrees, Team A takes the pair.
  If the values are not equivalent, Team A returns both cards to their original
  position (face down). This is the end of the turn for Team A.

- Team B repeats the process.

- Teams alternate until no cards remain face down. The team with the most
  matches wins.

10-134.   In your Learning Log, describe the meaning of zero and negative exponents. That is, explain how to interpret x^0 and x^{-1}. Title this entry "Zero and Negative Exponents" and include today's date.

LOOKING DEEPER

MATH NOTES

Inductive and Deductive Reasoning

When you make a conclusion based on a pattern, you are using **inductive reasoning**. So far in this course, you have used inductive reasoning repeatedly to **generalize** patterns. For example, in Lesson 10.4.1 and in this lesson, you used patterns to generalize the facts that $x^m x^n = x^{m+n}$ and $(x^m)^n = x^{mn}$.

However, you can also make a conclusion based on facts, using logic. This is called **deductive reasoning**. You used deductive reasoning during this lesson when you determined that $x^{-1} = \frac{1}{x}$. See the logical deduction below.

Statement	Reason
Since $\frac{x^4}{x^5} = x^{-1}$,	This is true because $\frac{x^m}{x^n} = x^{m-n}$.
And since $\frac{x^4}{x^5} = \frac{x \cdot x \cdot x \cdot x}{x \cdot x \cdot x \cdot x \cdot x} = \frac{1}{x}$,	This is true because $\frac{x}{x} = 1$.
Therefore, $x^{-1} = \frac{1}{x}$.	$\frac{x^4}{x^5}$ equals both x^{-1} and $\frac{1}{x}$, so $x^{-1} = \frac{1}{x}$. (This is called the Transitive Property of Equality.)

10-135.   Which of the expressions below are equivalent to $16x^8$? Make sure you find *all* the correct answers!

a. $(16x^4)^2$

b. $8x^2 \cdot 2x^6$

c. $(2x^2)^4$

d. $(4x^4)^2$

e. $(2x^4)^4$

f. $(\frac{1}{16}x^{-8})^{-1}$

10-136.   Write the inequality represented
           by the graph at right.

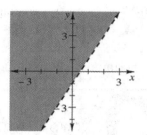

10-137.   Solve the system of equations below using any
           method. Check your solution.

$$8y - 1 = x$$
$$10y - x = 5$$

10-138.   Chad is entering a rocket competition. He
           needs to program his rocket so that when it
           is launched from the ground, it lands 20 feet
           away. In order to qualify, it must be 100
           feet off the ground at its highest point. What
           equation should he program into his rocket
           launcher to win? Let x represent the
           distance from the launch pad in feet and y
           represent the height of the rocket in feet.
           Draw a sketch of the rocket's path.

10-139.   Solve the quadratic equation below *twice*, once using the Quadratic Formula and
           once by completing the square. Which was easier?

$$x^2 - 10x + 21 = -4$$

10-140.   Simplify the rational expressions below.

    a. $\dfrac{x^2 - 8x + 16}{3x^2 - 10x - 8}$ b. $\dfrac{10x + 25}{2x^2 - x - 15}$

    c. $\dfrac{9x^4 y^3 z}{3x^4 y^3 z}$

10.4.3 How can I rewrite it?

Fractional Exponents and Scientific Notation

$$x^3 = x \cdot x \cdot x$$

So far you have discovered ways to deal with exponents when multiplying and dividing. You have also found ways to interpret expressions when the exponent is zero or negative. But what if the exponent is a fraction? And how can exponents help you rewrite numbers?

Today you will develop an understanding for fractional exponents and learn about scientific notation, a way to use exponents to rewrite very large or very small numbers.

10-141.   FRACTIONAL EXPONENTS

What happens when an exponent is a fraction? Consider this as you answer the questions below.

a.   Calculate $9^{1/2}$ with your scientific calculator. What is the result? Also use your calculator to find $49^{1/2}$ and $100^{1/2}$. What effect does having $\frac{1}{2}$ in the exponent appear to have?

b.   Based on your observation in part (a), predict the value of $4^{1/2}$ and $(7^{1/2})^2$. Then confirm your prediction with your calculator.

c.   Was the reasoning you used in part (a) an example of inductive or deductive reasoning? Refer to the Lesson 10.4.2 Math Notes box to help you decide.

10-142.   Danielle wants to understand why $9^{1/2}$ is the same as $\sqrt{9}$. Since exponents represent repeated multiplication, Danielle decided to rewrite the number 9 as $3 \cdot 3$. She then reasoned that $9^{1/2}$ is asking for 1 of the 2 repeated factors with a product of 9.

a.   Using Danielle's logic, find $16^{1/2}$. Confirm your answer with your calculator.

b.   What is the value of $8^{1/3}$? $125^{1/3}$? How can you use the same reasoning to find these values? Confirm your answers with your calculator.

c.   What about $27^{2/3}$? $32^{3/5}$? $25^{3/2}$? Use your calculator to find each of these values. Then apply Danielle's logic to make sense of what each of these expressions mean. Share any insight with your team members.

d.   Another name for $x^{1/3}$ is "cube root." This can be written $\sqrt[3]{x}$. What would be the notation for $x^{1/5}$? What should it be called?

10-143. Now that you have many tools to rewrite expressions with exponents, use these tools together to rewrite each of the expressions below. For example, $\sqrt{2^5} = (2^5)^{1/2} = 2^{5/2}$, since taking the square root of a number is the same as raising that number to the one-half power.

a. $(\sqrt{3})^4$

b. $9^{7/2}$

c. $\sqrt[3]{2^5}$

10-144. Match each expression below on the left (letters (a) through (h)) with an equivalent expression on the right (numbers 1 through 8). Assume $x > 0$.

a. $\sqrt{x^3}$ e. $\sqrt[3]{x^2}$ 1. x^{-2} 5. $\sqrt{x}$

b. $\dfrac{x^2}{x^5}$ f. 1 2. x 6. $x^{2/3}$

c. $(\sqrt[3]{x})^5$ g. $x^{-3}x^4$ 3. $x^{3/2}$ 7. $x^{5/3}$

d. $\dfrac{1}{x^2}$ h. $(x^{1/4})^2$ 4. x^0 8. x^{-3}

10-145. Exponents can also help you represent very large (and very small) numbers. For example, a very large number like the one below can be difficult to write out in complete form (called **standard form**).

3,000,000,000,000,000,000,000,000,000,000

Instead, you can write this number using **scientific notation**: $3 \cdot 10^{30}$. This shorthand notation is not only easier to write, but it also gives you an immediate sense of how large the number is. Since 10^{30} is 10 multiplied by itself thirty times, then you know that $3 \cdot 10^{30}$ is the number 3 with 30 zeros after it.

Similarly, $1.4 \cdot 10^8$ is 1.4 multiplied by 10 eight times. Thus $1.4 \cdot 10^8 = 140,000,000$.

Scientific notation is also useful for writing small numbers, such as 0.00024. Since $0.00024 = 24 \cdot \frac{1}{10,000}$, you can rewrite the number using scientific notation: $2.4 \cdot 10^{-4}$.

a. Scientists claim that the earth is about $4.6 \cdot 10^9$ years old. Write this number in standard form.

b. The average distance between the Earth and the sun is about 150,000,000,000 meters. Translate this number into scientific notation.

c. It takes light about $3.3 \cdot 10^{-9}$ seconds to travel one meter. Express this number in standard form.

10-146.   Scientific notation is not only a convenient way to write very large and very small numbers, but it also makes them easier to put into your calculator.

   a.   For example, multiply $5000 \cdot 20{,}000{,}000{,}000{,}000$ and write the answer in standard form. If these numbers cannot be entered into your calculator, then multiply them by hand on your paper.

   b.   Now multiply these same numbers by first changing each into scientific notation. For example, $5000 = 5 \cdot 10^3$. Express your answer in scientific notation.

   c.   Which method was easier and why?

LOOKING DEEPER

Laws of Exponents

MATH NOTES

In the expression x^3, x is the **base** and 3 is the **exponent**.

$$x^3 = x \cdot x \cdot x$$

The patterns that you have been using during this section of the book are called the **laws of exponents**. Here are the basic rules with examples:

Law	Examples	
$x^m x^n = x^{m+n}$ for all x	$x^3 x^4 = x^{3+4} = x^7$	$2^5 \cdot 2^{-1} = 2^4$
$\dfrac{x^m}{x^n} = x^{m-n}$ for $x \neq 0$	$x^{10} \div x^4 = x^{10-4} = x^6$	$\dfrac{5^4}{5^7} = 5^{-3}$
$(x^m)^n = x^{mn}$ for all x	$(x^4)^3 = x^{4 \cdot 3} = x^{12}$	$(10^5)^6 = 10^{30}$
$x^0 = 1$ for $x \neq 0$	$\dfrac{y^2}{y^2} = y^0 = 1$	$9^0 = 1$
$x^{-1} = \dfrac{1}{x}$ for $x \neq 0$	$\dfrac{1}{x^2} = (\tfrac{1}{x})^2 = (x^{-1})^2 = x^{-2}$	$3^{-1} = \dfrac{1}{3}$
$x^{m/n} = \sqrt[n]{x^m}$ for $x \geq 0$	$\sqrt{k} = k^{1/2}$	$y^{2/3} = \sqrt[3]{y^2}$

10-147.   Simplify each of the expressions below. Your final simplification should contain no negative exponents.

   a. $(5x^3)(-3x^{-2})$ b. $(4p^2q)^3$ c. $\dfrac{3m^7}{m^{-1}}$

10-148.   Neil A. Armstrong was the first person ever to walk on the moon. After his historic landing on July 20, 1969, he stepped onto the moon's surface and spoke the famous phrase, "That's one small step for a man, one giant leap for mankind."

His craft, Apollo 11, traveled 238,900 miles from Earth to reach the moon. How many feet was this? Express your answer in both standard form and in scientific notation. Round your decimal to the nearest hundredth. (Note: There are 5280 feet in each mile.)

10-149.   Solve the system of equations below by graphing. Write your solution(s) in (x, y) form.

$$y = -4x - 2$$
$$y = x^2 - 3x - 4$$

10-150.   Write and solve an inequality to represent the situation below. Write your solution as a sentence.

Vinita wants to rent a skateboard and only has $20. She found out that the shop will charge her $8 to rent the skateboard plus $3.75 per hour. She does not know how long she wants to rent it. What are her options?

10-151.   A motion detector can record the distance between a moving person and the detector. Examine the graphs below, each of which was generated when a different person walked in front of a motion detector. For each graph, describe the motion of the person. Did they walk quickly? Did they walk slowly? In what direction did they walk? If the motion is not possible, explain why not.

a.
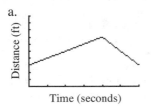

b.
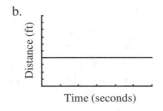

c.
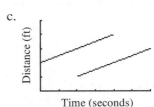

Chapter 10 Closure   What have I learned?

Reflection and Synthesis

The activities below offer you a chance to reflect on what you have learned during this chapter. As you work, look for concepts that you feel very comfortable with, ideas that you would like to learn more about, and topics you need more help with. Look for **connections** between ideas as well as **connections** with material you learned previously.

①   TEAM BRAINSTORM

With your team, brainstorm a list for each of the following topics. Be as detailed as you can. How long can you make your list? Challenge yourselves. Be prepared to share your team's ideas with the class.

Topics: What have you studied in this chapter? What ideas and words were important in what you learned? Remember to be as detailed as you can.

Ways of Thinking: What Ways of Thinking did you use in this chapter? When did you use them?

Connections: What topics, ideas, and words that you learned *before* this chapter are **connected** to the new ideas in this chapter? Again, make your list as long as you can.

②   MAKING CONNECTIONS

The following is a list of the vocabulary used in this chapter. The words that appear in bold are new to this chapter. Make sure that you are familiar with all of these words and know what they mean. Refer to the glossary or index for any words that you do not yet understand.

absolute value	**base**	boundary point
completing the square	equivalent equations	**exponent**
fraction buster	inequality	**looking inside**
number line	**perfect square form**	quadratic equation
Quadratic Formula	**rational expression**	**rewriting**
scientific notation	simplifying	solution
standard form for quadratics	**undoing**	

Continues on next page →

②   *Continues from previous page.*

Make a concept map showing all of the **connections** you can find among the key words and ideas listed on the previous page. To show a **connection** between two words, draw a line between them and explain the **connection**, as shown in the example below. A word can be **connected** to any other word as long as there is a **justified connection**. For each key word or idea, provide a sketch that illustrates the idea (see the example below).

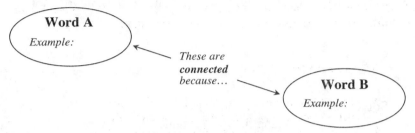

Your teacher may provide you with vocabulary cards to help you get started. If you use the cards to plan your concept map, be sure either to re-draw your concept map on your paper or to glue the vocabulary cards to a poster with all of the **connections** explained for others to see and understand.

While you are making your map, your team may think of related words or ideas that are not listed here. Be sure to include these ideas on your concept map.

③   SUMMARIZING MY UNDERSTANDING

This section gives you an opportunity to show what you know about certain math topics or ideas. Your teacher will give you directions for exactly how to do this.

④   WHAT HAVE I LEARNED?

This section will help you evaluate which types of problems you have seen with which you feel comfortable and those with which you need more help. Even if your teacher does not assign this section, it is a good idea to try these problems and find out for yourself what you know and what you need to work on.

Solve each problem as completely as you can. The table at the end of the closure section has answers to these problems. It also tells you where you can find additional help and practice on problems like these.

CL 10-152. Simplify the following expressions.

a. $\dfrac{x^2 y^3}{xy^2}$

b. $\dfrac{(x+2)^2 (x-4)}{(x+2)(x-4)}$

c. $\dfrac{x^2-x-6}{x-3}$

d. $\dfrac{5x^2-2xy+7}{5x^2-2xy+7}$

e. $\dfrac{x^2-5x+4}{x^2-x-12}$

f. $\dfrac{x^2-25}{x^2+10x+25} \div \dfrac{x-5}{x+3}$

CL 10-153. Solve the equations below using any method. How many solutions does each problem have?

a. $\frac{6x-5}{2x+1} + \frac{2x-7}{2x+1} = 2$

b. $\sqrt{x-5} + 10 = 15$

c. $|x - 7| = 22$

d. $(3x + 7)^2 = 144$

CL 10-154. Solve each inequality algebraically. Then represent your solution on a number line.

a. $5x - 7 \geq 2x + 5$

b. $6x - 29 > 4x + 12$

c. $x^2 \leq -4x + 5$

d. $|2x - 7| > 31$

CL 10-155. Solve the quadratic equation below three times: once by completing the square, once by factoring and using the Zero Product Property, and once by using the Quadratic Formula. Make sure you get the same answer using each method!

$$x^2 + 14x + 40 = -5$$

CL 10-156. Graph the system of inequalities at right and shade its solutions.

$y \geq \frac{2}{3}x - 7$

$y < -x + 4$

CL 10-157. Mario and Antoine are each in the middle of reading *War and Peace*. However, they just heard that something exciting happens on page 475. Even though each boy is at a different place in the book, they each agreed to read as fast as they can and to see who can get to page 475 first. Assume they each read at a constant, but different, rate.

a. After 2 hours of reading, Mario is on page 350 and Antoine is on page 425. Who will get to page 475 first? Can you tell? **Justify** your answer.

b. After 6 hours of reading, Mario is on page 450 and Antoine is on page 465. Who will get to page 475 first? Can you tell? **Justify** your answer.

c. What page was Mario on when they started the race? What page was Antoine on when they started?

d. At what rate does Mario read? At what rate does Antoine read?

e. *War and Peace* is 1400 pages long. After how many hours will each boy finish the book?

CL 10-158. For the equation $y = \frac{5}{3}x + 7$, find:

a. The equation of the line that is parallel to the given line and passes through the point (3, 2).

b. The equation of the line that is perpendicular to the given line and passes through the point (10, 4).

CL 10-159. Rewrite each of these expressions. Your answer should have no parentheses and no negative exponents.

a. $4(2x^{-3}y^5)^4$

b. $\dfrac{10x^3y^{-4}}{25x^5y^2}$

c. $12x^{-10}y^{53} \cdot (3x^5y^{-10})^4$

d. $\dfrac{m^2}{m^{-8}} \cdot \dfrac{3m^5}{m^9}$

CL 10-160. Check your answers to each problem above using the table at the end of the closure section. Which problems did you feel confident about? Which problems were hard? Use the table to make a list of topics you need help on and a list of topics you need to practice more.

⑤ **HOW AM I THINKING?**

This course focuses on five different **Ways of Thinking**: reversing thinking, justifying, generalizing, making connections, and applying and extending understanding. These are some of the ways in which you think while trying to make sense of a concept or to solve a problem (even outside of math class). During this chapter, you have probably used each Way of Thinking multiple times without even realizing it!

Review each of the Ways of Thinking with your class. Then choose three of these Ways of Thinking that you remember using while working in this chapter. For each Way of Thinking that you choose, show and explain where you used it and how you used it. Describe why thinking in this way helped you solve a particular problem or understand something new. (For instance, explain why you wanted to **generalize** in this particular case, or why it was useful to see these particular **connections**.) Be sure to include examples to demonstrate your thinking.

Answers and Support for Closure Activity #4
What Have I Learned?

Problem	Solution		Need Help?	More Practice
CL 10-152.	a. xy c. $x+2$ e. $\frac{x-1}{x+3}$	b. $x+2$ d. 1 f. $\frac{x+3}{x+5}$	Lessons 10.1.2 and 10.4.3 Math Notes boxes	Problems 10-3, 10-5, 10-16, 10-21, 10-97, 10-105, 10-123, and 10-128
CL 10-153.	a. $x = 3.5$ c. $x = 29$ or -15	b. $x = 30$ d. $x = \frac{5}{3}$ or $-\frac{19}{3}$	Lessons 10.1.4, 10.2.1, and 10.2.2 Math Notes boxes	Problems 10-22, 10-49, 10-63, 10-69, 10-73, and 10-94

Problem	Solution	Need Help?	More Practice

CL 10-154.

a. $x \geq 4$

b. $x > 20.5$

c. $-5 \leq x \leq 1$

d. $x > 19$ or $x < -12$

Need Help?: Lesson 9.2.2 Math Notes box, Lesson 10.2.4

More Practice: Problems 10-9, 10-74, 10-77, 10-78, 10-80, 10-90, 10-95, 10-107, and 10-116

CL 10-155. $x = -5$ or -9

Need Help?: Lessons 8.1.4, 8.2.3, 8.3.1, 8.3.2, and 10.2.4 Math Notes boxes

More Practice: Problems 10-106, 10-112, 10-114, and 10-139

CL 10-156.

Need Help?: Problems 9-57 and 9-57

More Practice: Problems 10-42 and 10-86

CL 10-157.

a. Cannot be determined because we do not know which pages Mario and Antoine were on before they started racing and we do not know the rates they are reading.

b. Mario and Antoine will get to page 475 at the same time. Each will arrive after another hour.

c. Mario: page 300, Antoine: page 405

d. Mario: 25 pages per hour, Antoine: 10 pages per hour

e. Mario: 44 hours, Antoine: 99.5 hours

Need Help?: Lesson 7.1.4 Math Notes box

More Practice: Problems 10-23 and 10-118

CL 10-158.

a. $y = \frac{5}{3}x - 3$

b. $y = -\frac{3}{5}x + 10$

Need Help?: Lesson 7.3.2 Math Notes box

More Practice: Problems 10-19, 10-31, 10-96, and 10-113

CL 10-159.

a. $\frac{64y^{20}}{x^{12}}$

b. $\frac{2}{5x^2y^6}$

c. $972y^{13}x^{10}$

d. $3m^6$

Need Help?: Lesson 10.4.3 Math Notes box

More Practice: Problems 10-123, 10-128, 10-135, and 10-147

458

11

FUNCTIONS AND RELATIONS

CHAPTER 11   Functions and Relations

So far in this course you have studied linear and quadratic functions extensively. In this chapter, you will explore new nonlinear functions and will learn how to describe a function completely. You will get to know the shapes and behaviors of many different functions and will be able to distinguish them by their graphs and rules. Many of the functions will look familiar because their rules relate closely to equations that you have already learned how to solve.

In this chapter, you will learn:

➢ How to find the domain and range of a function.

➢ How to recognize symmetry in a graph.

➢ How to determine if a relation is a function by looking at its table or graph.

➢ How to predict the shape of a graph by its rule.

➢ How to recognize the possible rule of a function by examining its graph.

➢ How different parameters in an equation affect the placement and direction of a graph.

Guiding Questions

Think about these questions throughout this chapter:

What does the graph look like?

Is there a pattern?

How does it grow?

Is it a function?

How can I describe it?

Chapter Outline

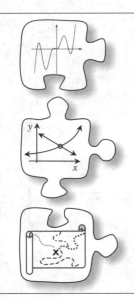

Section 11.1 This section is devoted to learning about special qualities of relations. You will start with an investigation of a parabola. Then you will learn about new ways to describe this relation and other relations better. Finally, you will investigate a variety of functions in order to describe them completely.

Section 11.2 This section clarifies the difference between intercepts and intersections. You will also predict the possible number of intersections in any system of multiple functions.

Section 11.3 This section brings closure to relations and functions with a treasure hunt focused on multiple representations of relations.

11.1.1 How can I describe a graph?

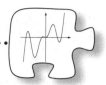

Describing a Graph

What does it mean to describe the graph of a rule completely? Today you will graph and investigate a new graph: $y = \sqrt{x}$.

11-1.   DESCRIBING A GRAPH

Your teacher will assign your team one of the rules below. On graph paper, graph your rule for x-values between –3 and 9. When your team is convinced that your graph is correct, discuss all the ways you can describe this graph. Then write as many summary statements about the graph as you can, such as, *"We noticed that as x gets larger, …"*

$$y = \sqrt{x}$$

$$y = \sqrt{x} + 1$$

$$y = \sqrt{x+2} - 1$$

$$y = \sqrt{x-1} + 3$$

$$y = -\sqrt{x}$$

$$y = -\sqrt{x} - 2$$

11-2.   PRESENT YOUR FINDINGS

With your team, create a poster that contains not only the graph of your rule but also all of your observations and summary statements from problem 11-1. Be thorough and complete. Remember that a main goal of this activity is to determine what items a "complete description" of a graph must contain, so be sure to include everything you can. Be prepared to present your poster to the class. Remember to give reasons for all statements that you make.

11-3.   As a class, examine the posters that were presented by the teams. Create a list of all the ways to describe a graph. Then, next to each description, create a question that will prompt you to look for this quality in the graphs of other rules you encounter.

Once your list is complete, copy the questions into your Learning Log. Title this entry "Graph-Investigation Questions" and include today's date.

11-4.   Find the dimensions of the generic rectangle shown at right and write its area as a sum and a product.

$-6x$	4
$9x^2$	$-6x$

11-5.   After noon, the number of people in Mal-Wart grows steadily until 6:00 PM. If the equation $y = 228 + 58x$ represents the number of people in the store x hours after noon:

   a.   How many people were in the store at noon?

   b.   At what rate is the number of shoppers growing?

   c.   When were there 402 shoppers in the store?

11-6.   Find the following absolute values.

   a. $|0.75|$ b. $|-99|$ c. $|4 - 2 \cdot 3|$ d. $|\pi|$

11-7.   Jacob discovered that the x-intercepts of a certain parabola are $(3, 0)$ and $(-1, 0)$, but now he needs to find the vertex. Can you get him started? What do you know about the vertex? Draw a sketch of this parabola to help you.

11-8.   When a family with two adults and three children bought tickets for an amusement park, they paid a total of $56.50. The next family in line, with four children and one adult, paid $49.50. Find the adult and child ticket prices by writing and solving a system of equations.

11-9.   Find the slope (m) and y-intercept (b) for each line below.

   a. $2x + 7y = 14$ b. $y = 6 - \frac{x}{3}$

   c. $y = \frac{10x-2}{2}$ d. $y = 3x$

11-10.   Solve the following inequalities for x.

   a. $4x - 1 \geq 7$ b. $3 - 2x < x + 6$

   c. $2(x - 5) \leq 8$ d. $\frac{1}{2}x > 5$

Algebra Connections

11-11.   Using your knowledge of exponents, rewrite each expression below so that there are
          no negative exponents or parentheses remaining.

    a. $\dfrac{4x^{18}}{2x^{22}}$

    b. $(s^4tu^2)(s^7t^{-1})$

    c. $(3w^{-2})^4$

    d. m^{-3}

11-12.   Match each graph below with the correct inequality.

    a. $y > -x + 2$ b. $y < 2x - 3$ c. $y \geq \frac{1}{2}x$ d. $y \leq -\frac{2}{3}x + 2$

    1)   2)   3)   4)

 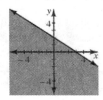 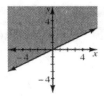

11-13.   Add, subtract, multiply, or divide the following rational expressions. Simplify your
          answers if possible.

    a. $\dfrac{12x^2+4x-1}{36x^2-12x+1} \cdot \dfrac{x^2-64}{2x^2+17x+8}$

    b. $\dfrac{2x^2-10x}{x^2-4} \div \dfrac{x^2-5x}{x^2-4x-12}$

11-14.   For the parabola $y = 2x^2 - 7x + 3$:

    a.   Give the coordinates of the y-intercept.

    b.   Give the coordinates of the two x-intercepts. Explain how you found them.

11-15.   Simplify each expression using the laws of exponents.

    a. $(x^2)(x^2y^3)$

    b. $\dfrac{x^3y^4}{x^2y^3}$

    c. $(2x^2)(-3x^4)$

    d. $(2x)^3$

11.1.2 What's the relationship?

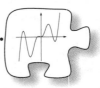

Relation Machines

In the next few lessons you will add to your list of what you can ask about a graph of a rule. Throughout this course, you have used rules that relate two variables (like $y = -2x^2 + 11x + 1$) to make graphs and find information. Today you will look more closely at how rules that relate two variables help establish a relationship between the variables. You will also learn a new notation to help represent these relationships.

11-16. **ARE WE RELATED?**

Examine the table of input (x) and output (y) values below. Is there a relationship between the input and output values? If so, state the relationship.

x	−3	−2	−1	0	1	2	3
y	8	3	0	−1	0	3	8

11-17. **RELATION MACHINES**

Each equation that relates inputs to outputs is called a **relation**. This is easy to remember because the equation helps you know how all the y-values (outputs) on your graph are **related** to their corresponding x-values (inputs).

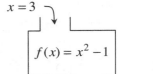

A relation works like a machine, as shown in the diagram below. A relation is given a name that can be a letter, such as f or g. The notation $f(x)$ represents the output when x is processed by the machine. (Note: $f(x)$ is read, "f of x.") When x is put into the machine, $f(x)$, the value of a function for a specific x-value, comes out.

Numbers are put into the relation machine (in this case, $f(x) = x^2 - 1$) one at a time, and then the relation performs the operation(s) on each input to determine each output. For example, when $x = 3$ is put into the relation $f(x) = x^2 - 1$, the relation squares it and then subtracts 1 to get the output, which is 8. The notation $f(3) = 8$ shows that the relation named f connects the input (3) with the output (8).

inputs

$x = 3$

$f(x) = x^2 - 1$

$f(3) = 8$

outputs

a. Find the output for $f(x) = x^2 - 1$ when the input is $x = 4$; that is, find $f(4)$.

b. Likewise, find $f(-1)$ and $f(10)$.

c. If the output of this relation is 24, what was the input? That is, if $f(x) = 24$, then what is x? Is there more than one possible input?

Algebra Connections

11-18. Find the relationship between x and $f(x)$ in the table below and complete the rule of the relation.

x	9	1	100	4	49		0	25	20
$f(x)$		1			7	4		5	

Relation: $f(x) = $ _____

11-19. Find the corresponding outputs or inputs for the following relations. If there is no possible output for the given input, explain why not.

a.
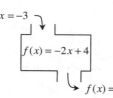

b.
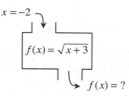

c.
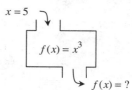

d.
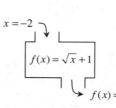

e.
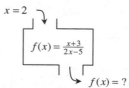

f.
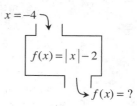

g.
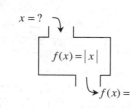

h.
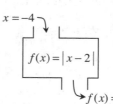

i.

11-20. Examine the relation defined at right. Notice that $g(1) = -1$; that is, when x is 1, the output (y or $g(1)$) is -1.

a. What is the output of the relation when the input is 2? That is, find $g(2)$.

b. Likewise, what are $g(-1)$ and $g(0)$?

c. What is the input of this relation when the output is 1? In other words, find x when $g(x) = 1$. Is there more than one possible solution?

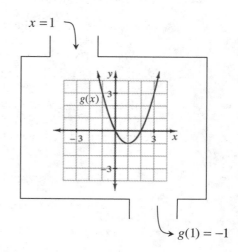

11-21. If $f(x) = x^2$, then $f(4) = 4^2 = 16$. Find:

    a. $f(1)$ b. $f(-3)$ c. $f(t)$

11-22. Find the equation of the line with slope $m = -\frac{4}{3}$ that passes through the point $(12, -4)$.

11-23. Marley thinks that the two lines below are perpendicular, but Bob thinks they are not. Who is correct and how do you know?

$$2x - 7y = 16$$
$$7x + 2y = 3$$

11-24. Ten minutes after he left his home, Gerald was 40 miles from his grandmother's house. Then, 22 minutes after he left, he was 34 miles from her house. If he was traveling toward his grandmother's home at a constant rate and reached her house after 90 minutes, how far away from her house does he live?

11-25. Use your method for multiplying and dividing fractions to simplify the expressions below.

    a. $\frac{x+2}{x-1} \cdot \frac{x-1}{x-6}$ b. $\frac{(4x-3)(x+2)}{(x-5)(x-3)} \div \frac{(x-1)(x+2)}{(x-1)(x-3)}$

    c. $\frac{(x-6)^2}{(2x+1)(x-6)} \cdot \frac{x(2x+1)(x+7)}{(x-1)(x+7)}$ d. $\frac{(x+3)(2x-5)}{(3x-4)(x-7)} \div \frac{(2x-5)}{(3x-4)}$

    e. $\frac{3x-1}{x+4} \div \frac{x-5}{x+4}$ f. $\frac{x-3}{x+4} \cdot \frac{3x-10}{x+11} \cdot \frac{x+4}{3x-10}$

11-26. Rewrite each expression below without negative or zero exponents.

    a. 4^{-1} b. 7^0 c. 5^{-2} d. x^{-2}

Algebra Connections

11.1.3 Can I predict the output?

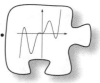

Functions

You have studied relations and have learned that each relation defines a relationship between the input and output values. But what happens when your relation gives you unpredictable results? That is, what happens when you cannot predict the output for a given input? Today you will study this situation and will be introduced to a special type of relation called a *function*.

11-27. **THE COLA MACHINE**

The cola machine at your school offers several types of soda. There are two buttons for your favorite drink, *Blast*, while the other drinks (*Slurp, Lemon Twister,* and *Diet Slurp*) each have one button.

a. Explain how the cola machine is a relation.

b. Describe the input and output of this soda machine.

c. While buying a soda, Ms. Whitney pushed the button for *Lemon Twister* and got a can of *Lemon Twister*. Later she went back to the same machine, but this time pushing the *Lemon Twister* button got her a can of *Blast*. Is the machine functioning consistently? Why or why not?

d. When Brandi pushed the top button for *Blast* she received a can of *Blast*. Her friend, Miguel, decided to be different and pushed the second button for *Blast*. He, too, received a can of *Blast*. Is the machine functioning consistently? Why or why not?

e. When Loutfi pushed a button for *Slurp*, he received a can of *Lemon Twister*! Later, Tayeisha also pushed the *Slurp* button and received a can of *Lemon Twister*. Still later, Tayeisha noticed that everyone else who pushed the *Slurp* button received a *Lemon Twister*. Is the machine functioning consistently? Explain why or why not.

f. When a relation is functioning consistently and predictably, we call that relation a **function**. What is the main difference between a relation that is a function and a relation that is not a function?

11-28.   Using your own words, write a definition of a function. Be prepared to share your definition with the class.

11-29.   Examine each of the relations below. Compare the inputs and outputs of each relation and decide if the relation is a function. Explain your reasoning. Use your definition of a function (from problem 11-28) to help you **justify** your conclusion.

a.

Button Number	1	1	2	4	2	3
Type of Candy	Stix	Stix	M&Ns	M&Ns	Duds	Duds

b.

x	7	-2	0	4	9	-3	6
$f(x)$	6	-3	4	2	10	-3	0

c.

x	3	-1	2	0	1	2	9
$g(x)$	4	-5	9	7	4	-8	2

d.

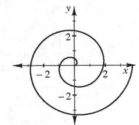

e.

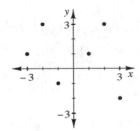

f.

x	$h(x)$
−8	11
4	3
11	−8
6	3
−8	11

g.

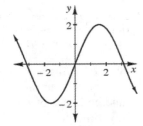

11-30.   Jade noticed that the line graphed at right is a function. "Hey – I think *all* lines are functions!" she exclaimed. Is she correct? Support your claim with a diagram.

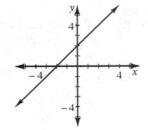

11-31.   In your Learning Log, describe what it means for a relationship to be a **function**. Think of another type of machine that you use on a regular basis and describe how it also operates as a function. Title this entry "Functions" and include today's date.

11-32.   If $g(x) = \sqrt{x-7}$, find $g(8)$, $g(32)$, and $g(80)$.

11-33.   Solve the system of equations below using any method. Be sure to check your solution.

$$5u + 6v = 2$$
$$u - 2v = 10$$

11-34.   Solve each equation below. Check each solution.

   a. $6 - (3 + x) = 10$

   b. $100(x + 3) = 200$

   c. $\frac{1}{3}x + 4 = x - 2$

   d. $\frac{4}{5} = \frac{x+2}{45}$

11-35.   Solve for x. Use any method. Check your solutions by testing them in the original equation.

   a. $|x - 3| = 5$

   b. $5|x| = 35$

   c. $|x + 1| = 2$

   d. $|x + 3| - 6 = -4$

11-36.   Rewrite each of the expressions below with no parentheses and no fractions. Negative exponents are acceptable in your answer.

   a. $(5a^{-2}b^3)^8 \cdot (5ab^{-2})^{-6}$

   b. $\frac{15x^{-5}y^2}{(3x^2)^2 \cdot y^{-3}}$

11-37.   **Multiple Choice:** Which line below is parallel to $y = -\frac{2}{3}x + 5$?

   a. $2x - 3y = 6$

   b. $2x + 3y = 6$

   c. $3x - 2y = 6$

   d. $3x + 2y = 6$

11.1.4 What can go in? What can come out?

Domain and Range

So far you have described relations using intercepts and symmetry. You also have noticed that sometimes relations are functions. Today you will finish your focus on relations by describing the inputs and outputs of relations.

11-38. Examine the graph of the relation $h(x)$ at right. Use it to estimate:

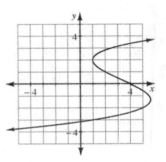

    a. $h(4)$

    b. $h(1)$

    c. $h(-4)$

    d.   Is this relation a function? Why or why not?

11-39. Examine the relation shown at right.

    a.   Find $f(-3)$, $f(0)$, and $f(2)$.

    b.   Find $f(3)$. What happened?

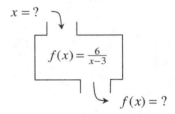

    c.   Are there any other numbers that cannot be evaluated by this relation? In other words, are there any other values that cannot be x? Explain how you know.

    d.   The set (collection) of numbers that can be used for x in a relation is called the **domain** of the relation. The domain is a description or list of all the possible x-values for the relation. Describe the domain of $f(x) = \frac{6}{x-3}$.

11-40.   Now examine $g(x)$ graphed at right.

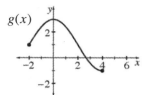

a.   Is $g(x)$ a function? How can you tell?

b.   Which x-values have points on the graph?
      That is, what is the domain of $g(x)$?

c.   What are the possible outputs for $g(x)$?
      This is called the **range** of the relation.

d.   Ricky thinks the range of $g(x)$ is: $-1, 0, 1, 2$, and 3. Is he correct? Why or
      why not?

11-41.   FINDING DOMAIN AND RANGE

The domain and range are good descriptors of a relation because they help you know
what numbers can go into and come out of a relation. The domain and range can
also help you set up useful axes when graphing and help you describe special points
on a graph (such as a missing point or the lowest point).

Work with your team to describe in words the domain and range of each relation
below.

a.

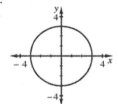

b.

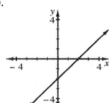

c.

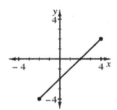

d.

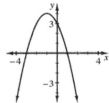

e.

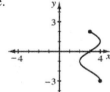

f.

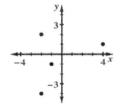

11-42.   Chiu loves tables! He has decided to make the table below for a relation $f(x)$ to help him find its domain and range.

x	-3	-2	-1	0	1	2	3
$f(x)$	5	0	-3	-4	-3	0	5

a.   From his table, can you tell what the domain of $f(x)$ is? Why or why not?

b.   From the table, can you tell the range of $f(x)$? Why or why not?

c.   Is using a table an effective way to determine the domain and range of a relation?

11-43.   Daniel is thinking about the relation shown at right.

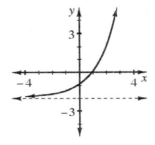

a.   He noticed that the curve continues to the left and to the right. What is the domain of this relation?

b.   He found out that the dotted line represents a boundary that the graph gets closer to but never touches or crosses. (Another name for this dotted line is **asymptote**.) How should Daniel describe the range?

11-44.   TEAM CHALLENGE

Sketch the graph of a relation that has a domain of all the numbers greater than or equal to –2 and a range of all the numbers less than or equal to 3. Is there more than one possible answer?

Algebra Connections

METHODS AND MEANINGS

Relations and Functions

A **relation** establishes a correspondence between its inputs and outputs (in math language called "sets"). For equations, it establishes the relationship between two variables and determines one variable when given the other. Some examples of relations are:

$$y = x^2, \ y = \tfrac{x}{x+3}, \ y = -2x + 5$$

Since the value of y usually depends on x, y is often referred to as the **dependent variable**, while x is called the **independent variable**.

The set of possible inputs of a relation is called the **domain**, while the set of all possible outputs of a relation is called the **range**. For example, notice that all the points on the graph at right have x-values that are greater than or equal to -3. The arrows on the graph indicate that the graph will continue to expand to the right. Thus, the entire domain is the set of numbers that are greater than or equal to -3. Likewise, since each y-value has a corresponding point on the graph, then the range is the set of all numbers. This is also referred to as the set of **all real numbers**. In the future, this course will refer to these as "all numbers."

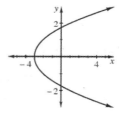

A **relation** is called a **function** if there exists <u>no more than one</u> output for each input. If a relation has two or more outputs for a single input value, it is not a function. For example, the relation graphed above is not a function because there are two y-values for each x-value greater than -3.

Functions are often given names, most commonly "f," "g," or "h." The notation $f(x)$ represents the output of a function, named "f" when x is the input. It is read "f of x." The notation $f(2)$, read "f of 2," represents the output of function f when $x = 2$. In the example at right, $f(2) = 10$.

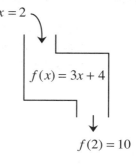

The equations $y = 3x + 4$ and $f(x) = 3x + 4$ represent the <u>same</u> <u>function</u>. Notice that this notation is interchangeable; that is, $y = f(x)$.

11-45. Which of the relations below are functions? If a relation is not a function, give a reason to support your conclusion.

a.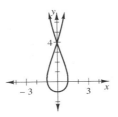

b.

x	y
-3	19
5	19
19	0
0	-3

c.

x	7	-2	0	7	4
y	10	0	10	3	0

d.

11-46. Find the x- and y-intercepts for the graphs of the relations in problem 11-45.

11-47. Marisol and Mimi walked the same distance from their school to a shopping mall. Marisol walked 2 miles per hour, while Mimi left 1 hour later and walked 3 miles per hour. If they reached the mall at the same time, how far from the mall is their school?

11-48. A line passes through the points A(−3, −2) and B(2, 1). Does it also pass through the point C(5, 3)? **Justify** your conclusion.

11-49. Solve each equation below for the indicated variable.

a. $3x - 2y = 18$ for x

b. $3x - 2y = 18$ for y

c. $rt = d$ for r

d. $C = 2\pi r$ for r

11-50. Simplify each expression below.

a. $\frac{3x^2 + 8x + 5}{x^2 - 5x - 6} \cdot \frac{2x - 5}{3x + 5}$

b. $\frac{x^2 + x - 12}{x^2 - x - 6} \div \frac{x - 5}{x^2 - 3x - 10}$

11.1.5 How can I describe this relation?

Investigating a New Relation

You are now familiar with the graphs of lines, parabolas, and square roots. What other types of relations can you study? Today you will use the questions your class generated in Lesson 11.1.1 to investigate several new relations. Your team will then report its findings to the class. Pay close attention to presentations! As you listen to the presentations of your classmates, you will learn about several new and interesting relations.

11-51.   NEW RELATIONS

Your teacher will assign your team a new relation from the list below. On graph paper, carefully graph your new relation. Be sure to include enough values in your table to show any unusual behavior of your graph. Then use your list of questions about relations to investigate your particular relation.

Write clear summary statements that describe your relation. Create a team poster for your relation with a graph and any observations and statements your team made. Be ready to present your poster to the class.

(1) $f(x) = \frac{1}{x}$ (2) $f(x) = x^3$

(3) $f(x) = \frac{1}{x^2}$ (4) $f(x) = 0.5^x$

(5) $f(x) = 2^x$ (6) $f(x) = \sqrt{16 - x^2}$

11-52.   On the resource page provided by your teacher, find a box for each of the relations listed in problem 11-51. As you listen to the presentations, take notes on each relation. Be sure to sketch a graph of the relation as well as list any special points or features. Remember to date this entry and place the resource page in your Learning Log.

11-53.   MATCH-A-GRAPH

Match each rule (a) through (f) with its corresponding graph below.

a. $f(x) = \sqrt{x-3}$ b. $f(x) = \frac{1}{x} + 1$

c. $f(x) = x^3 - 2$ d. $f(x) = \sqrt{4 - (x+2)^2}$

e. $f(x) = \frac{3}{x^2}$ f. $f(x) = 2^{x-2}$

1) 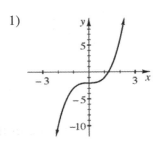   2) 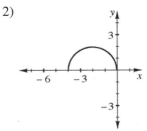   3)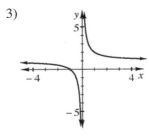

4) 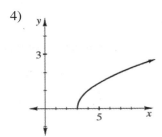   5) 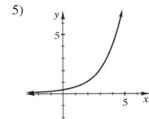   6)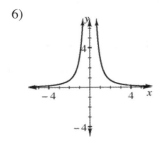

11-54.   For each relation graphed in problem 11-53, name the domain and the range.

11-55.   On the same set of axes, graph $y = |x|$ and $y = |x| + 2$. What is the same about these two graphs? What is different?

11-56.   Simplify the rational expression below. What values can x not be?

$$\frac{3x^2 + 11x - 20}{2x^2 + 11x + 5}$$

11-57.   Find the corresponding inputs or outputs for the following relations. If there is no
          solution, explain why not. Be careful: In some cases, there may be no solution or
          more than one possible solution.

a. $x = 8$

$$f(x) = |x|$$

$f(8) = ?$

b. $x = ?$

$$f(x) = 3 - \sqrt{x}$$

$f(x) = 2$

c. $k = -6$

$$f(k) = \frac{k}{2} + 1$$

$f(-6) = ?$

d. $x = 3$

$$f(x) = \sqrt{x - 5}$$

$f(3) = ?$

11-58.   Find the equation of a line that is perpendicular to $y = -\frac{1}{5}x + 11$ but goes through
          the point (6, 8).

11-59.   Solve each equation below for the given variable. Be sure to check your solution.

a. $6x - 11 = 3x + 16$

b. $-2(5 - 3x) + 5 = 9 + 3x$

c. $\frac{6}{k-2} = 10$

d. $\frac{4}{3x-1} = \frac{2}{x+3}$

11-60.   Simplify using only positive exponents.

a. $(3x^2 y)(5x)$

b. $(x^2 y^3)(x^{-2} y^{-2})$

c. $\frac{x^3}{x^{-2}}$

d. $(2x^{-1})^3$

11-61.   Find the inputs for the following relations with the given outputs. If there is no
          possible input for the given output, explain why not.

a. $x = ?$

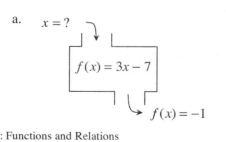

$$f(x) = 3x - 7$$

$f(x) = -1$

b. $x = ?$

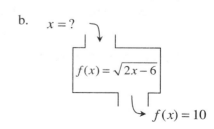

$$f(x) = \sqrt{2x - 6}$$

$f(x) = 10$

11-62.   One way to represent the solutions shown on the number line at right is $-3 \le x < 1$. For each number line below, write a similar mathematical sentence to describe the solutions for x.

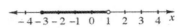

a.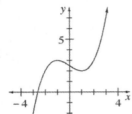

b.

c.

d.

11-63.   Which graphs below have a domain of all numbers? Which have a range of all numbers?

a.   b.   c.

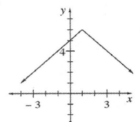
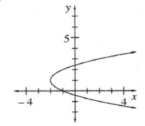

11-64.   Solve each of the following equations or systems.

a. $x^2 - 1 = 15$

b. $y = 3x - 2$
       $y = 4x + 3$

c. $x^2 - 2x - 8 = 0$

d. $2x^2 = -x + 7$

11-65.   Graph and shade the solution for the system of inequalities below.

$$y \le 4 + \tfrac{3}{4}x$$
$$y > -\tfrac{1}{2}x + 1$$

$11.1.6$ How does it change?

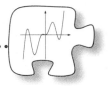

Transformation of a Function

11-66.   PROMOTION OPPORTUNITY

You and your co-workers at Functions of
America have received the following note
from your boss. Read the letter and
complete the task that follows.

To My Faithful Employees,

*I have been pleased to read in the
"Relations Daily" about the high
customer-service satisfaction ratings of
this company. Now I want to expand to
control the function-rental industry.*

*Before Functions of America can begin renting out our expensive graphs, I need an
equation attached to each one. That way, when a graph is returned to the company,
employees will be able to verify that it is the same function that was originally rented
to the customer. Also, if the graph of the function was damaged or switched for a
less sophisticated graph, we will then be able to prosecute the customer to the full
extent of the law.*

*Employees will be given a designated time to explore their new and innovative
function with a partner. Please be ready to report on how the numbers in a rule
change its graph.*

*At the end of the day, every employee will be challenged to identify the equation of a
function correctly by observing only its graph. Doing so will earn you a
management position. I wish all of you the best of luck.*

> *Sincerely,*
> *Freda Function, CEO, Functions of America*

Your Task: Your teacher will assign your team one of the functions below. Explore
the graph of your function as *a, h,* and *k* change values. Choose positive, negative,
and zero values for *a, h*, and *k* to uncover all possible patterns. Reflect on the
relationships you find between the graph and its equation. Discuss your observations
with your study team and record your results on paper.

(1) $f(x) = a(x-h)^3 + k$ (2) $f(x) = a(x-h)^2 + k$ (3) $f(x) = a\sqrt{x-h} + k$

(4) $f(x) = a|x-h| + k$ (5) $f(x) = \frac{a}{x-h} + k$ (6) $f(x) = 2^{a(x-h)} + k$

Problem continues on next page $\rightarrow$

11-66.   *Problem continued from previous page.*

Discussion Points

What is the goal of this investigation?

What is the best way to choose values of *a*, *h*, and *k* to see a pattern?

Further Guidance

11-67.   When you asked for clarification, your boss sent you the following note:

> *Dear Employees,*
>
> *Thank you for your questions. I am sorry I was so vague. In your report, I would like you to tell me:*
>
> 1. *How does the equation affect how "skinny" or "wide" the graph is?*
>
> 2. *What changes in the equation move the graph up or down? Left or right?*
>
> 3. *Is there a way to change the equation so that the function turns "upside down"?*
>
> *Use your graphing technology to test different values of a, h, and k to discover the answers to the questions above. Examine only one letter at a time so that you can find patterns quickly. For example, if you want to see what the value of a does to the graph of a function, then change a while you keep h and k the same.*
>
> *Good luck!*
> *Ms. Function*

—————   *Further Guidance*   —————
section ends here.

11-68.   PROMOTION CHALLENGE

Here is your opportunity to impress your boss. Find the equation for each relation graphed below. Remember the observations you made in problem 11-66 and pay close attention to details.

a.

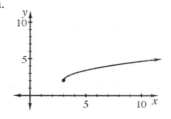

b.

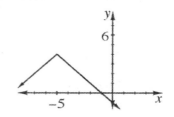

11-69.   EXTENSION

How do the domain and range of a function change when it moves? To answer this
question, examine what happens as the square-root function $f(x) = \sqrt{x}$ is moved
("translated").

a.   Describe the domain and range of $f(x) = \sqrt{x}$.

b.   Now describe the domain and range of $g(x) = \sqrt{x+2} - 3$.

c.   Are the domain and range for $f(x)$ and $g(x)$ above the same? If not, how are
they different?

11-70.   Match each rule below with its corresponding graph. Can you do this without
making any tables?

a. $y = |x-1|$ b. $y = |x| + 3$ c. $y = |x-1| + 3$

1)   2)   3)

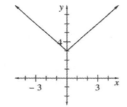   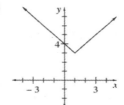   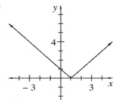

11-71.   Graph the rule $y = -x^2 + 4x$ and label its intercepts and vertex.

11-72.   If $f(x) = 7 + |x|$ and $g(x) = x^3 - 5$, then find:

a. $f(-5)$ b. $g(4)$ c. $f(0)$

d. $f(2)$ e. $g(-2)$ f. $g(0)$

11-73.   Solve for x in each equation below.

a. $2x = 8$ b. $2x + 2 = 10$

c. $6x + 2 - 4x = 10$ d. $2(3x+1) - 4x = 10$

e.   Check your solutions for the equations above. What do you notice?

11-74. Multiply each expression below using generic rectangles.

    a. $(4x-1)(3x+2)$ b. $(m+1)(3m-2)$ c. $(k-4)(6-5k)$

11-75. Solve the following inequalities for x. Graph your solutions on a number line.

    a. $3x-5 \le 7+2x$ b. $|x|-3<7$

    c. $5(2-x)+6>16$ d. $|x+2|>3$

11.2.1 Intercept or intersect?

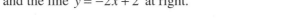

Intercepts and Intersections

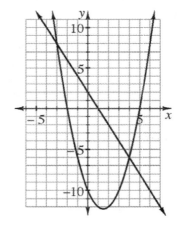

Now that you know about many kinds of functions, you will look more closely at intercepts and intersections. What is the difference between an intercept and a point of intersection? Think about this as you develop algebraic methods to find points where two functions cross. In the next few lessons you will have chances to practice your quadratic-solving skills as well as your newer solving skills from Chapter 10.

11-76. Examine the graphs of the parabola $y = x^2 - 3x - 10$ and the line $y = -2x + 2$ at right.

    a.   Name all x- and y-intercepts for the parabola.

    b.   Name all x- and y-intercepts for the line.

    c.   Where do the graphs intersect each other?

    d.   The words "intersect" and "intercept" look and sound a lot alike, but what do they mean? How are they alike? How are they different?

11-77.   Intercepts and intersections are similar, but they are not exactly the same. How can you tell which one you are looking for? Read the situations below and decide if the graphical solution would best be represented as an **intercept** or an **intersection**. Be prepared to defend your decision. Note: You do not need to solve the problem!

a.   A 5-gram candle on a birthday cake is lit. Two minutes after it is lit, the candle weighs 4.2 grams. How long will the candle burn?

b.   A local bowling alley charges you $4 to rent shoes and $3.50 for each game you play. Another alley charges you $7 to rent shoes and $2 for each game you play. How many games would you need to play in order for both alleys to charge you the same amount?

c.   Two months after Aliya's birthday, she had $450, while her sister Claudia had $630. Five months after her birthday, Aliya had $800, while Claudia had $920. How much did each person have on Aliya's birthday?

11-78.   Using a graph to find the intersection of two curves can be challenging when the rules are complicated or when the point of intersection ends up off the graph. Therefore, it helps to know another way to find the intersection without using a graph.

a.   Name the algebraic methods you already know to solve linear systems.

b.   Use one of the methods you listed in part (a) to solve for the intersection of $y = x^2 - 3x - 10$ and $y = -2x + 2$. Be sure to collaborate with your teammates and check your results along the way. Does the graph in problem 11-76 confirm your results?

11-79.   Solve the system of equations below for x and y. Write your solution(s) in the form (x, y). Then graph the system on the same set of axes and confirm your solution.

$$y = \frac{1}{x}$$
$$y = 2x + 1$$

11-80.   In your Learning Log, explain the difference between intercepts and intersections. Include a sketch or graph to help your explanation. Title this entry "Intercepts and Intersections" and include today's date.

11-81.   Find the output for the relation with the given input. $x = 1$
          If there is no possible output for the given input,
          explain why not.

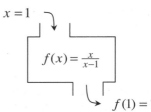

$$f(x) = \frac{x}{x-1}$$

$f(1) = ?$

11-82.   Examine the two lines
          graphed at right. Will these
          two lines intersect? Find the
          equation of each line and test
          your prediction.

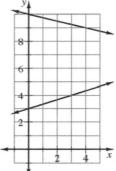

11-83.   For each line in problem 11-82,
          find the x- and y-intercepts.

11-84.   Which of the equations below is equivalent to $4(3x - 1) + 3x = 9x + 5$? More than
          one may be equivalent. **Justify** your answer.

          a. $12x - 4 + 3x = 9x + 5$ b. $12x - 1 + 3x = 9x + 5$

          c. $11x = 14x$ d. $15x - 4 = 9x + 5$

11-85.   Paula graphed a line and found that $f(-2) = 5$ and $f(0) = 2$. Graph this line and
          find its equation.

11-86.   Which of the relations below are functions? **Justify** your answer.

          a.   b.   c.

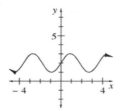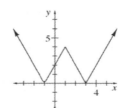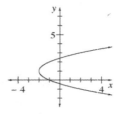

11-87.   For each graph in problem 11-86 above, name the domain and range.

11-88.   Examine the graphs in problem 11-86 again. Which, if any, have symmetry? Copy
          each graph on your paper and show any lines of symmetry.

11.2.2 How many points of intersection?

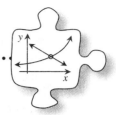

Pulling It All Together

In Lesson 11.2.1, you developed a method for finding the points of intersection of a line and a parabola. Today you will study different possibilities for lines and parabolas intersecting or not intersecting.

11-89.   As you have seen, sometimes a parabola and a line never intersect. However, if a parabola and a line do intersect, how many different intersection points can they have? How many intersections can two parabolas have? Do two parabolas *always* intersect?

On graph paper, sketch a graph that fits each description below. Not every graph is possible. As you graph, consider the questions above.

a.   A line and a parabola that intersect twice.

b.   A line and a parabola that intersect once.

c.   A line and a parabola that intersect more than twice.

d.   Two parabolas that intersect twice.

e.   Two parabolas that have an infinite number of intersections.

f.   Two parabolas that never intersect.

g.   Two parabolas that only intersect once.

11-90.   HOW MANY INTERSECTIONS?

When given a graph of two parabolas or a line and a parabola, it is usually easy to determine how many points of intersection they have. But how can you tell algebraically?

Your Task: Each team will be assigned one of the systems below. With your team:

- Use any algebraic solving method to find the point(s) of intersection for your team's system, if any exist. Examine your algebraic solution and decide what it indicates about the graph of the system. (That is, do the parabolas intersect once? Do they never intersect?)

- Once you have solved your team's system, have your teacher come to your team and listen to you explain your results. Use a graphing calculator (or sketch a graph using your graphing shortcuts) to verify your conclusion.

- If time allows, design a poster that shows the algebraic solution of your system as well as a sketch of the graph.

Systems:

a. $y = x^2$
    $y = 2x - 1$

b. $y = x^2 - 5x + 6$
    $y = -x^2$

c. $y = x^2 - 4x + 5$
    $y = -x^2 + 4x - 1$

d. $y = x^2 - x - 2$
    $y = x^2 + 2x + 1$

e. $y = x^2 - x - 2$
    $y = x - 6$

f. $y = 2x^2 + 3x - 9$
    $y = x - 5$

11-91.   ALGEBRA COMES TO THE RESCUE!

Darrel is so excited! When he called his local radio station during a contest, he was the 9th caller! The talk-show host, Maribel, explained that Darrel would win a brand-new graphing calculator if he answers this question correctly:

"*How many times do the parabola* $y = 2x^2 - 5x$
and the line $y = \frac{2}{3}x - 4$ *intersect?*"

a. Quickly, Darrel used his graphing calculator to graph the system – but then his calculator broke! Help him by graphing the system on your grapher. Time is running out… What should he tell Maribel?

b. Maribel paused and then asked, "*Are you **absolutely sure** that is your final answer?*" Help Darrel confirm his answer by solving the system algebraically. What is the correct answer?

11-92. Solve each quadratic equation below using any method you choose. Check your solutions.

a. $(5x-1)(x+3)=0$

b. $4x^2+10x-6=0$

c. $0.5x^2-3x+4.5=0$

d. $x^2+5x=14$

11-93. Use your graphing shortcuts to graph $f(x)=x^2-6x+5$.

a.   What is the vertex?

b.   Describe the domain and range of this relation.

11-94. Solve the following problem with a Guess and Check table. Write your solution as a sentence.

Mr. Ripley's fruit stand sells watermelons for $5 and apples for $2. Last weekend, he sold 40 pieces of fruit (all apples and watermelons) for $107. How many watermelons did he sell?

11-95. Find all points where the graphs of $y=x^2-3x+2$ and $y=2x+8$ intersect.

11-96. **Multiple Choice:** Which of the lines below is parallel to the line $5x-3y=11$?

a. $5x-3y=4$

b. $5x+3y=-2$

c. $3x-5y=11$

d. $3x+5y=-1$

11-97. **Multiple Choice:** Which expression below is a factor of $4x^2+8x-5$?

a. $2x-5$ b. $2x-1$ c. $2x+1$ d. $x+5$

11.3.1 Can I find it?

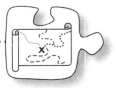

Relation Treasure Hunt

Now that you have many ways to describe a relation, you can use these ways to distinguish between different relations that are given in different representations.

11-98.   TREASURE HUNT

Today your teacher will give you several descriptive clues about different relations. (This information is also available online at www.cpm.org.) For each clue, work with your team (or a partner) to find all the possible matches among the relations posted around the classroom or provided on the resource page. Remember that more than one relation may match each clue. Once you have decided which relation(s) match a given clue, defend your decision to your teacher and receive the next clue. Be sure to record your matches on paper.

Your goal is to find the match (or more than one match) for each of **eight** clues. Once you and your team (or partner) have finished, only one relation will be left unmatched. That relation is the treasure!

11-99.   For each relation graphed below, describe the domain (input) and range (output).

a. 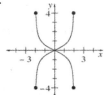   b. 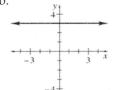   c. 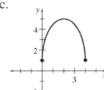   d.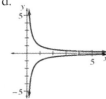

11-100.   For each relation graphed in problem 11-99, explain whether it is a function. If the relation is not a function, give a reason to support your claim.

11-101.   What number is not part of the domain of $f(x) = \frac{3}{x+5}$? How can you tell?

11-102.   Find the equation of the line perpendicular to $5x - 2y = 13$ that passes through the point (60, −20).

11-103.   Find all of the points at which the parabolas below intersect. Write your solution(s) in (x, y) form.

$$y = x^2 + 5x - 4$$
$$y = x^2 + x - 12$$

11-104.   The diagram at right shows one way to represent the fraction $\frac{1}{7}$.

    a.   Draw a similar diagram to represent $\frac{3}{7}$.

    b.   What is $\frac{1}{7} + \frac{3}{7}$? Use your diagram to **justify** your answer.

    c.   Use a new diagram to add $\frac{3}{5} + \frac{4}{5}$.

11-105.   Rewrite each of the expressions below. Avoid leaving negative exponents in your solution.

    a. $\left(\frac{2x}{y^2}\right)^2$ b. $\left(6x^3\right)\left(3x^{-1}y\right)$ c. $\frac{(xy)^{-1}}{(x^2y^3)^{-1}}$

Chapter 11 Closure What have I learned?

Reflection and Synthesis

The activities below offer you a chance to reflect on what you have learned during this chapter. As you work, look for concepts that you feel very comfortable with, ideas that you would like to learn more about, and topics you need more help with. Look for **connections** between ideas as well as **connections** with material you learned previously.

①   TEAM BRAINSTORM

     With your team, brainstorm a list for each of the following topics. Be as detailed as you can. How long can you make your list? Challenge yourselves. Be prepared to share your team's ideas with the class.

Topics: What have you studied in this chapter? What ideas and words were important in what you learned? Remember to be as detailed as you can.

Ways of Thinking: What Ways of Thinking did you use in this chapter? When did you use them?

Connections: What topics, ideas, and words that you learned *before* this chapter are **connected** to the new ideas in this chapter? Again, make your list as long as you can.

② MAKING CONNECTIONS

The following is a list of the vocabulary used in this chapter. The words that appear in bold are new to this chapter. Make sure that you are familiar with all of these words and know what they mean. Refer to the glossary or index for any words that you do not yet understand.

domain	**function**	graph
input	intersection	output
range	**relation**	rule
solution	x-intercept	$x \rightarrow y$ table
y-intercept		

Make a concept map showing all of the **connections** you can find among the key words and ideas listed above. To show a **connection** between two words, draw a line between them and explain the **connection**, as shown in the example below. A word can be **connected** to any other word as long as there is a **justified connection**. For each key word or idea, provide a sketch that illustrates the idea (see the example below).

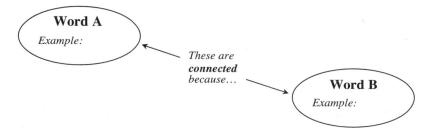

Your teacher may provide you with vocabulary cards to help you get started. If you use the cards to plan your concept map, be sure either to re-draw your concept map on your paper or to glue the vocabulary cards to a poster with all of the **connections** explained for others to see and understand.

While you are making your map, your team may think of related words or ideas that are not listed above. Be sure to include these ideas on your concept map.

③ SUMMARIZING MY UNDERSTANDING

This section gives you an opportunity to show what you know about one or more topics or ideas. Your teacher will give you directions for exactly how to do this.

④ **WHAT HAVE I LEARNED?**

This section will help you evaluate which types of problems you have seen with which you feel comfortable and those with which you need more help. Even if your teacher does not assign this section, it is a good idea to try these problems and find out for yourself what you know and what you need to work on.

Solve each problem as completely as you can. The table at the end of the closure section has answers to these problems. It also tells you where you can find additional help and practice on problems like these.

CL 11-106. For each of the representations below, decide if the relation represented is a function. **Justify** your answer.

a.

x	y
4	8
7	8
45	7
52	–6
7	9
13	0

b.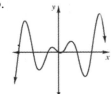

c.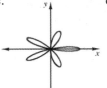

d. $2x + 3y = 4$

CL 11-107. Examine the relation $h(x)$ defined at right. Then estimate the values below.

a. $h(1)$

b. $h(3)$

c. x when $h(x) = 0$

d. $h(-1)$

e. $h(-4)$

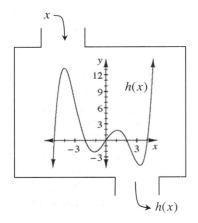

CL 11-108. Consider the parabola $y = 2x^2 + 6x - 20$.

a.   Find this parabola's x- and y-intercepts.

b.   Find where this parabola intersects the line $y = 3x + 1$.

Algebra Connections

CL 11-109. Solve for the given variable, if possible. Be sure to check your solution.

a. $\frac{3x}{5} - x = \frac{1}{2}(18 - 2x)$

b. $\sqrt{3y + 8} = 5$

c. $|2m - 7| = 16$

d. $(-x + 8)^2 \geq 16$

e. $\frac{3x-2}{x+5} = \frac{14}{16}$

f. $12 > |3x + 15|$

CL 11-110. For each system of equations below, find all points of intersection.

a. $2x + 3y = 7$
$-3x - 5y = -13$

b. $y = 2x^2 - 12x + 18$
$y = x^2 + 4x - 10$

c. $y = 2x - 4.5$
$18 = 8x - 4y$

CL 11-111. Simplify the expressions below. Each answer should have no parentheses or negative exponents.

a. $\dfrac{(x+3)^3}{3x^2 - 11x - 70} \div \dfrac{x^2 + 6x + 9}{x - 7}$

b. $\dfrac{(24a^{12}b^0c^{-3})(4a^{-3}c^2)}{(6a^4b^3)^2}$

CL 11-112. Check your answers using the table at the end of the closure section. Which problems do you feel confident about? Which problems were hard? Use the table to make a list of topics you need help on and a list of topics you need to practice more.

⑤ HOW AM I THINKING?

This course focuses on five different **Ways of Thinking**: reversing thinking, justifying, generalizing, making connections, and applying and extending understanding. These are some of the ways in which you think while trying to make sense of a concept or to solve a problem (even outside of math class). During this chapter, you have probably used each Way of Thinking multiple times without even realizing it!

Review each of the Ways of Thinking with your class. Then choose three of these Ways of Thinking that you remember using while working in this chapter. For each Way of Thinking that you choose, show and explain where you used it and how you used it. Describe why thinking in this way helped you solve a particular problem or understand something new. (For instance, explain why you wanted to **generalize** in this particular case, or why it was useful to see these particular **connections**.) Be sure to include examples to demonstrate your thinking.

Answers and Support for Closure Activity #4
What Have I Learned?

Problem	Solution	Need Help?	More Practice
CL 11-106.	a. not a function b. function c. not a function d. function	Lessons 11.1.3 and 11.1.4, Lesson 11.1.4 Math Notes box	Problems 11-29, 11-38(d), 11-40(a), 11-45, 11-86, and 11-100
CL 11-107.	a. 2 b. -4 c. $-5, -2, 0, 2, 4$ d. -2 e. 13	Lesson 11.1.2, Lesson 11.1.4 Math Notes box	Problems 11-20 and 11-38
CL 11-108.	a. x-intercepts $(2, 0)$ and $(-5, 0)$, y-intercept $(0, -20)$ b. approximately $(2.6, 8.8)$ and $(-4.1, -11.2)$	Lessons 11.2.1 and 11.2.2	Problems 11-14, 11-71, 11-76, 11-78(b), 11-90, and 11-95
CL 11-109.	a. 15 b. $y = \frac{17}{3}$ c. $m = \frac{23}{2}, -\frac{9}{2}$ d. $x \le 4$ or $x \ge 12$ e. 3 f. $-9 < x < -1$	Lessons 9.2.2, 10.1.3, 10.1.4, 10.2.1, and 10.2.3 Math Notes boxes	Problems 11-10, 11-35, 11-59, and 11-75
CL 11-110.	a. $(-4, 5)$ b. $(2, 2)$ and $(14, 242)$ c. Infinite solutions because the two lines coincide.	Lessons 11.2.1 and 11.2.2	Problems 11-33, 11-64(b), 11-78, 11-79, 11-90, 11-95, and 11-103
CL 11-111.	a. $\frac{x+3}{3x+10}$ b. $\frac{8a}{3b^6c}$	Lessons 10.1.2 and 10.4.3 Math Notes boxes	Problems 11-13, 11-15, 11-25, 11-36, 11-50, and 11-105

12

Algebraic Extensions

CHAPTER 12   Algebraic Extensions

As the title of this chapter suggests, during this chapter you will revisit and build upon many of the topics you have studied so far in this course. For example, you already have learned how to simplify, multiply, and divide rational expressions. In this chapter, you will develop a method to add and subtract them as well.

You will also revisit quadratics and will apply your techniques for problem solving to solve new kinds of word problems.

Finally, you will pull together the knowledge and tools you have gained throughout this course to solve a series of meaningful and challenging problems.

Guiding Questions

Think about these questions throughout this chapter:

Is there a shortcut?

How can I rewrite it?

What's the connection?

Is there another way?

In this chapter, you will learn:

➢ How to add and subtract rational expressions.

➢ How to factor a difference of squares or a perfect square trinomial quickly without using a generic rectangle.

➢ How to solve word problems involving rates of work and mixtures of quantities.

➢ How to derive the Quadratic Formula by completing the square.

➢ How to provide thorough mathematical justification for predictions and solutions.

Chapter Outline

Section 12.1 You will expand your ability to rewrite expressions by learning new ways to factor special quadratics and to add and subtract rational expressions.

Section 12.2 You will learn how to solve word problems about making mixtures and working together.

$x = \frac{-b \pm \sqrt{b^2 - 4ac}}{2a}$

Section 12.3 You will learn how to derive the Quadratic Formula.

Section 12.4 You will apply the mathematics you have learned throughout this course to analyze a challenging tile pattern, make a prediction about a burning candle, analyze an interesting inequality, and find the maximum area of a pen for a cow.

12.1.1 Is there a shortcut?

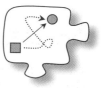

Factoring Shortcuts

Are there any types of quadratics that you can factor quickly without using a generic rectangle? If so, what do these quadratics look like and how can you recognize them? Today your team will examine the factored forms of many different quadratics and look for patterns and shortcuts for factoring certain types of quadratics.

12-1.   SPECIAL QUADRATICS

Your team will be assigned several of the quadratics below to factor (if possible). Look for similarities and differences among the expressions below and their corresponding factored forms. Be prepared to share your factors with the class. Then work as a class to sort the quadratics into groups based on the patterns you find in their factored forms.

a. $x^2 - 49$ b. $x^2 + 2x - 24$ c. $x^2 - 10x + 25$

d. $9x^2 + 12x + 4$ e. $5x^2 - 4x - 1$ f. $4x^2 - 25$

g. $x^2 - 6x + 9$ h. $x^2 - 36$ i. $7x^2 - 20x - 3$

j. $4x^2 + 20x + 25$ k. $x^2 + 4$ l. $9x^2 - 1$

12-2.   Which of the following quadratics fit the patterns you found in problem 12-1? Factor each of the following expressions using your new shortcuts, if possible.

a. $25x^2 - 1$ b. $x^2 - 5x - 36$ c. $x^2 + 8x + 16$

d. $9x^2 - 12x + 4$ e. $9x^2 + 4$ f. $9x^2 - 100$

12-3.   Special quadratics, like $9x^2 - 100$ in part (f) of problem 12-2, can be factored quickly once you discover the pattern. But why do the patterns you found in problem 12-1 work?

a.   A quadratic in the form $a^2x^2 - b^2$ is called a **difference of squares**. Use a generic rectangle to prove that $a^2x^2 - b^2 = (ax - b)(ax + b)$. Be ready to share your work with the class.

b.   A quadratic in the form $a^2x^2 + 2abx + b^2$ is called a **perfect square trinomial**. Use a generic rectangle to prove that $a^2x^2 + 2abx + b^2 = (ax + b)^2$. Be ready to share your work with the class.

12-4.   In your Learning Log, describe how to factor a difference of squares
         and a perfect square trinomial. Be sure to include an example of
         each type. Title this entry "Factoring Shortcuts" and include today's
         date.

12-5.   Use your factoring shortcuts to simplify the following expressions.

   a. $\dfrac{x^2-9}{x^2-6x+9}$

   b. $\dfrac{2x+5}{4x^2-25} \cdot \dfrac{2x-5}{x+7}$

   c. $\dfrac{x^2+x-20}{x^2-16} \cdot \dfrac{x^2+9x+20}{x^2+10x+25}$

   d. $\dfrac{x^2+12x+36}{x^2-25} \div \dfrac{x+6}{x+5}$

12-6.   Solve the following equations for x.

   a. $4x - 6y = 20$

   b. $\frac{1}{2}(x-6) = 9$

   c. $\frac{4}{3x} + \frac{6}{x} = 9$

   d. $3 + \sqrt{5-x} = 5$

12-7.   Simplify each expression below. Your answer should contain no parentheses and no
         negative exponents.

   a. $(-\frac{2}{3}x^5 y^{1/3})^0$

   b. $(25^{1/2} x^5)(4x^{-6})$

   c. $5t^{-3}$

   d. $\left(\dfrac{x^4 y}{x}\right)^3$

12-8.   Examine the graphs of relations $f(x)$ and $g(x)$ at right.
         Use the graph to approximate the values below (if
         possible).

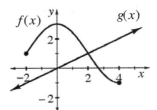

   a. $f(0)$ b. $g(4)$ c. $f(5)$

   d. $g(0)$ e. $g(2)$ f. $f(2)$

12-9.   Solve the equations and inequalities below by completing the square.

   a. $x^2 - 2x - 3 \le 0$

   b. $x^2 + 4x = 3$

   c. $x^2 + 12x + 39 > 0$

   d. $x^2 - 3x - 13.75 = 0$

12-10.   Describe how you add and subtract fractions that have a common denominator.

   a.   Add or subtract the fractions below. Draw a diagram to show that your answer is correct.

        i. $\frac{8}{11} - \frac{3}{11}$

        ii. $\frac{x}{6} + \frac{2}{6}$

   b.   What if you are given two fractions to add or subtract and the denominators are not the same? Add the fractions below and check your result on your calculator.

        $$\frac{1}{3} + \frac{2}{5}$$

12.1.2 How can I rewrite it?

Adding and Subtracting Rational Expressions

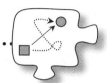

So far in this course you have learned a lot about rational expressions. You have learned how to simplify complex algebraic fractions by factoring the numerators and denominators. You have also learned how to multiply and divide rational expressions. What else is there to learn? Today you will develop a method to add and subtract algebraic fractions.

12-11.   With your team, review your responses for homework problem 12-10. Verify that everyone obtained the same answers and be prepared to share how you added fractions with the class.

   $\frac{8}{11} - \frac{3}{11}$ $\frac{x}{6} + \frac{2}{6}$ $\frac{1}{3} + \frac{2}{5}$

12-12.   Examine each expression below. For each one:

   •   Use your understanding of adding fractions to add the algebraic expressions.

   •   Simplify your solutions, if possible.

   a. $\frac{2x}{2x^2+x-21} + \frac{7}{2x^2+x-21}$

   b. $\frac{5x}{x^2-2x-3} - \frac{15}{x^2-2x-3}$

   c. $\frac{3x+9}{8x^2-50} - \frac{x+4}{8x^2-50}$

   d. $\frac{x^2+5x-2}{3x^2+2x-8} + \frac{2x^2-3x-6}{3x^2+2x-8}$

12-13.   What if the algebraic fractions do not have the same denominator? With your team, discuss how to add the fractions below. Be prepared to **justify** your strategy with the class.

a. $\dfrac{x}{3x+1} + \dfrac{2x^2-2}{(x-5)(3x+1)}$ b. $\dfrac{9-3x}{(x+3)(x-3)} + \dfrac{2x}{x+3}$

12-14.   Estacia wants to learn more about excluded values.

a.   Explain to Estacia why x cannot be 4 in the expression $\dfrac{x+2}{x-4}$.

b.   Find the excluded values of x in each of the expressions of problem 12-13.

c.   With your team, create an expression that has the excluded values of $x \neq -6$ and $x \neq \frac{1}{3}$. Be prepared to share your expression to the class.

12-15.   In your Learning Log, explain how to add and subtract rational expressions. Be sure to include an example. Title this entry "Adding and Subtracting Rational Expressions" and include today's date.

12-16.   Use your understanding of adding fractions to add the algebraic expressions below. Then simplify your solutions, if possible.

a. $\dfrac{5m+18}{m+3} + \dfrac{4m+9}{m+3}$ b. $\dfrac{3a^2+a-1}{a^2-2a+1} - \dfrac{2a^2-a+2}{a^2-2a+1}$

12-17.   Solve the equations and inequalities below. Check your solutions, if possible.

a. $\left|5x+8\right| \geq -4$ b. $x^2 + x - 20 < 0$

c. $2x^2 - 6x = -5$ d. $\dfrac{5}{9} - \dfrac{x}{3} = \dfrac{4}{9}$

12-18.   Multiply the expressions below using generic rectangles.

a. $(5m-1)(m+2)$ b. $(6-x)(2+x)$

c. $(5x-y)^2$ d. $3x(2x-5y+4)$

Algebra Connections

12-19.   Examine the graphs of each relation below. Decide if each is a function. Then describe the domain and range of each.

a.

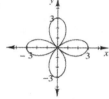

b.

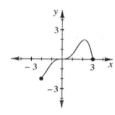

12-20.   Graph the function $g(x) = \frac{x+2}{x-1}$ on graph paper and name all x- and y-intercepts. What happens at $x = 1$?

12-21.   If $f(x) = 3x - 9$ and $g(x) = -x^2$, find:

a. $f(-2)$ b. $g(-2)$ c. x if $f(x) = 0$ d. $g(m)$

12.1.3   How can I rewrite it?

· ·

More Adding and Subtracting Rational Expressions

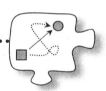

Today you will complete your work with rational expressions. By the end of this lesson you will know how to add, subtract, multiply, and divide rational expressions.

12-22.   Review what you learned in Lesson 12.1.2 by adding and subtracting the expressions below. Leave your solutions as simplified as possible.

a. $\frac{5}{8} + \frac{1}{6}$

b. $\frac{8}{9} - \frac{2}{3}$

c. $\frac{x+5}{x+2} + \frac{2x+1}{x+2}$

d. $\frac{x^2-3}{(x+5)(2x-1)} + \frac{x}{2x-1}$

12-23.   Examine the expression below.

$$\frac{2x-1}{3x^2+13x+4} + \frac{x+3}{x^2-3x-28}$$

a.   With your team, decide how you can alter the expression so that the fractions have a common denominator. Be ready to share your idea with the class.

b.   If you have not already do so, add the fractions. Then simplify the result, if possible.

c.   Repeat the process to subtract the expressions below. Simplify the result, if possible.

$$\frac{2}{x+4} - \frac{4x-x^2}{x^2-16}$$

12-24.   PULLING IT ALL TOGETHER

You now know how to add, subtract, multiply, and divide rational expressions. Pull this all together by simplifying the following expressions.

a. $\dfrac{x^2-3x-10}{x^2-4x-5} \div \dfrac{x^2-7x-18}{2x^2-5x-7}$

b. $\dfrac{2x^2+x}{(2x+1)^2} - \dfrac{3}{2x+1}$

c. $\dfrac{15x-20}{x-5} \cdot \dfrac{x^2-2x-15}{3x^2+5x-12}$

d. $\dfrac{4}{2x+3} + \dfrac{x^2-x-2}{2x^2+5x+3}$

e. $\dfrac{6x-4}{3x^2-17x+10} - \dfrac{1}{x^2-2x-15}$

f. $\dfrac{x^2-x-2}{4x^2-7x-2} \div \dfrac{x^2-2x-3}{3x^2-8x-3}$

 METHODS AND MEANINGS

MATH NOTES

Adding and Subtracting Rational Expressions

In order to add and subtract fractions, the fractions must have a common denominator. One way to do this is to change each fraction so that the denominator is the **least common multiple** of the denominators. For the example at right, the least common multiple of $(x+3)(x+2)$ and $x+2$ is $(x+3)(x+2)$.

$$\frac{4}{(x+2)(x+3)} + \frac{2x}{x+2}$$

The denominator of the first fraction already is the least common multiple. To get a common denominator in the second fraction, multiply the fraction by $\frac{(x+3)}{(x+3)}$, a form of the number 1.

$$= \frac{4}{(x+2)(x+3)} + \frac{2x}{x+2} \cdot \frac{(x+3)}{(x+3)}$$

Multiply the numerator and denominator of the second term.

$$= \frac{4}{(x+2)(x+3)} + \frac{2x(x+3)}{(x+2)(x+3)}$$

Distribute the numerator, if necessary.

$$= \frac{4}{(x+2)(x+3)} + \frac{2x^2+6x}{(x+2)(x+3)}$$

Add, factor, and simplify the result.

$$= \frac{2x^2+6x+4}{(x+2)(x+3)} = \frac{2(x+1)(x+2)}{(x+2)(x+3)} = \frac{2(x+1)}{(x+3)}$$

12-25.   Add, subtract, multiply, or divide the following rational expressions. Simplify your answers, if possible.

a. $\frac{2x}{3x^2+16x+5} + \frac{10}{3x^2+16x+5}$

b. $\frac{x^2-x-12}{3x^2-11x-4} \cdot \frac{3x^2-20x-7}{x^2-9}$

c. $\frac{2x^2+8x-10}{2x^2+15x+25} \div \frac{4x^2+20x-24}{2x^2+x-10}$

d. $\frac{16x-12}{4x^2+5x-6} - \frac{3}{x+2}$

12-26.   Examine the graph of $f(x)=|x-3|+1$ at right.
          Use the graph to find the values listed below.

          a. $f(3)$ b. $f(0)$

          c. $f(4)$ d. $f(-1)$

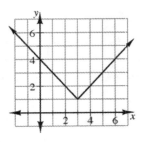

12-27.   Use the graph of $f(x)=|x-3|+1$ in problem 12-26
          to solve the equations and inequalities below. It may
          be helpful to copy the graph onto graph paper first.

          a. $|x-3|+1=1$ b. $|x-3|+1\leq 4$

          c. $|x-3|+1=3$ d. $|x-3|+1>2$

12-28.   Solve the quadratic below *twice*: once by factoring and using the Zero Product
          Property and once by completing the square. Verify that the solutions match.

          $$x^2+14x+33=0$$

12-29.   Match each graph below with its domain.

          a.   D: All values of x b.   D: $x>-2$ c.   D: $x\leq 3$

          1)   2)   3)

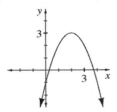   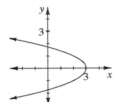   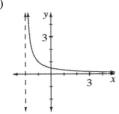

12-30.   Graph the two functions below and find all points where they intersect. List all
          points in the form (x, y).

          $$f(x)=x^2-3x-10$$
          $$g(x)=-5x-7$$

12.2.1   How can I solve it?

Solving Work Problems

So far in this course you have learned to solve many different types of word problems using a variety of tools. During Section 12.2, you will complete your understanding of solving word problems by focusing on two new types: those that involve rates of work and those that involve a mixture of quantities.

12-31.   MOWING THE LAWN

The National Mall, located in Washington, D.C., is a mile-long rectangular lawn surrounded by several museums and famous monuments. It has been the site of many major historical and political events.

The lawn is cared for by two teams of gardeners. It takes one team (working alone) 10 hours to mow the lawn, while it takes the other team 15 hours to cut the entire lawn area.

Your Task: With your team, determine how long it would take to mow the entire lawn if both teams of gardeners work together. Create a diagram on graph paper to represent the work done by each team. Write and solve an equation for this situation. Be sure to define your variable(s).

Discussion Points

What is the goal of this task?

About how many hours would it take to mow the lawn if they worked together? Make an estimate. Is it more or less than 10 hours? Why?

Does it matter how big the lawn is? Why or why not?

How much of the lawn does each team of gardeners mow in one hour? How can you tell?

12-32. To help solve problem 12-31, analyze what each piece of information gives you.

a. One team of gardeners can mow the lawn in 10 hours. How much of the lawn can this team mow in one hour? Draw a diagram to represent how much of the lawn this team can mow in one hour.

b. The other team of gardeners can mow the lawn in 15 hours. How much of the lawn can this second team mow in one hour? Draw a diagram to represent how much of the lawn this team can mow in one hour.

c. When the two teams of gardeners work together, how much of the lawn is mowed per hour? Explain how you got your answer.

d. How long will it take for both teams of gardeners to mow the entire lawn? Explain how you got your answer.

e. Write and solve an equation to represent this situation. Be sure to define your variables.

─────────────   *Further Guidance*   ─────────────
                 section ends here.

12-33. Hong can staple the programs for graduation in 30 minutes. However, since Eva has an electric stapler, it only takes her 10 minutes. If they work together, how long will it take to staple the programs? Be ready to share your work with the class.

12-34. It takes Frederick 8 minutes to wash his dad's truck. When he works with his sister, it takes them only 6 minutes. How long would it take his sister to wash the truck alone? Write and solve an equation for this situation.

12-35. Ellie estimates that it would take 3 students 2 hours to hang 50 streamers for the prom. If she has 5 students hang streamers for 3 hours, how many streamers could be hung? Explain how you found your answer.

12-36.   Solve the quadratic equation below *twice*, once by completing the square and once by using the Quadratic Formula. Leave all solutions in exact form. Verify that your solutions from each method match.

$$x^2 + 11 = 8x$$

12-37.   Susan can paint her living room in 2 hours. Her friend, Jaime, estimates it would take him 3 hours to paint the same room. If they work together, how long will it take them to paint Susan's living room?

12-38.   Write and solve an equation (or system of equations) for the situation below. Define your variable(s) and write your solution as a sentence.

Jessica has 147 coins that are all dimes and quarters. The number of quarters is 6 fewer than twice the number of dimes. What is the value of her coins?

12-39.   Which of the following expressions are equivalent to $12x^6$? (Note: More than one answer is possible!)

a. $3(2x^3)^2$

b. $(6x^8)(2x^{-2})$

c. $(144x^{12})^{1/2}$

d. $\dfrac{60x^{10}y}{5x^4y}$

12-40.   Find the equation of $f(x)$ graphed at right.

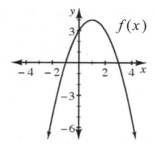

12-41.   Solve each equation or inequality below, if possible. Check your solution.

a. $-(x-3)(x+1) = 4$

b. $10|x-3| > 40$

c. $(x-5)^3 = 8$

Chapter 12: Algebraic Extensions

12.2.2 How can I solve it?

Solving Percent Mixture Problems

Today you will continue to develop ways to apply your problem-solving techniques to solve word problems as you examine a new type of problem: percent mixture problems.

12-42. GET OUT THE VOTE

In an election for school president, 40% of 7th graders and 90% of 8th graders voted for John. If 1000 students voted in the election, and if John ended up with 72% of the votes, how many students are in each grade at John's school? Assume that John's school only contains 7th and 8th grades. Explain how you found your answer.

12-43. This year, the math club decided to make candy gifts for graduates. They will mix Choco-nuts, which cost $1 per ounce, with Munchies, which cost $2 per ounce. They would like their candy bags to weigh 4 ounces and cost $5.40. How much of each type of candy should be used per bag?

12-44. Antoine works in the paint department at his local hardware store. He is trying to create a new color of paint using two different colors in stock: powder blue, which is made with 2% blue (the rest is white), and spring blue, which is 10% blue (the rest is white). He wants to end up with one gallon of paint made with 4% blue. How much of each color should he use?

12-45. In your Learning Log, describe what you know about solving percent mixture problems. Explain in your own words how to set up an equation or use Guess and Check to help solve this type of problem. Be sure to include an example. Title this entry "Percent Mixture Problems" and include today's date.

12-46. How much coffee costing $6 a pound should be mixed with 3 pounds of coffee costing $4 per pound to create a mixture costing $4.75 per pound?

12-47. If $g(x) = \sqrt{x-3} + 1$, find the values below. If there is no solution, **justify** your conclusion.

a. $g(7)$ b. $g(4)$ c. $g(8)$ d. $g(2)$

12-48. Graph the function $f(x) = |x-3| - 1$ and label all of its special points.

12-49. Add, subtract, multiply, or divide the expressions below. Leave your answer as simplified as possible.

a. $\dfrac{4x^2-13x+3}{5x^2+23x-10} \cdot \dfrac{5x-2}{x^2+6x-27} \cdot \dfrac{x^2+5x-36}{4x-1}$ b. $\dfrac{x^2-9}{x^2+6x+9} \div \dfrac{x^2-x-6}{x^2+4}$

c. $6 + \dfrac{3}{x+1}$ d. $\dfrac{5}{x} - \dfrac{10}{x^2+2x}$

12-50. Find the point(s) of intersection of the line and parabola below. Be sure to check each point by substituting it back into both equations.

$$y = 3x^2 - 5x + 2$$
$$y = 4x + 2$$

12-51. Solve the following quadratic equations by completing the square, if possible. Leave your answers in *exact* form. Check your solution(s).

a. $x^2 - 14x = -24$ b. $x^2 + 6x - 9 = 0$

c. $x^2 - 198x + 9797 = 0$ d. $x^2 - 9x = 15.75$

12.3.1   How can I derive it?
••• $x = \dfrac{-b \pm \sqrt{b^2-4ac}}{2a}$

Deriving the Quadratic Formula

In Chapter 9 you learned how to solve quadratic equations with the Quadratic Formula and the Zero Product Property. At the time, you had not yet learned how to complete the square of a quadratic equation and thus were not able to derive the Quadratic Formula by completing the square. You now have the tools to derive the Quadratic Formula by completing the square. To do this, you will start with the equation $ax^2 + bx + c = 0$ and will solve for x to prove that:

$$x = \dfrac{-b \pm \sqrt{b^2-4ac}}{2a}$$

12-52.   DERIVATION OF THE QUADRATIC FORMULA

The steps below outline a proof that if
$ax^2 + bx + c = 0$, then $x = \frac{-b \pm \sqrt{b^2 - 4ac}}{2a}$.

Fold a piece of lined paper in half
vertically, make a crease, and then
unfold the paper. Copy the algebraic
steps shown below onto the left-hand
side of your paper. Write your answer
to each question to the right of the
corresponding algebraic step.

Problem: Solve the equation $ax^2 + bx + c = 0$.

1. $ax^2 + bx = -c$ What was done to get this?

2. $x^2 + \frac{b}{a}x = -\frac{c}{a}$ What was done to get this?

Now complete the square.

3. $x^2 + \frac{b}{a}x + \frac{b^2}{4a^2} = \frac{b^2}{4a^2} - \frac{c}{a}$ Why did we choose $\frac{b^2}{4a^2}$?

4. $(x + \frac{b}{2a})^2 = \frac{b^2}{4a^2} - \frac{c}{a}$ What was done to get this?

5. $(x + \frac{b}{2a})^2 = \frac{b^2 - 4ac}{4a^2}$ What was done to get this?

You're very close! Now solve for x.

6. $x + \frac{b}{2a} = \pm \frac{\sqrt{b^2 - 4ac}}{2a}$ Why is there a $\pm$ symbol?

7. $x = -\frac{b}{2a} \pm \frac{\sqrt{b^2 - 4ac}}{2a}$ What was done to get this?

Finally, simplify the result.

8. $x = \frac{-b \pm \sqrt{b^2 - 4ac}}{2a}$ What was done to get this result?

12-53.   Use the Quadratic Formula to solve the following quadratic equations. Be sure to
check your solutions, if possible.

a. $8x^2 + 14x - 15 = 0$ b. $5m + 0.5m^2 - 3 = 0$

c. $k^2 - 10k = -30$ d. $4x^2 - 25 = 0$

12-54. Solve the quadratics below by first completing the square. Leave your solutions in exact form.

a. $x^2 - 10x + 22 = 0$ b. $x^2 + 2x = 18$

12-55. Ms. Speedi's favorite recipe for fruit punch requires 12% apple juice. How much pure apple juice should she add to 2 gallons of punch that has 8% apple juice to meet her standards?

12-56. Graph the function $g(x) = \sqrt{x - 3} + 1$ on graph paper. Describe its domain and range.

12-57. Use the graph of $f(x)$ at right to find the following values.

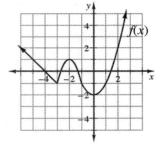

a. $f(1)$ b. $f(-6)$

c. $f(0)$ d. $f(-3)$

12-58. Factor the quadratics below using any method.

a. $x^2 - 81$ b. $x^2 + 12x + 36$

c. $4x^2 - 4x - 3$ d. $16x^2 - 25$

12-59. Where do the two parabolas below intersect? Show how you know.

$$y = x^2 + 4x - 2$$
$$y = x^2 - 3x + 5$$

12-60. Write three different single-term expressions that are equivalent to x^{-2}. At least one expression should use division and another should use multiplication. Show how you know that your expressions are equivalent.

Chapter 12: Algebraic Extensions

12.4.1 How can I make a prediction?

Using Data and Trend Lines to Make Predictions

In today's activity, you will use data to make a prediction. As you work, remember to find all the **connections** you can between different representations.

12-61.   THE BURNING CANDLE

Today is your friend's birthday. You want to surprise her by walking into the room carrying a piece of cake with a lit candle. However, you only have one candle and you are not sure it will stay lit long enough. Can you predict when the candle will burn out?

Your Task: Collect data for your burning candle that will help you predict when it will burn out. Collect data for at least two minutes (but no more than three minutes to save the candle for the surprise!). Then analyze the data and make a prediction. Your analysis must include:

- At least three representations of the data.

- An explanation of how you can use the equation to determine when the candle will burn out.

Discussion Points

What data should be collected as the candle burns?

What should the graph of the data look like?

Which representation can help you determine the most accurate prediction?

Further Guidance

12-62.   Start by collecting data from the burning candle. Record its weight at various times after it has started to burn. (The candle's weight is easier and safer to measure than its height.) Make sure you let the candle burn for at least two minutes, but no more than three minutes. Also be sure you get at least five data points. When all the data is collected, blow the candle out.

12-63.   Let x represent the time (in seconds) since the candle started to burn, and let y represent the weight of the candle. Make an $x \to y$ table showing the data you collected for the burning candle.

12-64.   With your team, decide how the axes should be scaled for a graph of the candle data. Then graph the data you have collected. Agree with your teammates on a trend line that best fits the data, and add it to your graph.

12-65.   Use your trend line to determine when the candle will burn out as you answer the questions below.

   a.   Write the equation for your trend line.

   b.   What do you know about the point on the graph at which the candle burns out? Do you know the value of either x or y at this point?

   c.   Use your equation and your answer to part (b) to solve for the time when the candle will burn out.

12-66.   Aura thinks the solution to the systems of equations at right is (–2, 4) while Edison thinks the solution is (2, –2). Teresito thinks they are both wrong. Who is correct? **Justify** your answer.

$$3x + 2y = 2$$
$$5x - 12 = y$$

12-67.   Evaluate the expression below when $x = 27$ and $y = 16$.

$$6x^{2/3}y^{1/4} \cdot x^{-1}y^{1/2}$$

12-68.   Graph the function $h(x) = -\sqrt{3 - x}$. Use inequalities to describe its domain and range.

12-69.   If $f(x) = \frac{-5}{x+2}$ and $g(x) = (x - 2)^3$, find each output value below (if possible). If it is not possible, explain why not.

   a. $f(-2)$ b. $g(-1)$ c. $g(4)$ d. $f(-7) + g(1)$ e. $f(3) - g(2)$

12-70.   James used the Distributive Property and got $6m - 12$. Find an expression that he could have started with.

12-71.   Find all of the points at which the parabolas below intersect. Write your solution(s) in (x, y) form.

$$y = x^2 - x + 12$$
$$y = 2x^2 + 3x + 7$$

12.4.2   What do I know about the pattern?

Analyzing Non-linear Tile Patterns

Remember tile patterns? When you first studied tile patterns, most of the patterns you studied grew linearly. You now have the tools to analyze more complex patterns and can apply what you know about non-linear equations. Today your team will use multiple representations to analyze and make predictions about a complex tile pattern.

12-72.   TEAM PATTERN CHALLENGE

Your teacher will assign your team one of the tile patterns below to analyze.

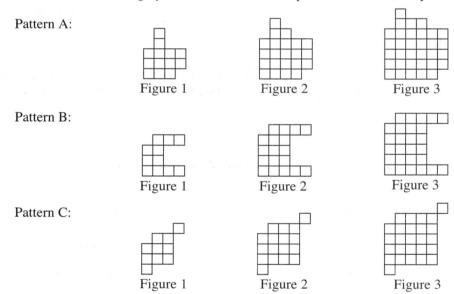

Pattern A:

Figure 1   Figure 2   Figure 3

Pattern B:

Figure 1   Figure 2   Figure 3

Pattern C:

Figure 1   Figure 2   Figure 3

Your Task: With your team, analyze your pattern completely. Create a stand-alone poster that shows all the things you discovered about your tile pattern. Your poster must also include the information described below.

Problem continues on next page →

12-72.   *Problem continued from previous page.*

Pattern Analysis:

- Figures 0 through 4.
- An $x \rightarrow y$ table.
- A graph.
- A sketch and description of the 100th figure.
- A rule for the xth figure.

Using the Rule:

- How can you rewrite your rule? Use algebra to simplify your rule.
- Use your rule to make predictions about figures in your pattern that you cannot draw.
    - How many tiles are in Figure 538?
    - *Pattern A*: Which figure will have 555,022 tiles?
      Pattern B: Which figure will have 491,403 tiles?
      Pattern C: Which figure will have 608,401 tiles?

12-73.   If a tile pattern can be described by the equation $y = (x-1)(x+1) + x + 2$, where x represents the figure number and y represents the number of tiles, find each of the following.

a.   The number of tiles in Figure 307.

b.   The number of the figure that contains 169,333 tiles.

12-74.   Solve the equations and inequalities below. Write your solutions in exact form.

a. $\frac{3}{4} - \frac{x}{3} = \frac{7-x}{4}$ b. $(b-4)^2 < 12$

c. $|3+x| - 9 \le 21$ d. $5n^2 - 11n + 2 = 0$

12-75.   Graph the parabola described by the following equation by finding its x-intercepts and vertex.

$$y = 3x^2 - 10x + 2$$

12-76. For $f(x) = \frac{x^2}{x+5}$ and $g(x) = \sqrt{3x-2}$, find the following, if possible.

a. $f(6)$ b. $g(17)$ c. $f(-5)$ d. $g(-2)$

e. $g(-1) - f(2)$ f. $f(4) + g(2)$ g. $g(x+2)$ h. $f(x-1)$

12-77. Add or subtract the following rational expressions. Then simplify your solutions, if possible.

a. $\frac{x-4}{2x^2+9x-5} + \frac{x+3}{x^2+5x}$ b. $\frac{4x^2-11x+6}{2x^2-x-6} - \frac{x+2}{2x+3}$

12-78. **Multiple Choice:** Which of the following expressions is equivalent to $x^2 - 12x + 40$?

a. $(x-6)^2 + 4$ b. $(x-6)^2 + 28$

c. $(x-12)^2 + 4$ d. $(x-12)^2$

12-79. Examine the graph of the relation at right.

a. Use inequalities to name its domain and range.

b. Is this relation a function? How can you tell?

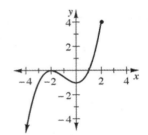

12-80. If a tile pattern can be described by the equation $y = (x-1)(x+2) + x$, where x represents the figure number and y represents the number of tiles, find each of the following.

a. The number of tiles in Figure 211.

b. The number of the figure that contains 6558 tiles.

12-81. Erika can mow her family's lawn in 3 hours. Her little brother can do it in 5 hours. How long will it take them to mow the lawn if they work together?

12-82. Find the equation of the line parallel to $3x + 2y = 10$ that goes through the point $(4, -7)$.

12-83. Rich has $1,268,714 and is spending $2,742 per day. Fred, on the other hand, has $231,384 and is saving $100 per day. When will they have the same amount of money saved? How much will each have at that time?

12-84.   **Multiple Choice:** For which of the following equations or inequalities is $x = -1$ a solution?

   a. $(x+3)^2 > 4$ b. $\frac{x+5}{2} = 2x^2$ c. $\sqrt{x+6} = 25$ d. $x^2 + 5x + 6 = 0$

12.4.3   What do I know about the inequality?

Investigating a Complex Function

Over the course of this year, you have studied many different kinds of functions and inequalities: linear, quadratic, absolute values, square roots, and others. Today you will use the tools you have learned to analyze a new and interesting inequality.

12-85.   FUNKY FUNCTION

   The following relation combines two functions you have studied to make a new kind of graph.

$$f(x) = \left| 3 - 2x - x^2 \right| + 2$$

   Your Task: With your team, create a *complete* description of the graph of $f(x)$.

Discussion Points

What does a complete description of a graph include?

How can you graph a relation when
you have no idea what it will look like?

Apply and Extend

12-86.   For the function $f(x) = \left| 3 - 2x - x^2 \right| + 2$, find $f(14)$.

12-87.   Use your graph and rule to find every x-value for which $\left| 3 - 2x - x^2 \right| + 2 = 6$.

12-88.   What if the equation in problem 12-85 were an inequality instead? Consider the inequality $y > \left| 3 - 2x - x^2 \right| + 2$. How would you need to change your graph to represent the solutions for $y > \left| 3 - 2x - x^2 \right| + 2$? **Justify** your conclusion.

12-89.   Is $(-5, 7)$ a solution to $y < \sqrt{x^2 + 24}$? Show how you know.

12-90.   The graphs of several relations are shown below. Decide if each is a function. If the relation is not a function, explain why not.

a. 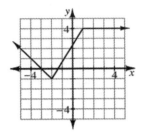   b. 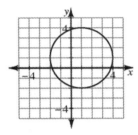   c.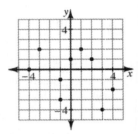

12-91.   Solve the quadratics below by completing the square. Leave your solutions in exact form.

a. $x^2 - 6x - 12 = 0$ b. $x^2 - 3 = 4x$

12-92.   Determine the number of solutions for each of the quadratics below. Note: You do not need to solve the quadratics.

a. $(x - 5)^2 = -6$ b. $312x^2 + 514x + 181 = 0$

c. $(x + 3)^2 - 10 = 0$ d. $4x^2 + 49 = 28x$

12-93.   Jeremiah inherited his grandmother's very large coin collection at the end of the year 2000. Since then, he has been giving away or selling the coins from the collection. The table at right shows the decreasing number of coins in his collection for the past six years.

Year	# of Coins
2000	1617
2001	1552
2002	1498
2003	1453
2004	1401
2005	1344

a.   Find the equation of a line that best fits Jeremiah's data.

b.   At this rate, when should Jeremiah expect to be out of coins?

12-94.   If $f(-1) = 7$ and $f(3) = 8$, and if the graph of $f(x)$ is a line:

a.   Graph the line on graph paper.

b.   Find the equation for $f(x)$.

c.   If $g(x)$ is a line that is perpendicular to $f(x)$, what is its slope?

12.4.4   What is the largest area?

Using Algebra to Find a Maximum

In this final activity, you will **connect** and **apply** much of your knowledge from throughout the course to solve a challenging problem.

12-95.   FENCING LESSONS

Lucy wants to be a farmer, just like her dad. Her father says he will give her some cows to raise if she can build them a good pen. Lucy saves her money and buys 30 meters of fencing material. She will use it to build a rectangular pen against one wall of her family's barn, as shown in the picture at right.

Lucy has come to you for help. She wants to build a pen for her cows that gives them as much possible area to roam. How long should each side of the fence be to give the cows as much roaming area as possible? How can you convince Lucy that the pen is the largest?

Your Tasks:

- Create a poster showing all four representations of this situation.

- On your poster, include a drawing of the pen with the largest possible area. State its dimensions (width and height) and its area.

- Use multiple representations to **justify** your conclusion that this is the largest pen.

Discussion Points

What is the goal of this problem?

What can x and y represent in this situation?

What are the possible dimensions
of the rectangular pen?

How can you collect and represent data
about the different-sized pens?

12-96.   MAKING A TABLE

Start by trying out some different-sized pens to see which ones appear to give the largest area. Your teacher will show you how to use string to make models of possible pens.

a.   Start an $x \rightarrow y$ table for this situation. Let x be the length of the sides of the pen that are attached to the barn and let y represent the enclosed area. Use your string model to try out at least four other sets of pen dimensions. Calculate the area for each pen you try and enter your data into your table.

b.   Of all the pens you have tried so far, which dimensions have created the largest possible roaming area for the cows? Do you think this is the largest area possible? Why or why not?

12-97.   MAKING A GRAPH

A graph can help you analyze the data.

a.   Graph the data from problem 12-96. Be careful about how you scale your axes, so that all the possible pens will fit on your graph.

b.   Is there a point on the graph where x is almost as big as it can possibly be? Do you have a point on your graph where x is almost as small as it can possibly be? If you are missing pens like these, build an example of each one using your string, enter the lengths and areas in your table, and plot the points on your graph.

c.   Should the x-intercepts be included on your graph? Discuss this with your team and **justify** your conclusions. What do the x-intercepts of this graph represent?

12-98.   ANALYZING THE GRAPH

a.   Looking at the points you have plotted so far, can you see what the general shape of the graph will be? If so, sketch in what you think the whole graph should look like. If not, build some more pens with your string to fill in the sections of the graph where you do not have enough points. When you see the general shape of the graph, sketch it.

b.   Find the point on your graph representing the pen with the greatest area. What are the dimensions of this pen?

c.   Use your graph to approximate the greatest possible enclosed area.

Algebra Connections

12-99.   WRITING AN EQUATION

      a.   If length of the sides that are attached to the barn are x meters long, and if she has only 30 meters of barbed wire, write an expression for the width of the pen in terms of x.

      b.   Now write an equation for y, the area of the space enclosed by the fence, in terms of x. Simplify your equation.

      c.   What kind of graph should this equation have? Does it match your graph?

      d.   In your equation from part (b), set $y = 0$ and find the roots of the resulting equation. Does your graph from problem 12-98 confirm these roots?

      e.   Use your equation to find the vertex of the graph. Does your graph confirm this result?

      f.   Use your new results to find the largest possible roaming area Lucy can give her cows. What are the dimensions of this pen? Is this answer more precise than the one you got from your graph? How do you know?

12-100.   SHOWING YOUR WORK

Finally, put together a poster showing your work on this problem. Be sure to include all four representations of the situation. Use the equation and the graph to **justify** to Lucy which dimensions the pen should have.

12-101.   Find the lowest point of the graph of the function $f(x) = 3x^2 + 15x - 18$. Explain how you know it is the lowest.

12-102.   Solve each equation.

      a. $\sqrt{y^2 + 5} = 3$ b. $\frac{x^2 + x - 6}{x + 3} = 6$

12-103.   Find the point(s) of intersection of the system of equations below. Show all your work.

$$y = 5x - 22$$
$$y = x^2 - 6x + 8$$

12-104.   Graph the function $f(x) = \frac{5}{x-2}$. Use inequalities to describe its domain and range.

12-105.   How much candy costing $8 a pound should be mixed with 6 pounds of candy costing $10 a pound to create a mixture costing $8.50 a pound?

12-106.   Write and solve an equation to answer the question below.

Lorena and Lena both work in the library. Lorena has already returned 38 books to the shelves and can shelve 16 books an hour on average. Lena, on the other hand, has already returned 52 books to the shelves and can shelve 20 books per hour on average. If together they started with a total of 252 books to return on the shelves, how much longer should it take them?

12-107.   Find the point of intersection of the two functions below using any method. Describe how you found your solution.

$$y = 2x + 9$$
$$y = x^2 - 2x - 3$$

12-108.   Find the equation of the line perpendicular to $3x - y = 4$ that goes through the point $(-12, 4)$.

12-109.   Graph the inequality $y > |x - 2| + 1$ on graph paper.

12-110.   Determine the number of solutions for each of the quadratics below. *Note*: You do not need to solve the quadratics.

a. $(x - 2)^2 = -3$ b. $6x^2 - x - 2 = 0$

c. $4x^2 - 4x + 1 = 0$ d. $427x^2 + 731x - 280 = 0$

Algebra Connections

Additional Topics 1.4

Polynomial Division

This lesson is designed to follow Lesson 8.3.3.

In Chapter 5, you developed a strategy to multiply polynomials. Today, you will **reverse your thinking** to develop a strategy to divide polynomials. As you work today, use the questions below to stimulate mathematical conversation:

How can we represent it?

Will this strategy always work? If not, is there another strategy?

How can we verify our solution?

AT-29. Use a generic rectangle to multiply $(x + 2)(3x - 5)$.

    a. What is $(3x^2 + x - 10) \div (x + 2)$? How do you know?

    b. Likewise, determine $(3x^2 + x - 10) \div (3x - 5)$.

AT-30. Now consider the problem $(2x^2 + 11x + 12) \div (x + 4)$. How can you use a generic rectangle to find this **quotient** (the result of division)? With your team, find a way to complete the generic rectangle set up for you at right. As you work, answer the questions below in any order to help you make sense of the process.

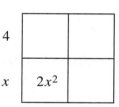

- Why are the terms x and 4 placed outside the generic rectangle, while the term $2x^2$ was placed inside the rectangle?

- What is the quotient? That is, what is $(2x^2 + 11x + 12) \div (x + 4)$?

- How can you verify your solution?

AT-31. What if the expression in problem AT-30 were instead $(2x^2 + 11x + 13) \div (x + 4)$?

    a. How would that change your result? Discuss this with your team and be ready to share your **conjecture** (educated guess) with the class.

    b. Now predict the result for $(2x^2 + 11x + 10) \div (x + 4)$. Then, as a class, find a way to verify your prediction.

Problem continues on next page →

AT-31.   *Problem continued from previous page.*

   c.   Compare your strategy of dividing polynomials with that of
        long division, as presented in the Math Notes box in this
        lesson. In your Learning Log, describe the similarities and
        differences of the different strategies. Title this entry
        "Division of Polynomials" and include today's date.

AT-32.   Find each quotient below. Verify your work.

   a. $\frac{4x^2 + 4x - 35}{2x + 7}$ b. $(10x^3 + 13x^2 - 3x) \div (5x - 1)$

   c. $(3m^2 + 20m + 10) \div (3m + 2)$ d. $(9x^2 - 3x + 1) \div (3x)$

MⒺTHODS AND MEANINGS

Dividing Polynomials

MATH NOTES

   In Chapter 5, you developed a strategy to multiply polynomials. To
divide polynomials, such as dividing $(3x^2 + 31x + 41)$ by $(x + 9)$ you
must **reverse** the process.

Two strategies for dividing polynomials are demonstrated below.

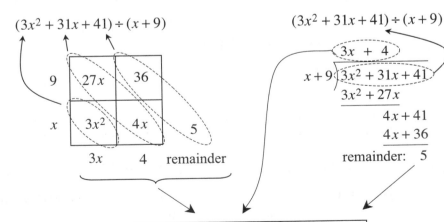

Using a Generic Rectangle:

$(3x^2 + 31x + 41) \div (x + 9)$

Using Long Division:

$(3x^2 + 31x + 41) \div (x + 9)$

Result: $(3x + 4)$ with remainder 5

Thus, $(3x^2 + 31x + 41) \div (x + 9) = (3x + 4)$ with remainder 5 or $3x + 4 + \frac{5}{x+9}$.

Algebra Connections

AT-33.   Use the strategies that you developed in this lesson to divide the following
polynomials.

a. $(x^2 + 6x - 16) \div (x - 2)$ b. $(x^2 + 6x - 14) \div (x - 2)$

c. $(3n^2 + 10n + 7) \div (3n + 1)$ d. $\frac{y^2 - 9y + 14}{y - 3}$

AT-34.   Use your knowledge of the properties of numbers to determine if the following
assertions are true or false.

a. $\sqrt{4}\sqrt{9} = \sqrt{4 \cdot 9}$ b. $\sqrt{64} - \sqrt{1} = \sqrt{64 - 1}$

c. $\sqrt{16} + \sqrt{4} = \sqrt{16 + 4}$ d. $\sqrt{100} \div \sqrt{25} = \sqrt{100 \div 25}$

e.   Based on your work in parts (a) through (d), write a conjecture (a statement
based on your observations) about which operations allow you to combine
square roots.

AT-35.   Test your conjecture from part (e) of problem AT-34 by rewriting the following
expressions, if possible. Confirm your answer with a calculator. If necessary, alter
your conjecture.

a. $\sqrt{10}\sqrt{3}$ b. $\sqrt{2} + \sqrt{1}$ c. $\sqrt{18} \div \sqrt{2}$ d. $\sqrt{6} - \sqrt{2}$

e. $\sqrt{19} + \sqrt{3}$ f. $\sqrt{24}\sqrt{6}$ g. $4\sqrt{9} - 2\sqrt{9}$ h. $\frac{\sqrt{28}}{\sqrt{7}}$

AT-36.   Determine if the following statements are sometimes, always, or never true. **Justify**
your conclusion. For each, assume that x and y are each positive or zero.

a. $\sqrt{x} + \sqrt{y} = \sqrt{x + y}$ b. $\sqrt{x}\sqrt{y} = \sqrt{xy}$

c. $(\sqrt{x})^2 = x$ d. x is greater than $\sqrt{x}$

AT-37. While diving from a platform which is 10 meters (roughly 32.8 feet) above the pool below, Hu's height above water was $h = -16t^2 + 4t + 32.8$ (where t is measured in seconds and h is measured in feet).

a. For how many seconds was Hu in the air after he left the platform? Write and solve an equation to find your answer.

b. How high was Hu in the air one second after he left the platform? Show how you got your answer.

AT-38. While working on a problem, Jed wrote the equation of a line below.

$$y - (-8) = \tfrac{3}{4}(x - 1)$$

a. What is the slope of his line?

b. Name at least one point this line must pass through. Explain how you found your answer.

c. Change his equation so that the result is perpendicular to Jed's line, and through the point $(-5, 6)$.

Glossary

absolute value   The absolute value of a number is the distance of the number from zero. Since the absolute value represents a distance, without regard to direction, it is always non-negative. Thus the absolute value of a negative number is its opposite, while the absolute value of a non-negative number is just the number itself. The absolute value of x is usually written "$|x|$". For example, $|-5| = 5$ and $|22| = 22$. (p. 389)

Additive Identity Property   The Additive Identity Property states that adding zero to any expression leaves the expression unchanged. That is, $a + 0 = a$. For example, $-2xy^2 + 0 = -2xy^2$. (p. 53)

Additive Inverse Property   The Additive Inverse Property states that for every number a there is a number $-a$ such that $a + (-a) = 0$. For example, the number 5 has an additive inverse of -5; $5 + (-5) = 0$. The additive inverse of a number is often called its opposite. For example, 5 and -5 are opposites. (p. 72)

Additive Property of Equality   The Additive Property of Equality states that equality is maintained if the same amount is added to both sides of an equation. That is, if $a = b$, then $a + c = b + c$. For example, if $y = 3x$, then $y + 1.5 = 3x + 1.5$. (p. 249)

algebra tiles   An algebra tile is a manipulative whose area represents a constant or variable quantity. The algebra tiles used in this course consist of large squares with dimensions x-by-x and y-by-y; rectangles with dimensions x-by-1, y-by-1, and x-by-y; and small squares with dimensions 1-by-1. These tiles are named by their areas: x^2, y^2, x, y, xy, and 1, respectively. The smallest squares are called "unit tiles." In this text, shaded tiles will represent positive quantities while unshaded tiles will represent negative quantities. (p. 41)

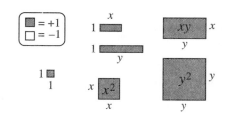

area   For this course, area is the number of square units needed to fill up a region on a flat surface. In later courses, the idea will be extended to cones, spheres, and more complex surfaces. (p. 5)

Area = 15 square units

Associative Property of Addition   The Associative Property of Addition states that if a sum contains terms that are grouped, the sum can be grouped differently with no effect on the total. That is, $a + (b + c) = (a + b) + c$. For example, $3 + (4 + 5) = (3 + 4) + 5$. (p. 53)

Associative Property of Multiplication   The Associative Property of Multiplication states that if a product contains terms that are grouped, the product can be grouped differently with no effect on the result. That is, $a(bc) = (ab)c$. For example, $2 \cdot (3 \cdot 4) = (2 \cdot 3) \cdot 4$. (p. 53)

asymptote   A line that a graph of a curve approaches as closely as you wish. An asymptote is often represented by a dashed line on a graph. For example, the graph at right has an asymptote at $y = -3$. (p. 472)

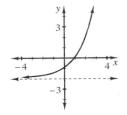

average   See "mean."

axes   In a coordinate plane, two number lines that meet at right angles at the origin (0, 0). The x-axis runs horizontally and the y-axis runs vertically. See the example at right. (p. 10)

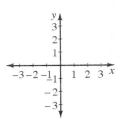

b   When the equation of a line is expressed in $y = mx + b$ form, the constant b gives the y-intercept of the line. For example, the y-intercept of the line $y = -\frac{1}{3}x + 7$ is 7. (p. 149)

base (1) When working with an exponential expression in the form a^b, a is called the base. For example, 2 is the base in 2^5. (5 is the exponent, and 32 is the value.) (Also see "exponent.") (p. 452) (2) When working with geometric figures, the term "base" may be applied to a side of a triangle, rectangle, parallelogram, or trapezoid. "Base" may also be applied to the face of a prism, cylinder, pyramid, or cone.

binomial   An expression that is the sum or difference of exactly two terms, each of which is a monomial. For example, $-2x + 3y^2$ is a binomial. (pp. 193, 329)

boundary line or curve   A line or curve on a two-dimensional graph that divides the graph into two regions. A boundary line or curve is used when graphing inequalities with two variables. For example, the inequality $y < \frac{2}{3}x + 2$ is graphed at right. The dashed boundary line has equation $y = \frac{2}{3}x + 2$. A boundary line is also sometimes called a "dividing line." (p. 393)

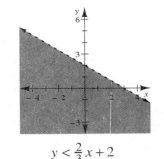

$$y < \frac{2}{3}x + 2$$

boundary point   The endpoint of a ray or segment on a number line where an inequality is true. For strict inequalities (that is, inequalities involving < or >), the point is not part of the solution. We find boundary points by solving the equality associated with our inequality. For example, the solution to the equation $2x + 5 = 11$ is $x = 3$, so the inequality $2x + 5 \geq 11$ has a boundary point at 3. The solution to that inequality is illustrated on the number line at right. A boundary point is also sometimes called a "dividing point." (p. 386)

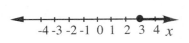

closure properties of rational numbers   The closure properties of rational numbers state that the product or sum of two rational numbers is a rational number. For example, $\frac{1}{2}$ and $\frac{3}{4}$ are both rational numbers; $\frac{1}{2} + \frac{3}{4}$ is $\frac{5}{4}$; and $\frac{5}{4}$ is a rational number. Also, 2.2 and 0.75 are both rational numbers; $2.2 \cdot 0.75$ is 1.65; and 1.65 is a rational number. (p. 214)

coefficient (numerical)   A number multiplying a variable or product of variables. For example, -7 is the coefficient of $-7xy^2$. (p. 255)

coincide   Two graphs coincide if they have all their points in common. For example, the graphs of $y = 2x + 4$ and $3y = 6x + 12$ coincide; both graphs are lines with a slope of 2 and a y-intercept of 4. When the graphs of two equations coincide, those equations share all the same solutions and have an infinite number of intersection points. (p. 252)

combining like terms   Combining two or more like terms simplifies an expression by summing constants and summing those variable terms in which the same variables are raised to the same power. For example, combining like terms in the expression $3x + 7 + 5x - 3 + 2x^2 + 3y^2$ gives $8x + 4 + 2x^2 + 3y^2$. When working with algebra tiles, combining like terms involves putting together tiles with the same dimensions. (p. 57)

common denominator   A common denominator of a group of fractions is an expression that has the denominators of each of the fractions as a factor. For example, if we are simplifying the sum $\frac{2}{x+3} + \frac{5x}{7} + \frac{3x-8}{2}$, we might use $14(x + 3)$ as a common denominator for all three terms. (p. 503)

common factor   A common factor is a factor that is the same for two or more terms. For example, x^2 is a common factor of $3x^2$ and $-5x^2y$. (p. 338)

Commutative Property of Addition   The Commutative Property of Addition states that if two terms are added, the order can be reversed with no effect on the total. That is, $a + b = b + a$. For example, $7 + 12 = 12 + 7$. (p. 45)

Commutative Property of Multiplication   The Commutative Property of Multiplication states that if two expressions are multiplied, the order can be reversed with no effect on the result. That is, $ab = ba$. For example, $5 \cdot 8 = 8 \cdot 5$. (p. 45)

complete graph   A complete graph includes all the necessary information about a line or a curve. To be complete, a graph must have the following components: (1) the x-axis and y-axis labeled, clearly showing the scale; (2) the equation of the graph written near the line or curve; (3) the line or curve extended as far as possible on the graph with arrows if the line or curve continues beyond the axes; (4) the coordinates of all special points, such as x- and y-intercepts, shown in (x, y) form. (p. 120)

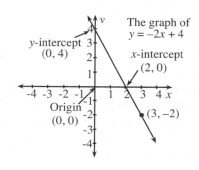

completing the square   In this course, we use completing the square to convert a quadratic equation in standard form into perfect square form. To complete the square, we add (or subtract) a constant to (or from) both sides of the equation so that the quadratic expression can be factored into a perfect square. For example, when given the quadratic equation $x^2 - 6x + 4 = 0$, we can complete the square by adding 5 to both sides. The resulting equation, $x^2 - 6x + 9 = 5$, has a left-hand side we can factor, resulting in the perfect square form quadratic equation $(x - 3)^2 = 5$. (p. 444)

conclusion   In an "If...then..." statement, the "then" portion is called the conclusion. For example, in the statement "*If* $x = 3$, *then* $x^2 = 9$," the conclusion is "$x^2 = 9$." (Also see "hypothesis.") (p. 241)

consecutive numbers   Integers that are in order without skipping any of them. For example, 8, 9, and 10 are consecutive numbers. (p. 256)

congruent   Two shapes are congruent if they have exactly the same size and shape. For example, the two triangles at right are congruent.

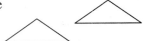

constant   A symbol representing a value that does not change. For example, in the equation $y = 2x + 5$, the number 5 is a constant. (p. 255)

continuous graph   A graph whose points are connected with an unbroken line or curve is called a continuous graph. A continuous graph can be traced with a pencil without ever lifting the pencil to move from one point on the graph to another point. For example, the graphs shown below are both continuous. (Also see "discrete.") (p. 102)

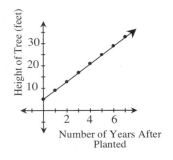

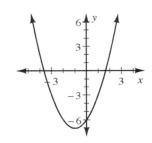

coordinate(s)   The number corresponding to a point on the number line or an ordered pair (x, y) that corresponds to a point in a two-dimensional coordinate system. In an ordered pair, the x-coordinate appears first and the y-coordinate appears second. For example, the point $(3, 5)$ has an x-coordinate of 3. (pp. 8, 10)

coordinate plane   A flat surface defined by two number lines meeting at right angles at their zero points. A coordinate plane is also sometimes called a "Cartesian Plane." (p. 10)

coordinate system   A system of graphing ordered pairs of numbers on a coordinate plane. An ordered pair represents a point, with the first number giving the horizontal position relative to the x-axis and the second number giving the vertical position relative to the y-axis. For example, the diagram at right shows the point $(3, 5)$ graphed on a coordinate plane. (p. 8)

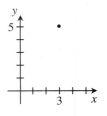

counterexample An example showing that a statement has at least one exception; that is, a situation in which the statement is false. For example, the number 4 is a counterexample to the hypothesis that all even numbers are greater than 7. (p. 192)

deductive reasoning See "justify."(p. 448)

degree (1) The degree of a monomial is the sum of the exponents of its variables. For example, $3x^2y^5$ has degree 7, because the sum of the exponents (5+2) is 7. (2) The degree of a polynomial in one variable is the degree of the term with the highest exponent. For example, $3x^5 - 4x^2 - x + 7$ has degree 5, because the highest exponent to which x is raised is 5. (3) The degree of a polynomial in more than one variable is the highest sum of the exponents among the terms. For example, $2x^5y^3 - 4x^2y^4z^3 - xy^5 + 3y^2z - 12$ has degree 9, because the sum of the exponents in the second term is 9 and no term has a higher exponent sum.

dependent variable When one quantity depends for its value on one or more others, it is called the dependent variable. For example, we might relate the speed of a car to the amount of force you apply to the gas pedal. Here, the speed of the car is the dependent variable; it depends on how hard you push the pedal. The dependent variable appears as the output value in an $x \rightarrow y$ table, and is usually placed relative to the vertical axis of a graph. We often use the letter y for the dependent variable. When working with functions or relations, the dependent variable represents the output value. (Also see "independent variable.") (pp. 110, 473)

difference of squares A polynomial that can be factored as the product of the sum and difference of two terms. The general pattern is $x^2 - y^2 = (x+y)(x-y)$. Most of the differences of squares found in this course are of the form $a^2x^2 - b^2 = (ax+b)(ax-b)$, where a and b are nonzero real numbers. For example, the difference of squares $4x^2 - 9$ can be factored as $(2x+3)(2x-3)$. (p. 497)

dimensions The dimensions of a flat region or space tell how far it extends in each direction. For example, the dimensions of a rectangle might be 16 cm wide by 7 cm high. (p. 22)

discrete graph A graph that consists entirely of separated points is called a discrete graph. For example, the graph shown at right is discrete. (Also see "continuous.") (p. 102)

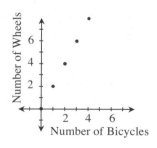

discriminant For quadratic equations in standard form $ax^2 + bx + c = 0$, the discriminant is $b^2 - 4ac$. If the discriminant is positive, the equation has two roots; if the discriminant is zero, the equation has one root; if the discriminant is negative, the equation has no real-number roots. For example, the discriminant of the quadratic equation $2x^2 - 4x - 5$ is $(-4)^2 - 4(2)(-5) = 56$, which indicates that that equation has two roots (solutions).

Distributive Property We use the Distributive Property to write a product of expressions as a sum of terms. The Distributive Property states that for any numbers or expressions a, b, and c, $a(b+c) = ab + ac$. For example, $2(x+4) = 2 \cdot x + 2 \cdot 4 = 2x + 8$. We can demonstrate this with algebra tiles or in a generic rectangle. (p. 198)

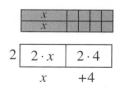

dividing line   See "boundary line."

dividing point   See "boundary point."

domain   The set of all input values for a relation or function. For example, the domain of the function graphed at right is $x \geq -3$. (p. 473) For variables, the domain is the set of numbers the variable may represent. (Also see "range.")

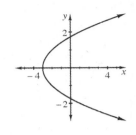

Elimination Method   A method for solving a system of equations. The key step in using the Elimination Method is to add or subtract both sides of two equations to eliminate one of the variables. For example, the two equations in the system at right can be added together to get the simplified result $7x = 14$. We can solve this equation to find x, then substitute the x-value back into either of the original equations to find the value of y. (pp. 250, 264)

$$5x + 2y = 10$$
$$2x - 2y = 4$$

equal   Two quantities are equal when they have the same value. For example, when $x = 4$, the expression $x + 8$ is equal to the expression $3x$ because their values are the same. (p. 68)

Equal Values Method   A method for solving a system of equations. To use the Equal Values Method, take two expressions that are each equal to the same variable and set those expressions equal to each other. For example, in the system of equations at right, $-2x + 5$ and $x - 1$ each equal y. So we write $-2x + 5 = x - 1$, then solve that equation to find x. Once we have x, we substitute that value back into either of the original equations to find the value of y. (p. 176)

$$y = -2x + 5$$
$$y = x - 1$$

equation   A mathematical sentence in which two expressions appear on either side of an "equals" sign (=), stating that the two expressions are equivalent. For example, the equation $7x + 4.2 = -8$ states that the expression $7x + 4.2$ has the value –8. In this course, an equation is often used to represent a rule relating two quantities. For example, a rule for finding the area y of a tile pattern with figure number x might be written $y = 4x - 3$. (p. 68)

equation mat   An organizing tool used to visually represent two equal expressions using algebra tiles. For example, the equation mat at right represents the equation $2x - 1 - (-x + 3) = 6 - 2x$. (p. 69)

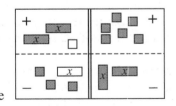

equivalent   Two expressions are equivalent if they have the same value. For example, $2 + 3$ is equivalent to $1 + 4$. (p. 19)   Two equations are equivalent if they have all the same solutions. For example, $y = 3x$ is equivalent to $2y = 6x$. Equivalent equations have the same graph. (p. 205)

evaluate   To evaluate an expression, substitute the value(s) given for the variable(s) and perform the operations according to the order of operations. For example, evaluating $2x + y - 10$ when $x = 4$ and $y = 3$ gives the value 1. (p. 49)

exponent In an expression of the form a^b, b is called the exponent. For example, in the expression 2^5, 5 is called the exponent. (2 is the base, and 32 is the value.) The exponent indicates how many times to use the base as a multiplier. For example, in 2^5, 2 is used 5 times: $2^5 = 2 \cdot 2 \cdot 2 \cdot 2 \cdot 2 = 32$. For exponents of zero, the rule is: for any number $x \neq 0$, $x^0 = 1$. For negative exponents, the rule is: for any number $x \neq 0$, $x^{-n} = \frac{1}{x^n}$, and $\frac{1}{x^{-n}} = x^n$. (Also see "laws of exponents.") (p. 452)

expression An expression contains one or more numbers and/or variables. Each part of the expression separated by addition or subtraction signs is called a "term." For example, each of these is an expression: $6xy^2$, 24, $2.5q - 7$, $\frac{y-3}{4+x}$. (p. 47)

expression comparison mat An expression comparison mat puts two expression mats side-by-side so they can be compared to see which represents the greater value. For example, in the expression comparison mat at right, the left-hand mat represents –3, while the right-hand mat represents –2. Since $-2 > -3$ the expression on the right is greater. (p. 55)

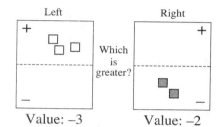

expression mat An organizing tool used to visually represent an expression with algebra tiles. An expression mat has two regions, a positive region at the top and a negative region at the bottom. The tiles on the expression mat at right represent a value of -3. (p. 47)

Value: –3

factor (1) In arithmetic: When two or more integers are multiplied, each of the integers is a factor of the product. For example, 4 is a factor of 24, because $4 \cdot 6 = 24$. (2) In algebra: When two or more algebraic expressions are multiplied together, each of the expressions is a factor of the product. For example, x^2 is a factor of $-17x^2y^3$, because $(x^2)(-17y^3) = -17x^2y^3$. (3) To factor an expression is to write it as a product. For example, the factored form of $x^2 - 3x - 18$ is $(x-6)(x+3)$. (p. 329)

factored completely A polynomial is factored completely if none of the resulting factors can be factored further using integer coefficients. For example, $-2(x+3)(x-1)$ is the completely factored form of $-2x^2 - 4x + 6$. (p. 337)

factored form A quadratic equation in the form $a(x+b)(x+c) = 0$, where a is nonzero, is said to be in factored form. For example, $-7(x+2)(x-1.5) = 0$ is a quadratic equation in factored form. (p. 438)

Fibonacci Sequence The sequence of numbers 1, 1, 2, 3, 5, 8, 13, ... Each term of the Fibonacci sequence (after the first two terms) is the sum of the two preceding terms. (p. 95)

Figure 0 The figure that comes before Figure 1 in a tile pattern. When representing a tile pattern with a graph, the y-intercept of the graph is the number of tiles in Figure 0. When representing a tile pattern with an equation in $y = mx + b$ form, b gives the number of tiles in Figure 0. (p. 142)

Algebra Connections

F.O.I.L.   An approach for multiplying two binomials. "F.O.I.L." stands for "First, Outer, Inner, Last." It describes the order in which to multiply the terms of two binomials to be sure to get all the products. For example, the equation below shows how to apply the F.O.I.L. method to multiply $(2x + 3)(x - 4)$.

$$(2x + 3)(x - 4) = \underset{firsts}{(2x)(x)} + \underset{outers}{(2x)(-4)} + \underset{inners}{(3)(x)} + \underset{lasts}{(3)(-4)} = 2x^2 - 5x - 12$$

fraction buster   "Fraction busting" is a method of simplifying equations involving fractions that uses the Multiplicative Property of Equality to rearrange the equation so that no fractions remain. To use this method, multiply both sides of an equation by the common denominator of all the fractions in the equation. The result will be an equivalent equation with no fractions. For example, when given the equation $\frac{x}{7} + 2 = \frac{x}{3}$, we can multiply both sides by the "fraction buster" 21. The resulting equation, $3x + 42 = 7x$, is equivalent to the original but contains no fractions. (p. 419)

function   A relation in which for each input value there is one and only one output value. For example, the relation $f(x) = x + 4$ is a function; for each input value (x) there is exactly one output value. In terms of ordered pairs (x, y), no two ordered pairs of a function have the same first member (x). (p. 473)

function notation   When a rule expressing a function is written using function notation, the function is given a name, most commonly "f," "g," or "h." The notation $f(x)$ represents the output of a function, named f, when x is the input. It is pronounced "f of x." For example, $g(2)$, pronounced "g of 2", represents the output of the function g when $x = 2$. If $g(x) = x^2 + 3$, then $g(2) = 7$. (p. 464)

generic rectangle   A type of diagram used to visualize multiplying expressions without algebra tiles. Each expression to be multiplied forms a side length of the rectangle, and the product is the sum of the areas of the sections of the rectangle. For example, the generic rectangle at right can be used to multiply $(2x + 5)$ by $(x + 3)$. (p. 218)

$$(2x + 5)(x + 3) = 2x^2 + 11x + 15$$

area as a product   area as a sum

graph   A graph represents numerical information spatially. The numbers may come from a table, situation (pattern), or rule (equation or inequality). Most of the graphs in this course show points, lines, and/or curves on a two-dimensional coordinate system like the one at right (pp. 8, 10) or on a single axis called a number line (see below). (p. 21) (See "complete graph.")

greater than   One expression is greater than another if its value is larger. We indicate this relationship with the greater than symbol ">". For example, $4 + 5$ is greater than $1 + 1$. We write $4 + 5 > 1 + 1$. (pp. 55, 377)

greatest common factor (GCF)   (1) For integers, the greatest positive integer that is a common factor of two or more integers. For example, the greatest common factor of 28 and 42 is 14.   (2) For two or more algebraic monomials, the product of the greatest common integer factor of the coefficients of the monomials and the variable(s) in each algebraic term with the smallest degree of that variable in every term. For example, the greatest common factor of $12x^3y^2$ and $8xy^4$ is $4xy^2$.   (3) For a polynomial, the greatest common monomial factor of its terms. For example, the greatest common factor of $16x^4 + 8x^3 + 12x$ is $4x$.

growth   One useful way to analyze a mathematical relationship is to examine how the output value grows as the input value increases. We can see this growth on a graph of a linear relationship by looking at the slope of the graph. (p. 142)

growth factor   When two quantities are in a linear relationship, the growth factor describes how much the output value changes when the input value increases by 1. For example, the $x \rightarrow y$ table at right shows a linear relationship with a growth factor of 6. The growth factor is equal to the slope of the line representing a linear relationship. The growth factor is also equal to the value of m when the relationship is represented with an equation in $y = mx + b$ form. (p. 205)

x	y
1	7
2	13
3	19
4	25

growth number   See "growth factor."

Guess and Check   A strategy for solving problems that starts with making a guess and then checking whether that guess is a correct solution to the problem. If the guess is not correct, the checking process helps suggest a closer next guess. The second guess is then checked. This process is repeated until a correct solution is found. Being organized is critical to using Guess and Check successfully. A table is one good way to organize your work. The Guess and Check process leads to writing equations to represent and solve word problems. (pp. 22, 65)

horizontal lines   Horizontal lines are "flat" and run left to right in the same direction as the x-axis. Horizontal lines have equations of the form $y = b$, where b can be any number. For example, the graph at right shows the horizontal lines $y = 3$ and $y = -2$. The slope of any horizontal line is 0. The x-axis has the equation $y = 0$ because $y = 0$ everywhere on the x-axis. (p. 291)

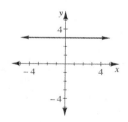

hypothesis   (1) A term scientists use to mean an "educated guess" (or what mathematicians call a conjecture), based on data, patterns, and relationships. For instance, having looked at many multiples of five, you might form a hypothesis that every multiple of five ends in the digit 0 or the digit 5.   (2) In an "If...then..." statement, the "if" portion is called the hypothesis. For example, in the statement "*If* $x = 3$, *then* $x^2 = 9$," the hypothesis is "$x = 3$." (Also see "conclusion.") (p. 241)

identity element for addition   0 is the identity element for addition because adding 0 to an expression leaves the expression unchanged. That is, $a + 0 = 0$. (Also see "Additive Identity Property.") (p. 53)

identity element for multiplication   1 is the identity element for multiplication because multiplying an expression by 1 leaves the expression unchanged. That is, $a(1) = a$. (Also see "Multiplicative Identity Property.") (p. 53)

Identity Property of Addition   See "Additive Identity Property."

Identity Property of Multiplication   See "Multiplicative Identity Property."

independent variable   When one quantity changes in a way that does not depend on the value of another quantity, the value that changes independently is represented with the independent variable. For example, we might relate the speed of a car to the amount of force you apply to the gas pedal. Here, the amount of force applied may be whatever the driver chooses, so it represents the independent variable. The independent variable appears as the input value in an $x \rightarrow y$ table, and is usually placed relative to the horizontal axis of a graph. We often use the letter x for the independent variable. When working with functions or relations, the independent variable represents the input value. (Also see "dependent variable.") (pp. 110, 473)

inductive reasoning   Drawing a conclusion based on a pattern. For example, having seen many multiples of 5 that end in the digit 0 or 5, you might use inductive reasoning to make a hypothesis or conjecture that *all* multiples of 5 end in the digit 0 or 5. (p. 448)

inequality   An inequality consists of two expressions on either side of an inequality symbol. For example, the inequality $7x + 4.2 < -8$ states that the expression $7x + 4.2$ has a value less than 8. (p. 352)

inequality symbols   The symbol $\leq$ read from left to right means "less than or equal to."   The symbol $\geq$ read from left to right means "greater than or equal to." The symbols $<$ and $>$ mean "less than" and "greater than," respectively. For example, "7<13" means that 7 is less than 13. (p. 377)

input value   The input value is the independent variable in a relation. We substitute the input value into our rule (equation) to determine the output value. For example, if we have a rule for how much your phone bill will be if you talk a certain number of minutes, the number of minutes you talk is the input value. The input value appears first in an $x \rightarrow y$ table, and is represented by the variable x. When working with functions, the input value, an element of the domain, is the value put into the function. (pp. 97, 464)

integers   The set of numbers { . . . –3, –2, –1, 0, 1, 2, 3, . . . }. (p. 15)

intersection   See "point of intersection."

irrational numbers   The set of numbers that cannot be expressed in the form $\frac{a}{b}$, where a and b are integers and $b \neq 0$. For example, π and $\sqrt{2}$ are irrational numbers. (p. 365)

justify   To use facts, definitions, rules, and/or previously proven statements in an organized way to convince an audience that a claim (or an answer) is valid or true. For example, you might justify your claim that $x = 2$ is a solution to $3x = 6$ by pointing out that when you multiply 3 by 2, you get 6. (p. 88)

lattice points   The points on a coordinate grid where the grid lines intersect. The diagram at right shows two lattice points. The coordinates of lattice points are integers. (p. 283)

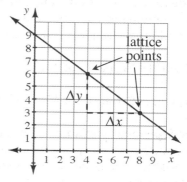

laws of exponents   The laws of exponents we study in this course are: (p. 452)

Law	Examples	
$x^m x^n = x^{m+n}$ for all x	$x^3 x^4 = x^{3+4} = x^7$	$2^5 \cdot 2^{-1} = 2^4$
$\frac{x^m}{x^n} = x^{m-n}$ for $x \neq 0$	$x^{10} \div x^4 = x^{10-4} = x^6$	$\frac{5^4}{5^7} = 5^{-3}$
$(x^m)^n = x^{mn}$ for all x	$(x^4)^3 = x^{4 \cdot 3} = x^{12}$	$(10^5)^6 = 10^{30}$
$x^0 = 1$ for $x \neq 0$	$\frac{y^2}{y^2} = y^0 = 1$	$9^0 = 1$
$x^{-1} = \frac{1}{x}$ for $x \neq 0$	$\frac{1}{x^2} = (\frac{1}{x})^2 = (x^{-1})^2 = x^{-2}$	$3^{-1} = \frac{1}{3}$
$x^{m/n} = \sqrt[n]{x^m}$ for $x \geq 0$	$\sqrt{k} = k^{1/2}$	$y^{2/3} = \sqrt[3]{y^2}$

least common multiple (LCM)   (1) The smallest common multiple of a set of two or more integers. For example, the least common multiple of 4, 6, and 8 is 24. (2) For two or more algebraic monomials, the product of the least common integer multiples of the coefficients of the monomials and the variable(s) in each algebraic term with the greatest degree of that variable in every term. For example, the least common factor of $12x^3 y^2$ and $8xy^4$ is $24x^3 y^4$. (p. 503)

"legal" moves   When working with an equation mat or expression comparison mat, there are certain "legal" moves you can make with the algebra tiles that keep the relationship between the two sides of the mat intact. For example, removing an x tile from the positive region of each side of an equation mat is a legal move; it keeps the expressions on each side of the mat equal. The legal moves are those justified by the properties of the real numbers. (p. 54)

less than   (1) One expression is less than another if its value is not as large. We indicate this relationship with the less than symbol "<". For example, $1 + 1$ is less than $4 + 5$. We write $1 + 1 < 4 + 5$. (p. 377) (2) We sometimes say that one amount is a certain quantity less than another amount. For example, a student movie ticket might cost two dollars *less than* an adult ticket. (p. 28)

Algebra Connections

"let" statement   A "let" statement is written at the beginning of our work to identify the variable that will represent a certain quantity. For example, in solving a problem about grilled cheese sandwiches, we might begin by writing "Let s = the number of sandwiches eaten." It is particularly important to use "let" statements when writing mathematical sentences, so that your readers will know what the variables in the sentences represent. (p. 233)

like terms   Two or more terms that contain the same variable(s), with corresponding variables raised to the same power. For example, $5x$ and $2x$ are like terms. (Also see "combining like terms.") (p. 57)

line of symmetry   A line that divides a shape into two pieces that are mirror images of each other. If you fold a shape over its line of symmetry, the shapes on both sides of the line will match perfectly. A shape with a line of symmetry is shown at right. (p. 342)

line of symmetry

linear equation   An equation in two variables whose graph is a line. For example, $y = 2.1x - 8$ is a linear equation. The standard form for a linear equation is $ax + by = c$, where a, b, and c are constants and a and b are not both zero. Most linear equations can be written in $y = mx + b$ form, which is more useful for determining the line's slope and y-intercept. (p. 205)

looking inside   "Looking inside" is a method of solving one-variable equations containing parentheses or an absolute value symbol. To use "looking inside," we first determine what the value of the entire expression inside the parentheses (or absolute value symbol) must be. We then use that fact to solve for the value of the variable. For example, to use "looking inside" to solve the equation $4(x + 2) = 36$, we first determine that $x + 2$ must equal 9. We then solve the equation $x + 2 = 9$ to find that $x = 7$. (p. 424)

m   When the equation of a line is expressed in $y = mx + b$ form, the constant m gives the slope of the line. For example, the slope of the line $y = -\frac{1}{3}x + 7$ is $-\frac{1}{3}$. (p. 149)

mathematical sentence   A mathematical sentence is an equation that uses variables to represent unknown quantities. For example, the mathematical sentence $b + g = 23$ might represent the fact that the total number of boys and girls in the class is 23. It is helpful to define variables using "let" statements before using them in a mathematical sentence. (Also see " 'let' statement.") (p. 232)

mean   The mean, or average, of several numbers is one way of defining the "middle" of the numbers. To find the average of a group of numbers, add the numbers together then divide by the number of numbers in the set. For example, the average of the numbers 1, 5, and 6 is $(1 + 5 + 6) \div 3 = 4$. (p. 11)

monomial   An expression with only one term. It can be a number, a variable, or the product of a number and one or more variables. For example, 7, $3x$, $-4ab$, and $3x^2y$ are each monomials. (p. 329)

multiple representations   See "representation" and "representations web."

Multiplicative Identity Property   The Multiplicative Identity Property states that multiplying any expression by 1 leaves the expression unchanged. That is, $a(1) = a$. For example, $437x \cdot 1 = 437x$. (p. 53)

Multiplicative Inverse Property   The Multiplicative Inverse Property states that for every nonzero number a there is a number $\frac{1}{a}$ such that $a \cdot \frac{1}{a} = 1$. For example, the number 6 has a multiplicative inverse of $\frac{1}{6}$; $6 \cdot \frac{1}{6} = 1$. The multiplicative inverse of a number is usually called its reciprocal. For example, $\frac{1}{6}$ is the reciprocal of 6. For a number in the form $\frac{a}{b}$, where a and b are non-zero, the reciprocal is $\frac{b}{a}$. (p. 72)

Multiplicative Property of Equality   The Multiplicative Property of Equality states that equality is maintained if both sides of an equation are multiplied by the same amount. That is, if $a = b$, then $a \cdot c = b \cdot c$. For example, if $y = 3x$, then $2(y) = 2(3x)$.

negative   A negative number is a number less than zero. Negative numbers are graphed on the negative side of a number line. (p. 15)

non-commensurate   Two measurements are called non-commensurate if no whole number multiple of one measurement can ever equal a whole number multiple of the other. For example, measures of 1 cm and $\sqrt{2}$ cm are non-commensurate, because no combination of items 1 cm long will ever have exactly the same length as a combination of items $\sqrt{2}$ cm long. (p. 42)

numeral   A symbol that names a number. For example, each of these is a numeral: 22.6, –19, 0.

numerical coefficient   See "coefficient."

opposite   Two numbers are opposites if they are the same distance from zero, but one is positive and one is negative. For example, 5 and –5 are opposites. The opposite of a number is sometimes called its additive inverse, indicating that the sum of a number and its opposite is zero. (p. 72)

order of operations   The specific order in which certain operations are to be carried out to evaluate or simplify expressions. The order is: parentheses (or other grouping symbols), exponents (powers or roots), multiplication and division (from left to right), and addition and subtraction (from left to right). (p. 49)

ordered pair Two numbers written in order as follows: (x, y). The primary use of ordered pairs in this course is to represent points in an x-y coordinate system. The first coordinate (x) represents the horizontal distance and direction from the origin; the second coordinate (y) represents the vertical distance and direction from the origin. For example, the ordered pair (3, 5) represents the point shown in bold at right. (p. 10)

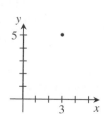

origin   The point on a coordinate plane where the x- and y-axes intersect is called the origin. This point has coordinates $(0, 0)$. The point assigned to zero on a number line is also called the origin. (p. 120)

output value   The output value is the dependent variable in a relation. When we substitute the input value into our rule (equation), the result is the output value. For example, if we have a rule for how much your phone bill will be if you talk a certain number of minutes, the amount of your phone bill is the output value. The output value appears second in an $x \rightarrow y$ table, and is represented by the variable y. When working with functions, the output value, an element of the range, is the value that results from applying the rule for the function to an input value. (pp. 97, 464)

parabola   A parabola is a particular kind of mathematical curve. In this course, a parabola is always the graph of a quadratic function $y = ax^2 + bx + c$ where a does not equal 0. The diagram at right shows some examples of parabolas. The highest or lowest point on the graph is called the vertex. (p. 106)

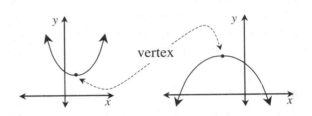

parallel   Two or more straight lines on a flat surface that do not intersect (no matter how far they are extended) are parallel. If two lines have the same slope and do not coincide, they are parallel. For example, the graphs of $y = 2x + 3$ and $y = 2x - 2$ are parallel (see diagram at right). When two equations have parallel graphs, the equations have no solutions in common. (p. 252)

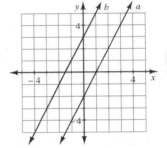

pattern   A pattern is a set of things in order that change in a regular way. For example, the numbers 1, 4, 7, 10, ... form a pattern, because each number increases by 3. The numbers 1, 4, 9, 16, ... form a pattern, because they are squares of consecutive integers. (p. 96) In this course, we often look at tile patterns, whose figure numbers and areas we represent with a table, a rule (equation), or a graph. (pp. 18, 93)

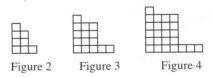

Figure 2   Figure 3   Figure 4

percent   A ratio that compares a number to 100. Percents are often written using the "%" symbol. For example, 0.75 is equal to $\frac{75}{100}$ or 75%. (p. 19)

perfect square form   A quadratic equation in the form $a(x + b)^2 = c$, where a is nonzero, is said to be in perfect square form. For example, $3(x - 12)^2 = 19$ is a quadratic equation in perfect square form. (p. 438)

perfect square trinomials   Trinomials of the form $a^2x^2 + 2abx + b^2$, where a and b are nonzero real numbers, are known as perfect square trinomials and factor as $(ax+b)^2$. For example, the perfect square trinomial $9x^2 - 24x + 16$ can be factored as $(3x-4)^2$. (p. 497)

perimeter   The distance around a figure on a flat surface. (p. 5)

Perimeter =
$5 + 8 + 4 + 6 = 23$ units

perpendicular   Two lines or segments that meet (intersect) to form a $90°$ angle. For example, the lines shown on the graph at right are perpendicular. If two perpendicular lines are graphed in an x, y-coordinate system, their slopes are opposite reciprocals. (p. 308)

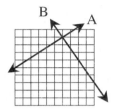

point of intersection   A point of intersection is a point that the graphs of two equations have in common. For example, (3, 4) is a point of intersection of the two graphs shown at right. Two graphs may have one point of intersection, several points of intersection, or no points of intersection. The ordered pair representing a point of intersection gives a solution to the equations of each of the graphs. (pp. 165, 252)

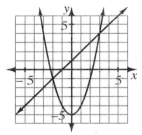

point-slope form   The point-slope form of the equation of a line is $y - k = m(x - h)$, where (h, k) are the coordinates of a point on the line, and m is the slope of the line. For example, a line with slope –4 passing through the point (5, 8) has the equation $y - 8 = -4(x - 5)$. To find the equation of the line in $y = mx + b$ form, we solve the point-slope form equation for y. (p. 314)

polygon   A two-dimensional closed figure of straight line segments ("edges" or "sides") connected end to end. Each side (or edge) intersects only the endpoints of its two adjacent sides (or edges). For example, the shape at right is a polygon.

polynomial   An expression that is the sum or difference of two or more monomials (terms). For example, $x^8 - 4x^6y + 6x^4y^2$ is a polynomial. (p. 329)

power   A number or variable raised to an exponent in the form x^n. See "exponent."

prediction   A rule (equation), table, or graph can be used to make a prediction about the value(s) a quantity will take that we have not yet seen. For example, we might analyze data about the height of a tree in each of its first three years of growth to predict how tall it will be at the end of year 4. (p. 97)

prime number   A positive integer with exactly two factors. The only factors of a prime number are 1 and itself. For example, the numbers 2, 3, 17, and 31 are all prime. 31 has no factors other than 1 and 31. (p. 241)

problem-solving strategies   This course incorporates several problem-solving strategies, specifically, making a guess and checking it, using manipulatives (such as algebra tiles), making systematic lists, collecting data, graphing, drawing a diagram, breaking a large problem into smaller subproblems, working backward, and writing and solving equations. For example, a student given the details of a cell-phone pricing plan and asked how many minutes would cost $29.95 might approach the problem by writing an equation and solving it, making a table of times and prices, graphing the relationship, or guessing and checking various numbers of minutes. (p. 2)

product   The result of multiplying. For example, the product of 4 and 5 is 20; the product of $3a$ and $8b^2$ is $24ab^2$. (p. 28)

proportion   An equation stating that two ratios (fractions) are equal. For example, the equation below is a proportion. A proportion is a useful type of equation to set up when solving problems involving proportional relationships. (p. 211)

$$\frac{68 \text{ votes for Mr. Mears}}{100 \text{ people surveyed}} = \frac{34 \text{ votes for Mr. Mears}}{50 \text{ people surveyed}}$$

quadrants   The coordinate plane is divided by its axes into four quadrants. The quadrants are numbered as shown in the first diagram at right. When graphing data that has no negative values, we sometimes use a graph showing only the first quadrant. (p. 10)

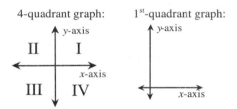

quadratic equation   An equation that can be written in the form $ax^2 + bx + c = 0$, where a, b, and c are real numbers and a is nonzero. A quadratic equation written in this form is said to be in standard form. For example, $3x^2 - 4x + 7.5 = 0$ is a quadratic equation. (p. 348)

quadratic expression   An expression that can be written in the form $ax^2 + bx + c$, where a, b, and c are real numbers and a is nonzero. For example, $3x^2 - 4x + 7.5$ is a quadratic expression. (p. 329)

Quadratic Formula   The Quadratic Formula states that if $ax^2 + bx + c = 0$ and $a \neq 0$, then $x = \frac{-b \pm \sqrt{b^2 - 4ac}}{2a}$. For example, if $5x^2 + 9x + 3 = 0$, then $x = \frac{-9 \pm \sqrt{9^2 - 4(5)(3)}}{2(5)} = \frac{-9 \pm \sqrt{21}}{10}$. (p. 357)

quadrilateral A polygon with four sides. For example, the shape at right is a quadrilateral. (p. 50)

radical   An expression in the form $\sqrt{a}$, where $\sqrt{a}$ is the positive square root of a. For example, $\sqrt{49} = 7$. (Also see "square root.") (p. 365)

radicand   The expression under a radical sign. For example, in the expression $3 + 2\sqrt{x - 7}$, the radicand is $x - 7$.

range   The set of all output values for a function or relation. For example, the range of the function graphed at right is $y > -2$. (Also see "domain.") (p. 473)

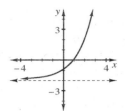

ratio   A ratio compares two quantities by division. A ratio can be written using a colon, but is more often written as a fraction. For example, we might be interested in the ratio of female students in a particular school to the total number of students in the school. This ratio could be written as 1521:2906 or as the fraction shown at right. (p. 211)

$$\frac{1521 \text{ female students}}{2906 \text{ total students}}$$

rational expression   An expression in the form of a fraction in which the numerator and/or denominator contain polynomials. For example, $\frac{x+2}{x^2+8x+12}$ is a rational expression. (pp. 409, 413)

rational numbers   Numbers that can be expressed in the form $\frac{a}{b}$, where a and b are integers and $b \neq 0$. For example, 0.75 is a rational number because it can be expressed in the form $\frac{3}{4}$. (p. 214)

real numbers   Irrational numbers together with rational numbers form the set of the real numbers. For example, the following are all real numbers: 2.78, -13267, 0, $\frac{3}{7}$, π, $\sqrt{2}$. All real numbers are represented on the number line. (p. 365)

reciprocal   The reciprocal of a nonzero number is its multiplicative inverse; that is, the reciprocal of x is $\frac{1}{x}$. For a number in the form $\frac{a}{b}$, where a and b are non-zero, the reciprocal is $\frac{b}{a}$. The product of a number and its reciprocal is 1. For example, the reciprocal of 12 is $\frac{1}{12}$, and $12 \cdot \frac{1}{12} = 1$. (Also see "Multiplicative Inverse Property.") (p. 72)

Reflexive Property   The Reflexive Property states that any expression is always equal to itself. That is, $a = a$. For example, $1627x^2 - 2 = 1627x^2 - 2$.

relation   An equation that relates inputs to outputs. For example, $y = \frac{4x}{x-3}$ and $x^2 + y^2 = 18$ are both relations. The set of input values to a relation is the domain, and the set of output values is the range. A relation can also be thought of as a set of ordered pairs. (p. 473)

representation   A representation expresses a relationship between quantities in a particular way. In this course, we emphasize four different ways of representing a numerical relationship: with a graph, table, situation (pattern), or rule (equation or inequality). (Also see "representations web.") (p. 161)

representations web   The representations web, or just "the web," is an organizational tool we use to keep track of connections between the four representations of numerical relationships emphasized in this course. As we learn how to move from one representation of a particular type of pattern to another, we record this by drawing an arrow on the web. For example, an arrow from "rule" to "graph" in the web might record our ability to draw the graph for a given equation. (Also see "representation.") (p. 161)

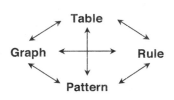

rewriting   To rewrite an equation or expression is to write an equivalent equation or expression. In this course, "rewriting" also refers to a method of solving one-variable equations. In "rewriting," we use algebraic techniques to write an equation equivalent to the original. This will often involve using the Distributive Property to eliminate parentheses. We then solve the equation using various solution methods, including perhaps rewriting again. For example, to solve the equation $4(x+2)=36$ by "rewriting," we use the Distributive Property to rewrite the equation as $4x+8=36$. We then solve this equation to find that $x=7$. (p. 424)

root   A root of an equation is a solution of the equation. For example, the roots of $(x-4)(2x+3)=0$ are $x=4$ and $x=-\frac{3}{2}$. When working with a function $f(x)$, the x-intercepts of the function's graph are the roots of the equation $f(x)=0$. (p. 344)

rule   A rule is an equation or inequality that represents the relationship between two numerical quantities. We often use a rule to represent the relationship between quantities in a table, a pattern, a real-world situation, or a graph. For example, the rule $y=0.4x+25$ might tell us how to find the total cost y in cents of talking on a pay phone for x minutes. (p. 93)

scale on axes   The scale on an axis tells you what number each successive mark on the axis represents. A complete graph has the scale marked with numbers on each axis. Each axis should be scaled so that each interval represents the same amount. (p. 105)

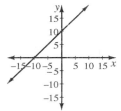

scientific notation   A number is expressed in scientific notation when it is in the form $a \cdot 10^n$, where $1 \le a < 10$ and n is an integer. For example, the number 31,000 can be expressed in scientific notation as $3.1 \cdot 10^4$. (p. 451)

similar figures   Similar figures have the same shape but are not necessarily the same size. For example the two triangles at right are similar. In similar figures, the measures of corresponding angles are equal and the lengths of corresponding sides are proportional. (p. 78)

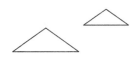

simple radical form   A number $r\sqrt{s}$ is in simple radical form if no square of an integer divides s and s is not a fraction; that is, there are no perfect square factors (square numbers such as 4, 9, 16, etc.) under the radical sign and no radicals in the denominator. For example, $5\sqrt{12}$ is not in simple radical form since 4 (the square of 2) divides 12. But $10\sqrt{3}$ is in simple radical form and is equivalent to $5\sqrt{12}$. (p. 365)

544

simplify   To simplify an expression is to write a less complicated expression with the same value. A simplified expression has no parentheses and no like terms. For example, the expression $3-(2x+7)-4x$ can be simplified to $-4-6x$. When working with algebra tiles, a simplified expression uses the fewest possible tiles to represent the original expression. (p. 55)

slope   A ratio that describes how steep (or flat) a line is. Slope can be positive, negative, or even zero, but a straight line has only one slope. Slope is the ratio $\frac{\text{vertical change}}{\text{horizontal change}}$ or $\frac{\text{change in } y \text{ value}}{\text{change in } x \text{ value}}$, sometimes written $\frac{\Delta y}{\Delta x}$. When the equation of a line is written in $y=mx+b$ form, m is the slope of the line. Some texts refer to slope as the ratio of the "rise over the run." A line has positive slope if it slopes upward from left to right on a graph, negative slope if it slopes downward from left to right, zero slope if it is horizontal, and undefined slope if it is vertical. (p. 291)

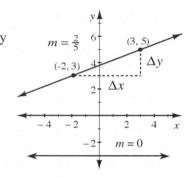

slope-intercept form   See "$y=mx+b$."

slope triangle   A slope triangle is a right triangle drawn on a graph of a line so that the hypotenuse of the triangle is part of the line. The vertical leg length is the change in the y-value (Δy); the horizontal leg length is the change in the x-value (Δx). We use the lengths of the legs in the triangle to calculate the slope ratio $\frac{\Delta y}{\Delta x}$. For example, the diagram at right shows a slope triangle with $\Delta y=2$, $\Delta x=4$. The slope of the line in the example is $\frac{2}{4}$, or $\frac{1}{2}$. (Also see "slope.") (p. 282)

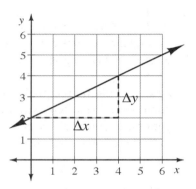

solution   The number or numbers that when substituted into an equation or inequality make the equation or inequality true. For example, $x=4$ is a solution to the equation $3x-2=10$ because $3x-2$ equals 10 when $x=4$. A solution to a two-variable equation is sometimes written as an ordered pair (x, y). For example, $x=3$ and $y=-2$ is a solution to the equation $y=x-5$; this solution can be written as $(3, -2)$. (pp. 128, 201, 245, 252)

solve   (1) To find all the solutions to an equation or an inequality (or a system of equations or inequalities). For example, solving the equation $x^2=9$ gives the solutions $x=3$ and $x=-3$. (pp. 68, 119, 170)   (2) Solving an equation for a variable gives an equivalent equation that expresses that variable in terms of other variables and constants. For example, solving $2y-8x=16$ for y gives $y=4x+8$. The equation $y=4x+8$ has the same solutions as $2y-8x=16$, but $y=4x+8$ expresses y in terms of x and some constants. (p. 203)

square numbers   The numbers in the pattern 1, 4, 9, 16, 25, ... That is, the squares of the counting numbers 1, 2, 3, 4, 5, ... are known as square numbers.

square root   A number a is a square root of b if $a^2 = b$. For example, the number 9 has two square roots, 3 and –3. A negative number has no real square roots; a positive number has two; and zero has just one square root, namely, itself. Other roots, such as cube root, will be studied in other courses. (Also see "radical.") (p. 365)

standard form for a number   See "standard notation."

standard form for quadratics   A quadratic expression in the form $ax^2 + bx + c$ is said to be in standard form. For example, the following are all expressions in standard form: $3m^2 + m - 1$, $x^2 - 9$, and $3x^2 + 5x$. (p. 335)

standard form of a linear equation   The standard form for a linear equation is $ax + by = c$, where a, b, and c are real numbers and a and b are not both zero. For example, the equation $2.5x - 3y = 12$ is in standard form. When you are given the equation of a line in standard form, it is often useful to write an equivalent equation in $y = mx + b$ form to find the line's slope and y-intercept. (p. 205)

standard notation   A number written out completely, showing all digits and without use of exponents is written in standard notation. For example, 31,000 is the standard notation for the number expressed by $3.1 \cdot 10^4$. Standard notation is also sometimes called "standard form."

starting value   In certain situations, the dependent variable has a starting value where the situation described in a problem begins. For example, if we are measuring the population of a town over time, that population will have some starting value when we begin our measurements. (p. 203)

substitution   Replacing one symbol with a number, a variable, or another algebraic expression of the same value. Substitution does not change the value of the overall expression. For example, suppose we are trying to evaluate the expression $13x - 6$ when $x = 4$. Since x has the value 4, we can substitute 4 into the expression wherever x appears, giving us the equivalent expression $13(4) - 6$. (p. 248)

Substitution Method   A method for solving a system of equations by replacing one variable with an expression involving the remaining variable(s). For example, in the system of equations at right the first equation tells you that y is equal to $-3x + 5$. We can substitute $-3x + 5$ in for y in the second equation to get $2(-3x + 5) + 10x = 18$, then solve this equation to find x. Once we have x, we substitute that value back into either of the original equations to find the value of y. (pp. 242, 248)

$$y = -3x + 5$$
$$2y + 10x = 18$$

Substitution Property   The Substitution Property states that if $a = b$, a can be replaced by b in any expression without changing the value of the expression. For example, if $x = 4$, $13x - 6$ has the same value as $13(4) - 6$.

sum   The result of adding two or more numbers. For example, the sum of 4 and 5 is 9. (p. 28)

Symmetric Property of Equality   The Symmetric Property states that if two expressions are equal, it does not matter which is stated first. That is, if $a = b$ then $b = a$. For example, $56 \div 8 = 7$, and $7 = 56 \div 8$.

symmetry   See "line of symmetry."

system of equations   A system of equations is a set of equations with the same variables. Solving a system of equations means finding one or more solutions that make each of the equations in the system true. A solution to a system of equations gives a point of intersection of the graphs of the equations in the system. There may be zero, one, or several solutions to a system of equations. For example, $(1.5, -3)$ is a solution to the system of equations at right; setting $x = 1.5$, $y = -3$ makes both of the equations true. Also, $(1.5, -3)$ is a point of intersection of the graphs of these two equations. (p. 165)

$$y = 2x - 6$$
$$y = -2x$$

system of inequalities   A system of inequalities is a set of inequalities with the same variables. Solving a system of inequalities means finding one or more regions on the coordinate plane whose points represent solutions to each of the inequalities in the system. There may be zero, one, or several such regions for a system of inequalities. For example, the shaded region at right is a graph of the system of inequalities that appears below it. (p. 391)

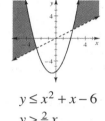

$$y \le x^2 + x - 6$$
$$y > \tfrac{2}{3}x$$

table   The tables used in this course represent numerical information by organizing it into columns and rows. The numbers may come from a graph, situation (pattern), or rule (equation). Many of the tables in this course are x-y tables like the one shown at right. (pp. 13, 23)

IN (x)	-2	4	1	6	-5
OUT (y)	-6	-2	-3	2	-9

term   A term is a single number, variable, or the product of numbers and variables. In an expression, terms are separated by addition or subtraction signs. For example, in the expression $1.2x - 45 + 3xy^2$, the terms are $1.2x$, -45, and $3xy^2$. (p. 57)

tile pattern   See "pattern."

Transitive Property of Equality   The Transitive Property of Equality states that if $a = b$ and $b = c$, then $a = c$. For example, if $x = 2y$ and $2y = 13$, then x must equal 13.

trend line   A line that represents a set of data. The trend line does not necessarily intersect each data point; it attempts to approximate the data, as in the example at right. Trend lines are often used to make predictions about future, unobserved data points. (p. 279)

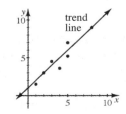

trinomial   A polynomial that is the sum or difference of exactly three terms, each of which is a monomial. For example, $x^2 + 6x + 9$ is a trinomial. (pp. 329)

twice Two times as much. For example, a twenty-dollar bill has *twice* the value of a ten-dollar bill. (p. 28)

undoing In this course, "undoing" refers to a method of solving one-variable equations. In "undoing," we undo the last operation that was applied to an expression by applying its inverse operation. We then solve the resulting equation using various solution methods, including perhaps undoing again. For example, in the equation $4(x+2) = 36$, the last operation that was applied to the left-hand side was a *multiplication* by 4. So to use "undoing," we *divide* both sides of the equation by 4, giving us $x+2=9$. We then solve the equation $x+2=9$ (perhaps by "undoing" again and subtracting 2 from both sides) to find that $x = 7$. (p. 424)

variable A symbol used to represent one or more numbers. In this course, letters of the English alphabet are used as variables. For example, in the expression $3x - (8.6xy + z)$, the variables are x, y, and z. (p. 41)

vertex (of a parabola) The vertex of a parabola is the highest or lowest point on the parabola (depending on the parabola's orientation). (p. 106)

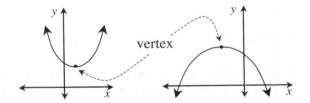

vertical lines Vertical lines run up and down in the same direction as the y-axis and are parallel to it. All vertical lines have equations of the form $x = a$, where a can be any number. For example, the graph at right shows the vertical lines $x = 4$ and $x = -1$. The y-axis has the equation $x = 0$ because $x = 0$ everywhere on the y-axis. Vertical lines have undefined slope. (p. 291)

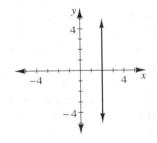

Ways of Thinking This course emphasizes five Ways of Thinking about mathematical ideas: justifying (explaining and verifying your ideas), generalizing (predicting behavior for any situation), making connections (connecting your ideas to other ways of seeing or to past or future learning), reversing thinking (solving problems "backward and forward"), and applying and extending (applying your knowledge to new contexts and extending it to help solve new problems). For example, when confronted with a new type of mathematical problem, you might solve it by reversing your thinking to work backwards or by trying to make connections to problems you have seen before. Once you have a solution, you might be asked to justify your solution or generalize it to a broader class of problems. Finally, you might then apply what you have learned on this problem to the next new type of problem that comes along. (p. 2)

web See "representations web."

x-axis See "axes."

x-coordinate See "coordinate."

x-intercept(s)   The point(s) where a graph intersects the x-axis. A graph may have several x-intercepts, no x-intercepts, or just one. We sometimes report the x-intercepts of a graph with coordinate pairs, but since the y-coordinate is always zero, we often just give the x-coordinates of x-intercepts. For example, we might say that the x-intercepts of the graph at right are (0, 0) and (2, 0), or we might just say that the x-intercepts are 0 and 2. (pp. 119, 301)

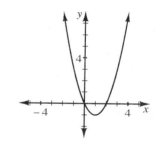

x→y table   An x→y table, like the one at right, represents pairs of values of two related quantities. The input value (x) appears first, and the output value (y) appears second. For example, the x→y table at right tells us that the input value 10 is paired with the output value 18 for some rule. (p. 94)

IN (x)	OUT (y)
	8
0	−2
− 4	−10
10	18
−2	
	198
0.5	

y-axis   See "axes."

y-coordinate   See "coordinate."

y-intercept(s)   The point(s) where a graph intersects the y-axis. A function has at most one y-intercept; a relation may have several. The y-intercept of a graph is important because it often represents the starting value of a quantity in a real-world situation. For example, on the graph of a tile pattern the y-intercept represents the number of tiles in Figure 0. We sometimes report the y-intercept of a graph with a coordinate pair, but since the x-coordinate is always zero, we often just give the y-coordinate of the y-intercept. For example, we might say that the y-intercept of the graph at right is (0, 2), or we might just say that the y-intercept is 2. When a linear equation is written in $y = mx + b$ form, b tells us the y-intercept of the graph. For example, the equation of the graph at right is $y = x + 2$ and its y-intercept is 2. (pp. 119, 298, 301)

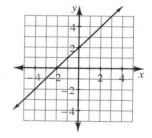

y = mx + b   When two quantities x and y have a linear relationship, that relationship can be represented with an equation in $y = mx + b$ form. The constant m is the slope, and b is the y-intercept of the graph. For example, the graph at right shows the line represented by the equation $y = 2x + 3$, which has a slope of 2 and a y-intercept of 3. This form of a linear equation is also called the slope-intercept form. (p. 149)

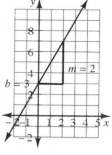

zero   A number often used to represent "having none of a quantity." Zero is neither negative nor positive. Zero is the identity element for addition. (pp. 51, 53, 346, 348)

Zero Product Property   The Zero Product Property states that when the product of two or more factors is zero, one of these factors must equal zero. That is, if $a \cdot b = 0$, then either $a = 0$ or $b = 0$ (or both). For example, if $(x + 4)(2x − 3) = 0$, then either $x + 4 = 0$ or $2x − 3 = 0$ (or both). The Zero Product Property can be used to solve factorable quadratic equations. (p. 349)

List of Symbols

+	plus (addition)	$\sqrt{}$	square root
−	minus (subtraction)	1:5	1 to 5 ratio
·	times (multiplication)	±	plus or minus
÷	divide by (division)	>	greater than
−1	negative one (negative integer)	<	less than
=	equals to	≥	greater than or equal
(x, y)	coordinates of a point	≤	less than or equal to
y = mx + b	slope-intercept form of a linear equation	x^2	x squared

1 ▪ 1   represents 1

1 ▭ represents y

1 ▭ x   represents x

y ▢ y^2 represents y^2

x ▢ x^2 represents x^2

x ▭ xy represents xy

Note: For this text, all unshaded tiles will represent negative quantities. For example, the tile ▢ represents −1.

Index
Student Version

Many of the pages referenced here contain a definition or an example of the topic listed, often within the body of a Math Notes box. Others contain problems that develop or demonstrate the topic. It may be necessary to read the text on several pages to fully understand the topic. Also, some problems listed here are good examples of the topic and may not offer any explanation. The page numbers below reflect the pages in the Student Version. References to Math Notes boxes are bolded.

Evaluate, 43, 46, **49**
Exact form, 426
Excluded values, 409, **413**, 470, 500
Exponents
    fractional, 450
    laws of, 446, **452**
    negative, 447
    rewriting, 442
    simplifying, 442, 446
Expression comparison mat, 55
Expression mat, 47
Expressions
    combining like terms, **57**
    comparing, 55, 59, 117
    evaluating, 43, 46, **49**
    factoring, **338**
    quadratic, **329**
    number of terms, **57**
    rational, 409, 410, **413**, 502
    representing on an expression mat, 47
    rewriting, 194, **198**, **218**, **338**
    simplifying, 52, **57**, 60, 64
    with exponents, 442

F

f(x), 464
Facilitator, 4
Factor, **329**
    common, 338
Factored form, **329**
Factoring
    completely, 338
    difference of squares, 334
    quadratics, **338**
    shortcuts, 497
    special cases, 334
    trinomials, 331, 332, 338
    with a diamond problem, 331, 332, **338**
    with a generic rectangle, 331, 332, **338**
    with algebra tiles, 327
Fencing Lessons problem, 519
Fibonacci numbers, **95**
Figure number, 100
Fractals, **82**
Fraction, **19**
    adding and subtracting, 499

Fraction Busters, 416, 418, **419**
Fractional exponents, 450
Fractions, algebraic, 409
    adding and subtracting, 499, 502,
        503
    multiplying and dividing, 412, **413**
    simplifying, 410, **413**
Function, 467
    definition of, **473**
    notation, **473**
Function Factory problems
    Functions of America, 340, 341
    Promotion Opportunity, 479
    Quality Control, 354, 355
Funky Function problem, 517

G

Generalizing, 133
Generic rectangles, 197, **198**, **218**
    factoring, 331, 338
    pattern with the diagonals, 328,
        332
Good Tipper problem, 108
Graph, **10**, **119**, 161
    axes, **119**
    complete, **119**
    from a pattern, 100, 139, 147
    from a rule, 105, 157
    from a table, 98, 105, 115
    of a non-linear inequality, 385
    of a system of inequalities, 391,
        392, **393**
    of an absolute value equation or
        inequality, 388
    of an inequality with two
        variables, 382, 385
    quadrant, 8, 10
    scaling axes, 106, 116, 278
    scatterplot, 278
    x- and *y*-intercepts, **301**
Growing, Growing, Growing
    problems, 18, 160
Growth factor, 142, 147, **205**, 282
Guess and Check, **65**
    problems, 26, 30
    table, 23, **65**

H

Highest point, 106
Horizontal change (delta x), **291**
Hypothesis, **241**, 384

I

Identity Properties, **53**
Iditarod Trail Sled Dog Race problem, 163
If ... then ... statement, **241**
Independent, 13, **110**, **473**
Inductive reasoning, **448**
Inequalities, 375
    boundary point, 376, **377**, **386**
    from word problems, 380
    solving by graphing, 432
    with absolute value, 432
    with one variable, 376, **386**
Inequality symbols, 350, **352**, **377**
Infinite solutions, **127**
Input, 464, **473**
Integers, **15**
Intercepts, 113, 119, 483
    shortcuts, 362
Intersection, 163, 165, **258**, 483
Inverse properties, **72**
Irrational numbers, 365

J

John's Giant Redwood problems, 98, 126
Justification, algebraic, 241
Justifying, 88

L

Lattice points, 283
Learning Logs, 24
Less than, **28**
Let statement, 233
Line Factory problems
    Line Factory Logo, 313
    Quality Control, 275
    Slope Walk, 293
    Take A Walk, 297
    Walk The Walk, 294

Linear equations
    finding the intercepts, 362
    from a graph, 156
    from a table, 150
    point-slope form, **314**
    slope-intercept form, 150, 203,
        205, **298**
    solving. *See* Solving equations
    standard form, 203, **205**
    through two points, 310
    $y = mx + b$ form, 203, **205**
Linear inequality
    boundary, 382
    graph, 382, 385
    solutions of, 382, 385
Lines of symmetry, **342**
Literal equations, 203
Logical conclusions, **241**, 384
Looking inside, 422, **424**
Lowest point, 106

M

m, 149, 150, 283, 285, 286, 290, **291**,
    298
Machine, relation, 464, 465, 467,
    473
Making connections, 36
Mathematical sentences, 231, 232,
    234, 236, 375
Mathography problem, 6
Mean, 11, 25
Minus, meaning of, 47
Mixture problems, 508
Mode, 70
Moe's Yo problem, 364
Monomial, **329**
More than, **28**
Motion detector, 293, 297
Multiple representations, 139, **161**
    connections between, 139, 152
    quadratic, 344
    quadratic web, 345
    web, 144, 173
Multiplicative Identity, **53**
Multiplicative Identity Property, **410**
Multiplicative Inverse Property, **72**
Multiplying binomials
    with algebra tiles, **192**
    with generic rectangles, 197, **218**
Multiplying integers, **24**

R

Range, 471, **473**
Ratio, 210, **211**
    slope, **291**
Rational expressions, 409
    adding and subtracting, 499, 502, **503**
    multiplying and dividing, 412, **413**
    simplifying, 410, **413**
Rational Numbers, **214**, 365
Ratios, equal, 212
Real numbers, 365
Reasoning
    deductive, **448**
    inductive, **448**
Reciprocal, **72**
Recorder/Reporter, 4
Rectangle
    area, **5**, 7, 191
    area as a product, **218**
    area as a sum, **218**
    building with algebra tiles, 193
    dimensions, **7**, 27, 46, 191
    generic, 197, **198**, **218**
    perimeter, **5**
Regions, 392
Relations, 465, 475
    domain, 470, 471, **473**
    function, 467
    input and output, 464
    range, **473**
    transformations, 479
Representations
    connections between, 139, 152
    multiple, **161**
    numeric, 11, 16, **19**
    web, 144, 159, **161**, 173
Resource Manager, 4
Reversing thinking, 184
Rewriting, solving by, 415, 416, 422, **424**
Rewriting expressions
    Distributive Property, 194, **198**
    multiplying binomials, **192**
    with exponents, **452**
Roots, 450
    of a parabola, 344, 350

Rule, 161
    from a graph, 149, 156
    from a pattern, 100, 139, 143, 148
    from a situation, 108
    from a table, 94, 97, 98, 150
    quadratic, from a graph, 354
    quadratic, from a situation or
        pattern, 345
    quadratic, from a table, 351

S

Saint Louis Gateway Arch problem,
    360
Sampling, 80, 81, 216
Save the Earth problem, 316
Scaling axes, 105, 115
Scatterplot, 163, 278
Scientific notation, 451
Search and Rescue problem, 395
Sierpinski Triangle, **82**
Silent Board Game, 97
Similar figures, **78**, 280
Simplifying expressions, 52, 60, 64
    by combining like terms, **57**
    on an expression mat, **60**
    recording your work, 64
    with algebra tiles, **60**
Slope, 281, 282, 283, **291**, **298**
    as a rate, 293
    negative, 285, 286, **291**
    of parallel lines, 288, 290, 308
    of perpendicular lines, 307, 308
    positive, 286, **291**
    triangles, 282, 285, 286, **298**, **314**
    undefined, **291**
    without a slope triangle, 290
    zero, 286, **291**
Slope-intercept form, 150, **205**, **298**
Solution, **127**
    checking, 118, **201**
    exact and approximate forms, 426
    infinite solutions, **127**
    no solution, **127**
    of a linear equation, 118, 382
    of a one-variable inequality, 376,
        386
    of a system of equations, **252**
    of a system of inequalities, 391,
        399
    of an inequality, 382, 385

Solving equations
    by completing the square, 436, 437, 438, 440, **444**
    by looking inside, 422, **424**
    by rewriting, 411, 414, 415, 416, 418, 422, **424**
    by undoing, 422, **424**
    checking solutions, **201**
    equations with absolute value, **430**
    equations with fractions, **419**
    inequalities with absolute value, 432
    linear, 68, **171**
    linear equations without algebra tiles, **171**
    literal equations, 203
    multiple methods, 421, **424**
    on an equation mat, 68
    quadratic equation with the Quadratic Formula, 357, **358**
    quadratic equations, **361**
    quadratic equations with the Zero Product Property, **349**
    recording your work, 117
    systems of equations, 170, 176, 242, **248**, 250, **264**, **287**
    with algebra tiles, 68
    without algebra tiles, 126
    word problems with an equation, **239**
    word problems with an inequality, 380
    word problems with Guess and Check, **65**, **236**
Solving inequalities
    with one variable, 376, **386**
Square, 336
Square root, 450
    graph of, 461
    simplifying, **365**
Square units, **5**
Standard form
    of a line, **205**
    of a number, 451
    of a quadratic, **335**, 357, **358**
Steepness, measurement of, 283, 285, **291**
Substitution Method, 242, **248**
Subtracting integers, **15**
Sum, **28**
    writing area as a sum. *See* Area as a sum

Symbol
    inequality, 350, **352**, **377**
    plus or minus (±), 357, **358**
    square root, 365
Symmetry, 341, **342**
Systems of equations, **165**, **252**
    Elimination Method, 250, **264**, **287**
    Equal Values Method, 176
    from a context, 164, 165
    linear, 164, 170, 171, **176**
Systems of inequalities, 391, 392, **393**, 398, 399
    solutions of, 391, 392, **393**

T

Table, **119**, 161
    from a graph, 123, 148
    from a pattern, 100, 139, 148
    from a rule, 105
    from a situation, 108
    Guess and Check, 23, **65**
Task Manager, 4
Team roles, 4
Term, **57**
Tile pattern, 18, 93, 139, 140, 142, 147, 160, 161
    finding a rule, 100
Tiles, algebra, 41, 42, 44
    building a square, **427**
    on an equation mat, 68, **69**
    on an expression mat, 52
    simplifying expressions, **60**
    to solve equations, 68
Times more than, **28**
Treasure Hunt problem, 488
Trend line, 279, 390
Trinomial, **329**
Twice, **28**

U

Undoing, 422, **424**
United Nations problems, 379, 385, 393, 398, 399
Units, **5**

V

Variable, 41
  defining, 233
  in mathematical sentences, 231
Vertex, **106**
Vertex of a parabola, 350
Vertical change (delta y), **291**

W

Water-Balloon Contest, 344, 351, 355
Ways of Thinking
  applying and extending, 224
  generalizing, 133
  justifying, 88
  making connections, 36
  reversing thinking, 184
Web, 144, 159, **161**, 173
  quadratic, 345
Word problems, 26, **65**
  involving mixture, 508
  involving work, 505, 506
  solving with an equation, **239**
  solving with Guess and Check, **65**, **236**
  solving a system of inequalities, 398
  solving with an inequality, 380
  vocabulary, **28**

Work problems, 505, 506
Writing equations, 232
  from word problems, 236
Writing inequalities
  from word problems, 395, 398

X

$x \rightarrow y$ table
  from a pattern, 100
x-axis, **10**
x-intercepts, 113, **119**, **301**
  roots of a parabola, 344, 350

Y

$y = mx + b$, 149, 150
Yao Ming, 14, 279
y-axis, **10**
y-intercepts, 113, **119**, 157, **205**, **298**, **301**

Z

Zero, **15**, 51, **60**, 346, 348
Zero Product Property, 346, 348, **349**